ETHICS

With Special Application
To The Nursing Profession

By

JOSEPH B. McALLISTER, S.S., Ph.D.

Assistant Professor of Philosophy

The Catholic University of America, Washington, D.C.

W. B. SAUNDERS COMPANY

Philadelphia and London

1947

MADE IN U. S. A.

IMPRIMI POTEST

John J. Lardner, S.S., S.T.D., Provincial.

NIHIL OBSTAT

Andrew Levatois, S.S., Censor deputatus, Baltimore.

IMPRIMATUR

Michael J. Curley, Archbishop of Baltimore and Washington.

PREFACE

The need which this book seeks to fill is not occasioned by the lack of texts in the field of professional adjustments or ethical guides for nurses. Rather it is an effort to satisfy a growing demand for an approach which stresses principles and attempts to give the nurse some understanding of the speculative basis behind the principles and their application.

In doing this the author is aware that principles should be applied. Even the firmest convictions based on the highest principles need to be made operative in the problems of daily life. So, while the theoretical element has been stressed, it has not been divorced from the challenges of moral living as well as moral thinking.

All too few people today have a mature notion why they act, or should act, as they do. This is not to deny that many men and women lead good lives. The point is: are they aware of the principles involved and the rational justification of the principles?

In turn it might be asked why they should be aware of the principles and their basis. The answer is the crying need of the time—basic convictions about moral principles. It would be wrong to think of contemporary life as immoral. It is rather unmoral. The moral problem has shifted from the question about the morality of a particular action to the question of whether there is any right or wrong at all—beyond the inconvenience or injury it may cause oneself or others.

There are forces, increasing in number and compounding in their threat to wholesome and happy living, which must be met. They are not being met by the good people who forthrightly lay down their judgments about moral right and wrong, yet who cannot explain what makes the conduct in question right or wrong.

The nurse for whom this work is intended is to take her place in contemporary society. As a professional woman she cannot escape the obligation which goes with her station. She should be a person who not only conducts herself properly but who acts morally through conviction, enlightened by mature and reasoned knowledge. It is one thing to do right; it is another to know why conduct is right. The modern nurse should be familiar with the deeper reaches of moral conduct.

Nurses have social responsibilities beyond the average. They need more than a question-and-answer type of ethical instruction. It is not enough for them to take good conduct on authority. They must be able to defend it, not only as it involves details but as it involves, as the slightest detail of life does involve, the question of whether there is any objective, permanent, knowable rightness or wrongness at all. Not to be able to give solid and reasonable explanations for their ethical judgments is to fail those who look to them for leadership.

The aim of this book is neither to command nor to exhort. It is to give a rational account of moral good. The moral life is the good life—vital, calling upon the best in human nature and promising the joy of struggle and the happiness of living to the fullest of human capacity.

Neither does this book propose to praise virtue. Virtue needs no praise. Once virtue is understood as corresponding to reality and evil to the absence of reality, it becomes evident that virtue must be pursued under penalty of forfeiting what is for what is not. It is equally evident how grievous and unphilosophical is the mistake of considering evil as pleasant and happy-making and virtue as something to be sought—but highly unpleasant. As Walter Lippmann said, "Were the nature of good and evil really made plain by moralists, their teachings would appear to the modern listener not like exhortations from without, but as Keats said of poetry: 'a wording of his own highest thoughts and . . . almost a remembrance' " (*Preface to Morals*, page 320).

Nor is it the purpose of this book to supply an answer to any and every moral problem which might arise. It is hoped that it will contribute to the nurse's conception of morality in its foundations and general principles. It remains for her to grasp the broad issues of life and to meet the challenge of daily problems with the surety of principles intelligently understood and prudently applied.

JOSEPH B. McALLISTER, S.S.

March, 1947

CONTENTS

PART I—GENERAL ETHICS

PART II—SPECIAL ETHICS

Section 1.   Ethics Regarding Self

Section 2.   Ethics Regarding Other Persons

Section 3.   Ethics Regarding God

Section 4.   Ethics Regarding the Family and the State

Part I

GENERAL ETHICS

Chapter 1

INTRODUCTION

1. PHILOSOPHY

Definition   Philosophy, of which ethics is one division, signifies *the love of wisdom*. According to its real meaning, however, it is defined as the science of beings in terms of their ultimate causes and principles in so far as these can be known by the light of human intelligence alone.

Definition explained   In the first place philosophy is a *science*, not just haphazard opinion. For science implies an organized body of truths arrived at by demonstration from adequate premises. Chemistry, physics, biology are sciences dealing with experimental fact, and for this reason are called positive sciences. Philosophy too is a science, but it concentrates not so much on facts as upon fundamental explanations. The phrase *of beings* indicates the material object of philosophy, or its general field. This includes everything that the human mind can comprehend by its natural powers. Obviously other sciences are active in the extensive field of all being; but their approaches are not identical. Each science has a special point of view which limits and specifies it. This special interest of a science is called its formal object, which, for philosophy, is indicated in the definition by the words *in terms of ultimate causes and principles*.

Principle   Though somewhat similar *cause* and *principle* are not synonyms. Of the two principle is the more vague. Anything from which something proceeds in any way whatsoever can be called a *principle*. Non-being is

3

the negative principle of being. Night can be termed the principle of day, or day the principle of night, depending on the point of view. In the order of causality severe cerebral hemorrhages are often the principle of death. And in the realm of thought the law of contradiction, that the same thing under the same aspect cannot be and not be at the same time, is a principle of knowledge. These examples, while showing the extensive application of principle, bring out also that principle includes cause, so that every cause is a principle. But the contrary is not true—every principle is not a cause.

Cause   For *cause* enriches the lean meaning of principle. Cause signifies a positive principle which contributes to the being or becoming of something else. Thus the micro-organism Rickettsia, carried by the louse, is considered the cause of one of the world's chief epidemic scourges, typhus. The physician cures the patient. The artist paints a portrait, and the child's hammer causes the dent in the living-room chair. The notion of cause, then, implies positive influence flowing from one thing to another and producing in the latter some sort of change known as the effect.

Kinds of   This notion of positive influence prevails even
causes—   when various kinds of causes are distinguished.
efficient   The *efficient cause* was illustrated in the ex-
and final   amples above: the physician, the artist, the child's hammer. It remains to notice the *final cause*, the *material cause* and the *formal cause*. The efficient cause is the productive cause. Its action *produces* the effect. The *final cause*, on the contrary,. *attracts* the effect. Final cause strikes a more familiar note under such names as end or objective or purpose or goal. Final cause answers the question: For what purpose or for whose sake does this thing exist or is this thing being done? Thus the physician gives a sedative in order to quiet the patient. The warrior sacrifices

his life for his country. The patient's welfare and the nation's safety are final causes.

Material and   To understand *material* and *formal* cause is
formal cause   more difficult. *Material cause* signifies *that out of which* something comes to be. It is the determinable, passive, potential principle of composite reality. On the other hand *formal cause* is the determining and active principle, which *makes a thing to be precisely what it is*. The formal cause characterizes a thing in the sense either of an object or an action, and distinguishes it from all other kinds of things. Material and formal cause may be illustrated crudely in the production of a statue. The stone is just so much stone as it lies in the sculptor's studio. The artist (the efficient cause) begins to work on it. He takes the mass of stone (the material cause) and slowly chisels it into the likeness of Florence Nightingale (the formal cause). When asked why he is working he might reply that he was making the statue to honor an heroic woman (the final cause).

Ultimate   Some causes are closer to their effects than
cause   others. To the question of how things come to be, the reply might be made that animals come from animals and trees from the seed of trees. Hydrogen and oxygen account for water, good soil bears rich crops and selective breeding produces fine cattle. All man's hard-won knowledge of nature's laws can inspire him to conquer space and time and make life more comfortable. All such knowledge is useful, but back of it is there not a larger explanation? Is there a cause behind all these causes which will account for them completely? When the question about the origin of things bears upon the proximate explanation of reality, it belongs to the positive sciences. When it stresses the cause behind the causes, demanding the ultimate, then it is philosophical. Consider this example.

Man   The physician understands human physiology quite well in terms of the various organs and functions. His knowledge belongs to the science of medicine. The biochemist has his specialized knowledge of man, and it too belongs to positive science. Empirical psychology by tests and measurements, experiments and introspection, has widened man's understanding of himself. But all this involves causes close to their effects, proximate causes they are called. Suppose it is now asked what man's nature really is: Is he merely material or exclusively spiritual or somehow a baffling mixture of both? Has he free will or does a relentless necessity bind his every gesture? What is his destiny—merely to be a fine physical specimen? A well-clothed, well-fed, well-housed and contented being? Or has he a goal in some way above all this? When the human intelligence is directed to such questions it is turning to philosophy. It is seeking explanations not merely in terms of the ordinary sciences but in the light of ultimates which will illumine the past and present and cast long beams into the future. Time and space dissolve. Accidentals disappear; the inquirer confronts truth behind truths and eventually reaches out to Truth Itself.

Human   The last phrase of the definition *by the light of*
intelligence   *human intelligence alone* emphasizes that philosophy does not rest upon authority—divine or human. This rational quality distinguishes philosophy from theology or, in other words, from that science which deals with God as He has revealed Himself to man. Philosophy does not build upon God's testimony but upon the natural rational powers which man has to understand his universe. The ordinary human powers of knowing, therefore, and not God's supernatural intervention, constitute the proper instrument of philosophical investigation. Philosophy, then, is a science. Its material object is all being; its formal object is the ultimate explanation of all being; and its tool is man's natural reason.

2. PHILOSOPHY AND THE POSITIVE SCIENCES

No contra-diction Whatever may be stated at times to the contrary, true philosophy and science do not and cannot contradict each other. They both spring from man's profound curiosity about the universe, so mysterious and yet so tantalizing to this thirst for knowledge. Truth cannot contradict truth, even though occasionally they may seem to. This apparent conflict between philosophy and the positive sciences arises because of the fact that each of them has its own field and mode of pursuing truth. Positive sciences, such as chemistry, physics, astronomy, biology, rest upon sensible fact, which is concrete, specific, individual, controlled by space and time. Philosophy, however, strives to probe beyond phenomena and the limitations of time and space, to grasp the broader, more universal underlying truth, which will give a systematic and intelligible explanation of the universe.

Positive sciences piecemeal; philosophy comprehensive In other words, whereas the positive sciences are piecemeal, philosophy attempts to gather all truths into a single comprehensible unity. This is why philosophy has been called the queen of the sciences. While each of the positive sciences investigates its own segment of truth in a limited field, philosophy tries to gather the truth of all fields into one all-embracive world-picture. Philosophy and the positive sciences can have the same material object, for example, both may deal with material bodies; but their respective points of view, that is, their formal objects, are different. Likewise the approach and attitude of the scientist and the philosopher are different, just as the principles governing their research are different.

3. VALUE OF PHILOSOPHY

Integration, appreciation, courage In the midst of the accumulating mass of knowledge and experience, which no one today can master in detail, philosophy aims first to formulate a world view by integrating the specialized contributions of the positive sciences with profoundest human wisdom. Secondly, philosophy helps a man to live reasonably by giving him an appreciation of his own worth and of his rôle and destiny in the universe. This knowledge steadies him in the face of contemporary emphasis upon action, propaganda, mass movements and machine activity, social theories and economic panaceas. When, in spite of all his efforts and good intentions, life rises up against him, philosophy can help him meet it with courage and understanding. Boethius (480–525) was not the first nor the last to lean upon philosophy in hours of trial.

Thought and Thirdly, philosophy educates a man to be
power thoughtful and reflective. Plato (428–348 B. C.) felt that a life lived without reflection was not a truly human life. Fourthly, philosophy preserves a man from the domination of primitive emotional impulses. It gives him poise, prepares him to think rather than capitulate to passion and prejudice.

Religion and Finally, there is the connection of philosophy
morality with religion and morality. Philosophy itself is neither religion nor morality. But true philosophy ought to cooperate with them. It can be their most powerful ally—just as false philosophies can be, and unfortunately have been, their most insidious enemies.

4. DIVISIONS OF PHILOSOPHY

Wolff's Because of its unity philosophy balks at divi-
divisions sions. Yet for the purpose of study some classification must be made and various ones have been proposed. For example, Aristotle (384–322 B.C.) spoke of physics, mathematics and theology as theoretical sciences and of ethics, economics and politics as practical sciences. Today it is more usual to follow, with some modifications, Christian Wolff's (1679–1754) plan, which has seven di-

visions: logic, epistemology, cosmology, psychology, ontology, natural theology and ethics.

Logic   *Logic* denotes the collection of practical rules and methods which aim to guide man in his thought processes, so that he may reason with order and facility towards truth. Strictly speaking, logic is not so much a part of philosophy as it is a tool or instrument of philosophy, just as it is for the other sciences.

Epistemology   *Epistemology* (criteriology, theory of knowledge) is the division of philosophy which investigates the power of the human mind to have certitude. It raises such questions as the truth-value of knowledge, the sources, standards, limitations of what men can know. It examines the trustworthiness of the senses as well as the products of man's intellectual and reasoning processes. Since the time of Descartes (1596–1650) and Immanuel Kant (1724–1804) epistemology has held the spotlight of philosophical inquiry—although it was not entirely overlooked by earlier thinkers, even ancient ones.

Cosmology   *Cosmology* studies the world of non-living things from a philosophical point of view. It tries to explain sensible reality, i.e., reality which falls under man's senses, not merely in terms of the mathematician or physicist or chemist or astronomer but in the light of principles which apply to the universe at large. Does the material universe show purposive activity? What is the nature of space and time? Can natural bodies be productive causes? What significance has physical law, and in what limits can it be said to be necessary? These are some of the problems of cosmology.

Rational psychology   *Rational psychology* concentrates upon living things. It includes plants and animals and that unique animal endowed with reason called man. Since he surpasses all other living bodies and embraces their perfections, psychology concentrates upon him. It thus becomes an inquiry into man as a living, sentient, rational being. Psychology as a branch of philosophy should not be confused with psychiatry. They both study man, but each from its own point of view. Psychiatry might be called medical psychology. It deals with the genesis, dynamics and manifestations of such disorders and undesirable functionings of the personality as disturb either the subject state of the individual or its relations with other persons.

Ontology *Ontology,* or metaphysics, is the most basic division of philosophy. But dealing as it does with being in the highest degree of abstraction it is not easy to define. To say that ontology is the science of being as such means little to the beginner in philosophy. It might be clearer to mention some typical problems of ontology: the nature of unity and truth and goodness and beauty, the validity of the notion of cause and the various kinds of causes, the interpretation of reality through ultimate concepts, such as substance and accident, potentiality and actuality, matter and form, essence and existence. Ontology formulates doctrines about the meaning of nature and its relation to the individual and its perfection in personality. While such investigations often are tedious, no one justly can deny their importance or scorn ontology because of its difficulties.

Natural *Natural theology,* or theodicy, reaches the most
theology sublime object of man's pursuit of truth. It seeks by the light of human reason alone (i.e., apart from divine revelation) to know whether a Supreme Being exists, what manner of being He is, what His relations are to the universe in terms of its original cause and its sustaining and intelligent director.

Ethics *Ethics,* or the philosophical science of morals, belongs to the practical sciences. Ethics studies such activities of men as bear the stamp of knowledge and freedom and deliberate choice, in order to establish the principles of order which they ought to have relative both to one another and to man's ultimate destiny. What man's highest good is and what his attitude should be towards the intermediate good things of this world are also questions which ethics considers.

5. ETHICS DEFINED

Nominal and real definition   *Ethics*, as a division of philosophy, is sometimes called the philosophy of conduct or moral philosophy. It comes from a Greek word meaning custom, usage, habit and, in the plural, disposition, temper, character. The corresponding Latin word signifies manners, morals, character. From the Latin *mores* come the English moral, morals, morality. So much for the etymology. By definition ethics is the philosophical science of human acts from the point of view of the order they should have regarding one another and man's ultimate destiny, which they ought to help him achieve.

Material object— human acts   The meaning of *philosophical science* has been given, but here must be indicated ethics' material and formal object. *Human acts* indicate the *material object*. Not all acts attributable to people are called human, but only those which are done with knowledge, freedom, and are willed. Such acts alone are moral. Other acts, such as digestion or the circulation of the blood, which do not spring from the rational will are called *acts of the man* to distinguish them from moral acts, or acts which do spring from the will. These last are truly *human acts* and furnish the subject matter of ethics.

Formal object   The special point of view, however, from which ethics considers these truly human acts is the *formal object*. They might be dealt with from many aspects, the physiological, the psychological or the pedagogical, to mention just a few. But ethics concentrates upon them from the aspect of *the order they should have re-*

garding one another and man's ultimate destiny. Order means an arrangement of these acts in a way to harmonize with man's rational nature. On this basis they merit being called good and honest, but falling short of this deserve such epithets as evil and unethical.

Ethics not the art of conduct   Though having certain similarities, ethics must not be confused with the art of conduct. Ethics aims to instruct reason, so that it can make correct judgments about the morality of human acts. Its business is to supply principles for man's moral guidance. On the other hand, the art of conduct seeks to strengthen the will and to apply ethical principles to actual living, to the struggle of doing right and avoiding evil. It must be obvious, however, that a balanced life, in other words the good life, demands that men and women combine correct ethical principles, or science, with a faithful application, or art, of those principles to daily living. From the practical point of view ethical principles and the art of conduct must be kept together. The science of ethics divorced from practice cannot lead a man to the good life and to his ultimate destiny. Yet, just as certainly, sincere but unenlightened conduct can lead to tragedy. The good life, the happy balanced existence demands the closest union of right science with vigorous and courageous living.

Ethics not statistical   A dangerous modern tendency is to consider ethics a product of statistical surveys of human conduct. The true science of ethics is not a mere tabulation of how men and women actually *have behaved* towards themselves and their social environment. Nor does ethics attempt to extract principles of right and wrong from empirical or statistical data. Such data when properly gathered and collated may have considerable value for the science of ethics. Yet they cannot themselves constitute ethics. The problem of ethics is not how men have acted but *how they should act.*

Ethics not
"codes" of
ethics
The science of ethics is not a "code of ethics." Generally these codes are rather arbitrary statements of conduct deemed proper for special groups. There are the "ethical codes" of doctors and lawyers. Some business houses use them to stimulate employees' efficiency and build up the confidence of patrons. Such "codes" may incorporate principles of conduct as established by the science of ethics, and to that extent they bind in conscience. But for the most part they do not bear on right or wrong in the moral sense—though, it ought to be noted, some of their stipulations may be reinforced by civil law.

Ethics and
nurse's code
The nursing profession has such a "code" or at least is tending to formulate one. It concerns the ideals and customs which are gradually evolving from the nursing profession itself and shaping the popular concept of the professional nurse. But it should be clear that such a "code" must sink roots into the science of moral philosophy if it is going to be anything more than etiquette or a morale booster or a bid for vocational growth, enthusiasm, professional spirit and pride. These objectives are legitimate enough, but they do not constitute ethics.

6. ETHICS AND PHILOSOPHY

Ethics part of
philosophy
Ethics is not a self-sufficient philosophical science. A complete philosophy includes ethics, so ethics implies a whole philosophy. Ethics without any or at best only weak metaphysical foundations is dangerous. Divorced from natural theology and sadly mistaken about the nature of man, it can betray its champions, no matter how great their sincerity, into unhappy theories and perhaps flagrant injustice and tragedy.

Ethics and
the Scholastic
synthesis
Scholastic philosophy is a system of which ethics is a part, an integral part. It is the system which is the harmonious synthesis. Upon it

ethics leans heavily. For example, ethics needs natural theology for the reasoned demonstration of God's existence and providential dominion over the world and everything in it. In rational psychology ethics finds man's free will and immortality vindicated and man's nature explained. Epistemology cooperates by defending man's ability to know truth with certitude and metaphysics sustains the use in ethics of such concepts as cause and effect, teleology, potency and act, matter and form, substance and accident, essence and personality. It must be remembered, then, that ethics is part of an integrated system. If it tries to arrogate the whole field of philosophy to itself, it is presumptuous. If it rests upon shallow or mistaken philosophical principles, it merely transmits their weaknesses. To survive and to safely guide men to virtue and to ultimate happiness ethics must rely upon the larger system and focus its light upon its own more specialized problems.

7. IMPORTANCE OF ETHICS

Furnishes   Ethics prevents the loss of a poorly planned
principles   life. Poor planning occurs when human existence meanders without principles or follows wrong ones. Sincerity and courage may bespeak good character but do not of themselves give enlightenment. This comes only from the apprehension of right principles. To ascertain these principles and to establish them on solid rational grounds are the burdens of ethics and suggest the important contribution ethics has for successful living.

Relations   Again—no human being ever outgrows his
with God and   need of God and fellow human beings. Men
fellow man   have naturally enduring relationships with the
Deity and with other men, and these contribute generously to human happiness or to human misery. Ethics aims to insure these relationships for men's welfare by founding them on right reason.

Ethics and practical problems
Today social unrest plagues the world. Labor's conflicts with the organizers of industry, disputes about the rights and prerogatives of ownership, seething human aspirations towards life and liberty and happiness, the State versus the person, and men's mutual rights and duties, not to mention these problems when magnified to international or world-wide scope, all of these questions pertain to the field of ethics, and in that science must find the beginnings of their solution.

Ethics inadequate
To emphasize that ethics cannot promise the last word on these questions does not at all minimize what it really has to offer. Ethics based on natural human reason can shed some light upon man's destiny and the principles leading to it. But it *cannot carry him all the way to the most luminous truth of his existence:* that his life and its ultimate goal transcend the merely natural limits of reason and that he has a destiny marked out not by a philosopher but by the Son of God.

8. AIM AND DIVISION OF COURSE

Nurse and leadership
What has been said about the importance of ethics applies in a special way to the nursing profession if that profession is to exercise the leadership it should. It is not enough for nurses to *do* what is right. Today in the face of many a challenge they must do what is right, of course; but also they must know *why* what they are doing is right and be able to defend it.

Moral and physical health
Nurses must be prepared for this leadership in the moral world for their own sake, certainly, but also for the benefit of their patients. Often their task is not only to win ill bodies back to health but to bring ailing minds to new and wholesome views of life. Physical health remains the chief concern of the nurse. Yet the intimate connection between health and the patient's emotional and rational and spiritual life is forcing

the medical profession to consider more than it ever did the patient's mental and spiritual condition.

The appeal of ethics Consequently ethics should appeal to the nurse for the regulation of her own life, for meeting the threats of a materialistic world speedily becoming non-moral, for the aid it can give her to help her patients, and for the contribution ethics can make to maintain the high ideals of the profession.

Division of course A course in ethics for nurses must fulfil these ends, and so falls into two major divisions. The first division deals with ethics in general, as this science of moral philosophy applies to all human beings. The second division treats of ethical problems with special application to the nursing profession.

READINGS

Charlotte A. Aikens: *Studies in Ethics for Nurses*, pp. 1–8.
Michael Cronin: *The Science of Ethics*, i, 1–27.
Etienne Gilson: *The Spirit of Medieval Philosophy*, pp. 1–41, 324–342, 364–381.
J. F. Leibell, ed.: *Readings in Ethics*, pp. 1–34.
Joseph A. Leighton: *The Field of Philosophy*, pp. 1–34.
Charles J. McFadden: *Medical Ethics for Nurses*, ch. 1.
Jacques Maritain: *An Introduction to Philosophy*.
R. P. Phillips: *Modern Thomistic Philosophy*, i, 1–19.

Chapter 2

BACKGROUND OF ACTION—THE HUMAN DIMENSIONS

1. INTRODUCTION

Human nature the key to the good life

In the world of daily experience, if a person wants to understand something, he looks at it to see what it is made of, what it can do, for what it can be used. The same sort of approach can be made to the study of man relative to the good life. A step towards defining the good life is to try to understand what human beings are by nature. For a knowledge of human nature can be a guide to the kind of life human beings ought to lead.

Human nature and man's activity

Human nature can be described in terms of man's activity and legitimate inferences based upon it. This, however, presents a bewildering picture. The difficulty springs from man's having so much in common with all the rest of creation— with what lies beneath him as well as with what soars above him. With the whole universe he is akin.

Human nature a unity of diversity

The picture of human activity is so complex that one or other aspects of it easily can be overlooked or be stressed unduly. To understand man, *all* the manifestations of his nature must be examined and taken into account. His unity must rest not upon the denial of any of his powers or the over simplification of his diversity. Rather this diversity is the very thing which needs closest attention, that it may be given due weight in judging what man most truly is.

Purpose—a The purpose then in giving the following
picture of sketch of human activities is to formulate a
human nature concept of human nature, to discover the
principle which reduces man's diversity to a dynamic unity
and makes a coherent pattern of human existence. It is important to remember that because man has much in common with the chemical and physical world it does not follow that he belongs to it entirely. Likewise man shows
striking resemblances with the plant and animal kingdoms.
But it does not follow that they can claim him exclusively.
Similarly man's powers of intellectual thought and willing
and his social needs show his affinity with the immaterial
world and the world of his fellow human beings. But they
do not justify his being considered simply as a disembodied
spirit or a pawn of society. The picture is tantalizingly complex; but must be reckoned with in any appreciation of
human nature and what ought to be expected of it.

Division Briefly, then, man will be considered in what
follows as sharing *existence* with non-living
things, *life* with plants, *sentient life* with the animals and
rational life with immaterial beings. This completes man's
portrait in the dimensions of his individual personal self.
But the picture still needs the finishing touches of man's
social characteristics.

A danger Such a composite picture of human nature
drawn from human activities carries the
danger of atomizing man, of breaking him down into distinct and separate departments of being and action. Let
it be constantly remembered that diverse and even opposed
as are some of his activities and the elaborate background
into which they are set, nevertheless they all spring from
the same being and must be attributed to him as the unitary,
autonomous thing he is. The reality and unique self-hood
of man must not be allowed to vanish in the complexity of
his analysis.

2. THE INORGANIC, NON-LIVING DIMENSION

Facts With so much stress laid upon vitamins and diet and radiotherapy and chemical and physical analysis, it seems pointless to insist upon human affinity with the non-living segment of creation. Any standard work on the chemistry of the human body reveals how human beings must be considered, and dealt with, as huge complexes of chemical and physical phenomena. Anabolism and catabolism, basic as they are in the life processes, draw heavily upon chemistry and physics. Today persons afflicted with diabetes can anticipate rather normal lives—provided they carefully balance sugar and insulin.

Their meaning To such an extent do chemical compounds, physical laws of motion and electricity and pressure, the facts and theories of the positive sciences enter into man's make-up and well-being that all too hastily some people conclude that man is nothing but these physical and chemical forces. Philip Wylie has one of his characters voice this conviction—

"It's just that I think life is a mechanical phenomenon," John answered. "Stop the brain—consciousness stops. Take the blood from a dog and it dies. Put it back, and it lives again. In between—it was dead. Protoplasm. Chemicals. An automaton. Like an automobile—which runs when you supply it with fuel and an electric spark."[1]

That man does manifest physical and chemical forces of the mechanical order is evident. That they compass his every being does scant justice to other human phenomena which are just as self-evident.

3. THE ORGANIC, LIVING DIMENSION

Vital properties Even the most elementary forms of life have characteristics which do not appear in merely

[1] *Night unto Night* (New York, Farrar and Rinehart, 1944), p. 83.

mechanical structures. Movement used to be considered a
test for life and still serves under some circumstances. But
today life is described in terms of organization, chemical
composition, growth, reproduction, metabolism and adaptive movements. When a thing shows these phenomena it
has life. They are called *vital properties*. All of them appear in
the smallest unit of life, the biological cell. An exception is
reproduction, which does not occur in the nerve cells of
adult human beings.

The cell   Though it is the simplest unit of life there is
            nothing simple about the *cell*. It is composed of
a material called protoplasm, which is semi-fluid, colorless,
translucent and viscid. In a typical cell two differentiations
appear: the cytoplasm and the nucleus. Under patient
study each reveals divisions of structure and function. The
cytoplasm seems to be chiefly involved in nutrition and excretion, in furnishing the cell's energy and reproduction. If
the nucleus is considered, again there is complexity of function. Here are found the chromosomes and genes, which
play such important rôles in transmitting hereditary characters. The concept of protoplasm must be taken with allowances for variations. The similarities, however, far outnum-
ber the dissimilarities in what is often referred to as the
agent of vital manifestations.

Chemical   The cell's diversity of organization and func-
composition   tion only reflects its equally complex chemical
composition. Protoplasm always contains carbon, oxygen,
hydrogen, nitrogen, sulfur and phosphorus. Frequently it
has chlorine, potassium, sodium, magnesium, calcium and
iron. Of these carbon, oxygen, hydrogen and nitrogen pre-
dominate, forming great varieties of compounds. Some of
these are simple; others are extremely complex, especially
the compounds of carbon.

Growth   *Growth* as characteristic of life means more
            than an increase in size. Some non-living

things, for example salt crystals, get bigger. But their "growth" is merely the addition of salt upon salt. New material of the same sort is brought into permanent contact with the old. The growth of living protoplasm is different. It takes material and energy from its environment and builds them into its own being. It is the bringing together of different things, one of which, the living being, changes the other into itself. Even this is not all. For along with increase of size usually goes multiplication of function.

Reproduction   Growth means an increase of size; *reproduction* signifies increase in the number of living beings. Life once was thought to come from non-living beings. But there is no evidence for this view in modern science. On the contrary, it insists that living things come only from living beings. This can happen in various ways, but it always signifies some separation of a new individual from preexisting life. Thus living things grow, reach their prime and preserve their kind by transmitting life to other individuals. They in turn repeat the cycle of existence, growth, reproduction, decline and death.

Metabolism   *Metabolism* signifies collectively the functions of building up and tearing down protoplasm. It involves getting food, taking it in and assimilating it. It means transforming the energy stored up in its own substance into the manifold activities of living. It denotes getting rid of waste by excretion. In short, the processes of living demand that the animal or plant, while remaining essentially unchanged, constantly undergo change. At the same time it is destroying and rebuilding itself.

Adaptive movement   Animals and plants survive only if they adjust themselves to their environment. If living things cannot get food, they die. But to get what they need, they must be stimulated. This stimulation takes various forms. It may be chemical, electrical, thermal, photic or mechanical, depending upon the protoplasmic system involved. Above all the living being responds as an individual. Structurally and functionally it adapts itself to its needs and environment. This *power of adaptation* is a significant attribute of life and clearly exposes the gulf which separates even the lowest forms of life from the non-living world.

Conclusions   From this survey of life's phenomena certain conclusions follow. One of the most important is that whereas life processes manifest profound and varied chemical and physical aspects, they are not *merely* chemical and physical. The differences can be summarized in the life processes of organization, chemical composition, growth, reproduction, metabolism and adaptive movements. Collectively these activities identify life and mark it off from non-living things. Then there is the unity which living things show, their fitness of structure and function to serve the well-being of the individual and the preservation of its kind.

The vital   Now what does this point to? What is the ex-
principle   planation of the unity and organization and
or soul   vital functions of living things and the chasm
which divides them from the non-living? What spells the difference? The answer here offered is the answer of the traditional Aristotelian philosophy. Living things have an inherent principle which non-living things do not have, a principle which is the explanation and source of the unique phenomena of life. It is called the vital principle or soul. It is not something extrinsic—as icing on a cake. It is of the very being of the individual, its partial and positive and determining factor, the source of its special mode of being and largely responsible for its characteristic operations.

4. THE SENTIENT, FEELING DIMENSION

Sensory   The unmistakable signs of life seen in the
phenomena   vegetative world appear also in human beings.

But in addition they manifest phenomena as strikingly different as the manner in which plant life itself differs from lifeless matter. These are the phenomena of *sensory knowing* and of *sensory desiring*.

Sensation defined   The basis of sensation is the nervous system, the study of which belongs to psychology. So too does any detailed treatment of sensation and appetition. But to continue the plan of understanding the nature of man by an examination of his activities, these sensory functions, which relate man to the animal kingdom, must be taken into consideration. *Sensation* may be defined as a conscious experience aroused by the stimulation of one of the sense organs. It involves a physical stimulus acting upon a sensory organ and producing some physiological modification. This begets a conscious psychological state in the subject. Thus sensation has three aspects: the physical, the physiological and the psychological.

External sensations enumerated   Such sensations as hearing and seeing, smelling and tasting appear in ancient as well as in recent tabulations. But the sensation of touch, which used to be counted as one of the five senses, today is subdivided into what are called somesthetic sensations. They include sensations of the skin, sensations of pressure and pain, coolness and warmth, sensations of movements in muscles and tendons and joints, sensations of equilibrium. Then, still classified under somesthetic, are the organic sensations—the need of food and drink and erotic experience, the need of micturating and defecating, the need of air and of change and, in the female, of lactation. Corresponding to the sensations of wanting these things are the organic sensations of satisfaction in having them. Finally, also somesthetic, are sensations of body weariness and illness and general well-being. These last signify the total impression from all contemporaneous organic sensations, as distinct from any special or well-defined sensation.

Internal   Quite different from the sensations just enu-
senses   merated are those which involve the internal
senses. These are the central, or synthetic, sense, the imagination, sense memory and instinct. As Brennan puts
it,[2] introspection reveals a "power of sifting, sorting, and
unifying the data of sensory experience into perceptual
wholes [*central sense*]; of summoning up mental pictures of
things that are absent and perhaps far removed [*imagination*]; of knowing, on the instant and without previous experience, what is good and what is bad for the organism
[*instinct*]; of remembering past events [*memory*]. It is absurd
to suppose that cognitive contents such as these should
originate solely as functions of the external senses. To account for the additional forms of knowledge which we have
just described, Thomas Aquinas [1225–1274] postulates the
existence of four internal senses, to each of which he as-
signs a special set of operations."

Sensory   By the sensory functions just mentioned human
desiring—   beings become aware of physical objects. But
appetition   the process does not stop with the act of bringing the object to the knowledge of the subject. There is a
reaction on the subject's part of tending toward the object
—or away from it if it be unpleasant. This activity is called
appetition. It is the operation of a sensory appetite, which
may be defined as "a power in virtue of which a sentient
being tends toward a consciously apprehended sensuous
good and away from a consciously apprehended sensuous
evil."[3]

Appetites in   Beings come into existence and endure on con-
themselves   dition that they get what they need. They all
good   have manifold wants, whose fulfilment marks

[2] Brennan, R. E.: *General Psychology* (New York, The Macmillan Co., 1937), p. 185. Material in brackets the author's.
[3] Bittle, C. N.: *The Whole Man* (Milwaukee, Bruce Publishing
Co., 1945), p. 246.

the being's progress toward perfection. These needs, resulting in tendencies towards certain objects, impel the being towards those very things which will contribute towards its development. *Considered in itself* every appetite is at least partially beneficial to the being and so must be considered good. Likewise its object, whose possession completes the being, must be considered good. So true is this that Aristotle (384–322 B.C.) defined the good as that which all things seek.

Appetites and evil   Yet human beings have appetites for things which will hurt them—or so it seems. The child wants too much cake and the father too much alcohol. Are not these appetites evil? The answer is that the specific good of a single appetite must not be confused with the general over-all good of the being. The cake and the alcohol are good and remain good considered in themselves and as the objects of the special appetites involved. But in relation to the person's *integral good* they appear evil because they deprive the being viewed in its completeness of the perfection it ought to have. Man does not have merely one or two appetites which can seek their own objects with total disregard of the well-being of the entire person. The appetites are many and varied. To the extent that an appetite is satisfied at the expense of the being's general welfare, that appetite and its object may be called evil or bad by analogy. Sentient animals, and this includes man, do not seek evil as evil. What they seek is always good. But whether it is good for them at this time and under these circumstances and from every aspect of their due perfection is quite another question.

Summary   The enumeration given of organic sensations ought to be recalled here. They were classified as sight, taste, hearing and smelling, the somesthetic sensations and the four internal senses of imagination, instinct, memory and the central, or synthetic, sense. Each of them can be viewed as a legitimate appetite, pointed towards securing the being's over-all perfection. When this suffers through some *inordinate* activity of the appetite there arises evil. But, let it be repeated, this privation makes neither the appetite nor the object evil in itself.

Feelings and   Along with sensory inclinations or aversions
emotions   and amplifying them go certain effects known as *feelings* and *emotions*. *Feeling*, as compared with emotion, is simpler and without noteworthy physiological changes, such as glandular secretions, peristalsis, modifications in respiration, pulse beat and electrical potential. *Emotion* involves the perception of something, an inclination towards it (or aversion from it) and finally the physiological changes mentioned. Yet it should be noted that the emotions flow from sensory processes and are not restricted to human beings. Animals have them. But in human beings they can overflow into the rational processes of understanding and willing.

5. THE RATIONAL, THINKING AND WILLING DIMENSION

Man   In order to form a just estimate of man's
immeasurably nature on the basis of his activities, all of them
above brute   must be considered. To say that human beings
animals   share existence with elements, life with plants, sentiency with animals states an important truth but does not do justice to *all* the human powers. There remain activities which immeasurably top the highest attainment of beasts. These un-animal characteristics fall under the title of rational, as opposed to non-rational, and are divided into rational knowledge, or intellection, and rational appetite, or volition.

RATIONAL KNOWLEDGE, INTELLECTION

Human   It does no injustice to the accomplishments of
achievements brute animals to contrast them with man's

most evident achievements. Wherever there are human beings, there is language—of perhaps unequal perfection but always beyond comparison with the instinctive cries of animals. Then consider man's artistic productions, his development of social organizations, his ingenious use of tools, his powers of adaptation to widely diverse environments, his ethical and religious codes. Even the briefest summary of human attainments strikes man off from brutish nature just as certainly as other facts establish some common ground between them.

Inference—the rational soul   Human culture, art, religion, morality, technology, fascinating in themselves, are vitally important here because of their implications. They show powers which brute animals do not have. They reveal man's ability to form abstract, universal concepts, to judge, to reason, to build upon the initial data of sense experience magnificent edifices of science and art. These facts point to the conclusion that man must be considered radically different from the brute. And the essential difference between them must lie in some principle which man has and which brute beasts do not have. This principle is the rational soul, the immaterial, incorporeal, spiritual, formative component of human beings.

RATIONAL APPETITE, VOLITION

The will   As sensory knowledge has a counterpart in sensory desire, so intellectual knowledge has its correlative in rational appetency, or will. Bittle[4] defines *will* as "the power to strive for an intellectually perceived good and to shun an intellectually perceived evil." Will, or volition, differs from a merely sensory act. It defies explanation in terms of sense images, feeling and emotions. Moreover the will ties up closely with the intellect, since it depends upon the intellect to perceive the good towards

[4] *The Whole Man*, p. 354.

which it tends and which it seeks. No merely sensory power can desire things which sense cannot apprehend, such as heroism, virtue, patriotism, knowledge of a scientific order, generosity, self-sacrifice. But these suprasensible things the intellect can and does know. They can be and actually are things which human beings want and strive to obtain. Yet to be desired they must be known, a fact which Thomas Aquinas stressed in his principle that nothing is willed which has not been known.

Object of the will—good in general   In the realm of sensory desire or appetition, no appetite seeks evil. An appetite and its object are called evil when they conflict with the general well-being of the creature. The desire for an unbecoming good produces some defect, some lack of perfection which the subject ought to have. Similarly the object of the will is good—but with this difference. Whereas the senses have their own special kind of good, the will tends to good in general, not to just this or that special kind of good but towards good as such, to all good as perfecting the human being.

Will determined to good in general   By nature man is destined to have what he needs for his perfection. This is just another way of saying that man's ultimate goal is good and all his fundamental urges focus upon it. Consequently the will cannot be neutral to good. Good must be sought and evil, its opposite, must be avoided. On this score there is no freedom. *Natural volition* describes this determination of the will and separates it from *deliberate volition.*

Free in regard to particular goods   Deliberate volition concerns particular goods, which because of their incompleteness cannot satisfy man's desire for perfect good. When he confronts several of such goods deliberate volition comes into play. He faces the decision of choosing some or none at all, and having decided on some he must decide which ones. Obviously he is making a choice, is deliberating. In connection with this type of volition man enjoys freedom or, as is usually said, the will is free.

Motive   This unique freedom deserves some further explanation; but first a word about motive. It is defined as "anything which inclines an individual to conscious activity."[5] The degree of influence of motive upon the will varies. But it may be safely said that as the motive becomes stronger, the will more easily, but not necessarily, moves in that direction. Notice that the person's decision or choice does not have to follow the strongest motive. It is the intellect's rôle to furnish motives, weigh them and pass judgment. But the motive as finally accepted and which brings the will into action may have been in itself inferior to the others. For this is the essence of freedom, that a man can be aware of the most compelling motive and yet disregard it.

Determinism   Opposed to human freedon is *Determinism*.
explained   This doctrine maintains that all the events in man's mental life are as antecedently conditioned as the processes of physical nature. All his actions are absolutely determined sequences of previous actions and states. All human conduct, whether good or bad, flows with the uniformity of the law of gravity from man's inner nature and external circumstances, from his total self and environment. These in turn are products of irresistible forces reaching back in an endless chain of succession. This theory implies that if a man could know all the antecedents of any given human act, even those traditionally called free, he would see why it and not its opposite was done. In other words, he would see that it came not as a matter of choice but as a matter of course—the necessitated result of inescapable antecedents.

[5] Rauth, J. E. and Sheehy, Sr. M. M.: *Principles of Psychology* (Milwaukee, Bruce Publishing Co., 1945), p. 66.

Moderate   On the other hand there is the doctrine of
indeterminism   *Moderate Indeterminism*, which has been men-
—its limi-   tioned. It regards man as determined to good
tations   in general but free in regard to particular
goods. Let it be noted that this does not mean that the acts
of the will are uncaused; rather adequate causes are im-
plied. Likewise Moderate Indeterminism takes into account
the myriad ways in which men are bound and without
freedom. It stresses man's obligation to condition his freedom by duly regarding himself and his relations to society.
It admits that some men and women in practice are such
slaves to their environment, upbringing, caste, passions,
habits and other determining factors that they may occasionally not realize their prerogative of freedom.

Its freedom   Conceding these limitations upon freedom,
             the Moderate Indeterminist claims that in
some instances men confront alternative courses. They may
act or not act (*freedom of exercise*) or they may choose one
object or action rather than another (*freedom of specification*).
Any number of motives may be perceived and their inequalities admitted. Yet even the most potent does not
force a man to follow its lead. With knowledge of them all,
he may spurn them all or follow the one of his choice. Even
though a person had complete knowledge of the man and
his character and his circumstances and conditioning, he
would not be sure antecedently what choice the man was
going to make.

Probability   This does not mean that a shrewd prediction
of prediction   could not be made. Knowledge of the person
and other items connected with his decision might suggest
his choice with considerable probability. But the Moderate
Indeterminist insists that one could not be sure, since the
man's choice does not follow as day the night the interlock-
ing network of his character and culture and other conditioning antecedents. All of these might be perfectly under-

stood, yet his decision might turn out to be disconcertingly unexpected.

Freedom and license Freedom of the will, or moral freedom, does not mean simply doing what one wants. W. G. Everett explains[6] that men are morally free only when they are completely determined to their conduct by a true moral standard. To the extent even to which one hesitates between right and wrong one is not morally free, for in this case evil solicits, attracts, influences one. Moral freedom results in harmony and a just expression of all the powers of the self, in contrast with the discord and strife which competing and uncontrolled appetites introduce into human nature. Moral freedom is secured through the rule of reason, which subordinates man's partial, conflicting aims and desires to the central aim of his life. The morally free life is the life that has won its unity, harmony and peace. The ideal of human freedom is not an undetermined will, but rather a freedom of life won through a will guided by true insight. Though free, men remain subject to all the requirements of a well-ordered polity. But their allegiance as moral freemen has been transferred from the rule of unorganized impulse and desire to the law of reason and truth.

Man an individual but also a person Man is *not* just a loose combination of activities found among the elements and plants and animals with the addition of suprasensory faculties of will and intellect. While manifesting great complexity, man just as certainly shows himself to be not many things but one single thing—*a person*. It is not enough to call him an individual. The earthworm is an individual and so is a fly on the screen. Individuality merely separates things on a material and spatial basis. But personality, while implying individuality, goes way beyond. It

[6] *Moral Values* (New York, Henry Holt & Co., 1918), pp. 357-358.

supposes the positive perfection of rationality. A person, then, is what a human being ought to be called—not merely an individual. *Person* is defined as a being whose nature it is to exist in itself, to have rationality, to be so complete that it does not need another being to complete its nature and that it cannot be transferred to another or be shared in by another.

All actions On the basis of his personal unity all man's *attributable* actions must be attributed to him. They may *to the person* be voluntary or not voluntary, elemental, vital, sentient or rational, yet all of them come from the same agent, from the man. He is their cause. Thus most truly it is not a man's eye that sees but the man. It is not his stomach which digests food. He digests his food. It is not his nervous system which reacts to a stimulus. He reacts. It is not his intellect that thinks or his will that decides. He thinks and he decides. Obviously human powers and faculties may be looked upon as the immediate principles of the actions which follow their operation. But in the last analysis all activities which proceed from the human composite must be attributed to that composite in the full unity of its personal wholeness.

Man's unity The explanation of man's personal unity rests *explained* upon the mutually perfecting action of the two incomplete principles constituting a human being. They are the body and the soul. The most fundamental principle of man's activity is his immaterial, spiritual soul. But it is not complete. It needs the body, not to be a soul, but to achieve the completeness of human nature. Likewise the body needs the soul to give it existence in the human composite. Together these two, the body, or the material principle, and the soul, or the formal principle, combine and of their incompleteness produce a complete man. But it is the higher and rational principle which gives man his unique perfection. It raises him above the brute beasts, separates him from all the rest of lower creation and relates him to the pure spirituality of the angels. It challenges him to live up to its high destiny or to pay the penalty of failure and accept in practice the brute beasts as his peers.

6. THE SOCIAL, SHARING DIMENSION

Man's complete portrait To think that the survey of man as inorganic, living, sentient and rational exhausts his nature is to overlook his relations with his fellow human beings. Man is not only a rational animal but a *social* animal. Today his social dimension is not only acclaimed but often exaggerated—probably this century's reaction to the extreme individualism of the nineteenth. It is not because of any doubt about the social aspects of human nature that it is considered here; but because a portrait of human nature without it would be grotesque.

The four basic societies Social means united together, held or done or shared in common. To say that men are naturally social signifies that by their innermost nature they need one another in order to realize a truly human existence. Man's need of union with his fellow men is shown from an analysis of the four basic societies. The society of *natural origin* is the union of man and woman in parenthood. The second is the *domestic or economic community*. It includes all the social oneness needed in managing a home, raising children, making a living, recreations, running a business. For these activities men must cooperate and work with one another. The third society is the *political community*, or the *State*, in which as citizens men unite to promote the common welfare. Finally there is the *ecclesiastical community*, in which human beings join for the purpose of serving God and saving their souls.

Man's needs In himself man is insufficient physically, mentally and morally. He has material needs for food and drink, for money and clothing and shelter, for health and sexual satisfaction and beauty and strength and activity. He has spiritual needs of growing in knowledge and in the love and practice of virtue. He needs to have friends and a legitimate pursuit of honor and fame and power and glory. And first and last men need God. These needs are not forced upon man from without. They spring from his very being.

Their satisfaction demands society   To some extent man can satisfy these needs by himself. But to be *adequately* met as they should, they require human cooperation. Apart from society they cannot be fulfilled. Man cannot bring himself into being any more than he can nourish himself in his earliest years. What many animals know by instinct, man has to learn, some of it by his own experience; but for the most part he builds on the knowledge he shares with others. And so on for all his other fundamental needs. Their satisfaction demands social relationships. Thus the need of human beings for one another plunges deep roots into human nature, with the result that, for their most ample development, men must help one another.

Social living natural   Society is not an accident, not a convenient arrangement, no mere product of man's arbitrary choice or enlightened prudence, not a makeshift creation for his self-preservation and well-being. Society is as much part of man's natural endowment as human nature itself. For man is as much a social being as he is a living, sentient, rational being. Man's unity amid so much complexity embraces the last complexity of social needs and social outlook and social responsibilities and rewards. Under threat of frustration man must live up to the rational demands of his social nature.

Man's social nature restated   The truth of man's social nature, which the thirteenth century Thomas Aquinas made so basic in his philosophy, is eloquently restated by George S. Fullerton. ". . . the ancient egoists, in setting before man their selfish and antisocial ideal of human conduct, made their appeal, not to the whole man, but only to a part of him. The normal man, whether savage or civilized, whether ancient or modern, cannot desire a life filled only with the objects which they set before him. Nor is the modern moralist, or as he prefers to style himself, 'immoralist,' Nietzsche, guilty of less gross a blunder. He rails at morality as commonly understood, calling it 'the morality of the herd,' and he recommends isolation, the repression of sympathy, and a contempt for one's fellows. To be sure, the 'herd' is a scornful rhetorical expression . . . for men do not, properly speaking, live in herds; but they do normally live in human societies of some sort, and they have the instincts and impulses which fit them to do so. The repression of such instincts and impulses does violence to their nature, and he who advocates other than a social morality should advocate it for some creature other than man. Man is a social creature, and, among the objects of his desire and will, he must give a prominent place to some which are distinctively social." [7]

READINGS

Celestine N. Bittle: *The Whole Man*, pp. 17–42; 273–301; 352–405; 463–563.

Robert E. Brennan: *General Psychology*, pp. 31–42; 96–109; 117–125; 321–345; 353–358; 418–427; 445–472.

Alexis Carrel: *Man the Unknown*.

Johann Lindworsky: *The Training of the Will*.

Thomas V. Moore: *Dynamic Psychology*.

J. E. Rauth and Sr. M. M. Sheehy: *Principles of Psychology*, pp. 17–31.

Sr. Roberta Snell: *Nature of Man in St. Thomas Aquinas Compared with the Nature of Man in American Sociology*, pp. 1–34.

Sr. Mary Joan of Arc Wolfe: *The Problem of Solidarism in St. Thomas*, pp. 54–117.

[7] *A Handbook of Ethical Theory*, p. 101, by permission of Henry Holt & Co., Inc. Copyright, 1922, by Henry Holt and Company.

Chapter 3

ULTIMATE GOAL OF ACTION—THE SUMMUM BONUM

1. INTRODUCTION

The question   On the basis of what man has been shown to be, what is the purpose or ultimate goal, the *summum bonum* of his existence?

Different orders   By nature man's appetites tend towards a confusing array of things, but these appetites cover a wide range of excellence. They are all good in their own order, but those orders in themselves differ hugely. There is the simple order of elements, the living order, the sentient order, and finally the rational and social order. A man can follow any of these orders. He can let any one of them dominate.

Man's choice   As Dr. Cabot wrote,[1] "You can use the toe of your boot to poke the fire; but it was not made for that and so it suffers. A poker does the work better and is none the worse for it. You can use a man as an adding machine, as a beast of burden, as ballast, cannon-fodder. But he comes off the worse for it, because only a small part of him is functioning. No power especially characteristic of him then guides the use to which he puts himself. If he smokes like a chimney, drinks like a fish, or drifts like a cloud, it is reasonable to suspect that something is wrong in him because he is not a chimney, a fish, or a cloud. If he guzzles like a hog, snarls like a wolf, or balks like a mule;

[1] Cabot, R. C.: *The Meaning of Right and Wrong* (New York, The Macmillan Co., 1936), pp. 72-73.

36

if he is as ruthless as a tiger, as imitative as a sheep, as mean-spirited as a cur, he is fighting the main trend of his own *human* nature, laid down in the structure of his body and of his mind."

Man's
highest
excellence

The sad fact is that man can let the lower orders prevail. But if he does *he fails to measure up to his highest excellence as a human being.* Man takes his unique worth from the truth that, while sharing something with the elements and plants and brute animals, he transcends them all in his powers of intellectual knowing and willing. For them must be allowed a non-animal principle, the rational soul. Its dignity gives man his excellence, and it is the soul's being which gives man his highest objective and purpose. His existence cannot realize merely the perfections of the plant or animal. Above all, and under threat of losing everything, it must realize his truly human powers and attain the goal of his highest perfection. The question then is: what is his ultimate goal or objective, or, as philosophers say, what is man's ultimate end? his *summum bonum?*

Objective end

When a man asks his son why he did something, he is asking the boy to give the purpose or end which he had in mind. Or suppose you ask a child why he is going home. He replies that he is going home for dinner. Suppose the dinner is waiting for him on the table. It exists independently of his thinking and his desire or appetite. It is an object for him to tend towards, to desire, to want and eventually to enjoy. As an object existing and sought after, the dinner is the *objective end.* Objective end may be defined as that for which something exists or is done and which completes and perfects a thing.

Subjective
end

However, for the boy on his way home to dinner the *enjoyment* of the meal exists only in his thought. It belongs to him as a thinking, imaginative subject. Understood in this sense the dinner is the *subjective end*. It is the possession of the object. It is the objective end realized and possessed. The dinner is not yet being enjoyed actually. It exists, this enjoyment of the object, only in the order of thought, in the intentional order. Distinguishing the end as objective and subjective doubles the original question: What is man's ultimate objective end? And what is his ultimate subjective end?

Ultimate ends   But first man's *ultimate* objective and subjective ends must be disengaged from merely intermediate or proximate ends. The ultimate objective end signifies that object which will satisfy all man's desires and leave nothing further to be sought after. Anything short of this will be intermediate or proximate. The ultimate subjective end means the ultimate objective end viewed as attained, as giving the satisfaction and perfection which it can confer by being possessed. But, it must be remembered that the ultimate subjective end exists as an end not actually but only in the order of promise, in the intentional order of thought, of anticipated possession and satisfaction.

Ultimate ends exist   Man has such an ultimate end, since it is evident that he has subordinated ends. Thus a farmer sows to reap; he reaps to sell his harvest; he sells his harvest to provide for his family; he provides for them in order to be a good husband and father. But the subordination of end to end cannot be continued endlessly. The ends being dependent postulate eventually a final end—the final end of a single series and in the last analysis of all series. This is the ultimate goal.

Same for all men   Furthermore it is the same for all men, since all men have the same sort of nature. People may disagree about this ultimate end. But, note well, in one way or another some ultimate objective is accepted. The disagreement about it does not change its character. It remains just what it is—like the dinner on the table waiting for the boy to come home. But it does vary subjectively according as men anticipate different kinds of satisfaction.

Satisfies   Finally man's ultimate end must satisfy his
highest   highest appetites. As a complex organism man
appetite   has manifold needs or desires or potentialities
to be realized. But varied and numerous as these appetites are they operate on different levels. They are not coordinate. They differ in dignity and importance. A thread of subordination runs through them, giving them their due order which they best realize when they best fit into the human pattern. But what establishes this pattern? Certainly not those inferior appetites which relate man to the plants and brute animals. Rather it is his *rational appetite*, or will, which is the principle of subordination. All man's lesser appetites and desires take their worth and excellence from their relation to the whole man under the over-all dominance of his rational will. It includes the other appetites as contained within its proper orientation.

2. ULTIMATE OBJECTIVE GOAL OF MAN'S EXISTENCE

Fundamental   Poets and novelists and dramatists as well as
ethical issue   philosophers have dealt with the theme of
man's *ultimate objective end*. They may not have used the technical terms, but the meaning stands: What is it that human beings want? What is it that will leave no further yearnings and bring the satisfaction of perfection or completeness without remorse or satiety? What is the highest good? Life's ultimate objective? This is the fundamental ethical issue.

Not wealth   Many inadequate replies have been made, at
               least in deed, by people who have set up
certain goals, given their all to reach them—only to reap the frustration of failure or the disillusionment of finding them miserably disappointing. One such common, but mistaken, goal is wealth. Some people want it without regard

for any other value; they make it the sole purpose of their existence. Notice that their mistake is not in craving riches but in craving them above everything else, in prizing them as life's supreme good. This they cannot be.

> Although the rich man from his mines of gold
> Dig treasure which his mind can never fill,
> And lofty neck with precious pearls enfold,
> And his fat fields with many oxen till,
> Yet biting cares will never leave his head,
> Nor will his wealth attend him being dead.

> (Boethius, *Consolation of Philosophy*, III, 3)

Philosophical proof   That is the way Boethius, who knew both riches and poverty, expressed his esteem of wealth. More philosophically it can be pointed out that whether riches be thought of in terms of natural wealth or simply as the accumulation of money they do not qualify as the highest good or ultimate end—as the *summum bonum* of life. For man seeks natural goods such as clothing and houses and food and drink and such needful things to preserve himself. They are not ultimates but merely means to his welfare or satisfaction. Riches in terms of money exist for the purpose of securing these goods. Money then is not an ultimate but an intermediary good. Unfortunately some persons think money can do everything. It can do a great deal. But to suppose it to be all-powerful is to make the fatal mistake of reducing all good to material and physical dimensions.

Not honor   The pursuit of honor has a higher appeal. Yet, worthy as honors may be, they do not satisfy as an ultimate end of human life. For honor is paid to man because of some exellence. It is a sign of, and testimony to, his merit. But what constitutes man's highest merit or virtue? Certainly not the honor which pays tribute to it! Furthermore, even when merited, honors are short-lived.

Consequently, persons who let honors be the absorbing pursuit of their lives may not be as unreasonable as the devotees of wealth, but they also are making a mistake about the ultimate goal of life.

Not reputation   Likewise they err who think of reputation or fame as life's highest good. For reputation and fame follow upon the recognition of some special goodness in a man; they do not constitute it. And consider how often reputation and fame rest upon skillful publicity and gullibility, and how quickly they pass!

Not power   Many a man who escapes the deception of money or honor or fame and reputation falls a victim to the illusions of power and might. Napoleon had his Saint Helena and Mussolini and Hitler have reaped the infamy of their ambitions. It takes little reflection to see that power cannot be man's ultimate goal. Power is a principle of action—not its end. And power according as it is directed can be a principle of evil as well as of good. What is going to give it direction? That will have to be something other than the power itself. It should be evident, then, that power is not an ultimate, much less the ultimate good of man.

Ultimate goal good   Wealth, honor, reputation and power fail to measure up as life's supreme goal. That goal, since it is man's highest good, must be good above everything else. It cannot embrace evil nor be a principle of evil. Yet wealth, honor, reputation and power occur among evil as well as among good men. Frequently they foment envy and hate, crimes and war. They fail also as ultimate goods, because they leave something further to be desired. For example, a man can have them all and yet suffer from bad health or some other handicap. Again, for the ultimate goal to be natural, it must correspond to inner drives of man's nature. Yet wealth and honor and reputation and power follow not so much from inner principles as from external causes. Often they are the result of good fortune—sometimes simply of shady dealings and hypocrisy.

Physical health proposed The view that man's ultimate good is physical health claims a large following today. Notice the implications of the familiar statement: When you have lost your health you have lost everything. In the same vein was President Ray Lyman Wilbur's command to his students: "Your real job here at Stanford is to learn to run your glands with their various endocrines."[2] A further example of the sublimation of physical health is the attitude of writers and physicians who consider direct abortion ethical when a mother's health demands it. They allow the intentional killing of the innocent for the sake of the mother's physical well-being. Thus in fact, if not in theory, bodily health is elevated to the supreme ethical criterion and goal of man.[3]

Physical health not the ultimate good What was said about wealth and honor and fame and power is applicable to physical health. It is a good and desirable thing. The objection to it rests in its being considered an ultimate, as the supreme good of life. The physical aspects of human nature have been given careful consideration. They spring essentially from the human constitution, of which they are component parts. But the physical is just a

[2] *Time*, October 9, 1939.

[3] As an example of the extremes to which physiological considerations can go cf. Givler, R. C.: *The Ethics of Hercules* (New York, Alfred A. Knopf, 1924), p. 3: "Ever since anatomists and physiologists first began to demonstrate that all the vital functions of man were dependent upon his intimate structure; and more recently that conduct and thought are in the strictest sense of the term functions of man's flesh, they have been laying the foundations . . . of a scrupulously natural science of ethics." And p. 9. ". . . we imply that just as man's body, by means of brain, sense organ, muscle and gland, makes, upon stimulation, all the mind it ever manifests, so likewise that same body of man, through the mechanisms just enumerated, creates ethical notions."

part; it is not the entirety of human nature. Man enjoys a mode of existence not merely higher than the animal or physical, but one which is radically different from the brute animal. Human nature takes its dignity from its rational principle. Its highest goods are the goods of the intellect and of the will. To insist that physical good is man's ultimate good is to divorce him from his most befitting good. It reduces him to the level of the brute in pursuit of the highest animal good, namely physical well-being. On the contrary, physical good exists for the higher good of man. The soul is the principle of integration, and the body with all its faculties exists for the soul.

Not bodily pleasures Bodily pleasures, which to all intent and purpose some people make the goal of their existence, cannot be man's ultimate good. For pleasure is something which follows upon the possession of something. It is not the thing itself but a property or quality of the thing possessed, either actually or in anticipation or in memory. Another objection resembles the one made to bodily health as the ultimate good. Man's satisfactions are not limited to physical pleasures. He has the higher delights of the soul. If pleasure were man's ultimate good, these would be more fitting to man than bodily pleasures.

Not the soul's spiritual good If man's physical well-being is not his ultimate end, may not the well-being of the soul be the supreme goal of life? Holiness, virtue, peace, intellectual knowledge, may not these goods of the soul be man's ultimate good and the supreme objective of existence? Again the reply is negative. No one denies these are superbly worth-while objectives, entirely harmonious with man's highest faculties. But they do not qualify as man's ultimate end. Notice that they are particular goods, whereas the proper object of the will has been shown to be not a particular good but good in general. Again it may be pointed out that man's ultimate happiness, since it is a perfection of his soul, is indeed a good residing in his soul. But that which produces this happiness is something outside of the soul—not the state itself of the soul.

Not particular goods taken collectively Though none of the goods mentioned can qualify as man's ultimate goal, perhaps, it may be thought, they might be the *summum bonum* if they are all taken together. However, it remains true that taken alone or collectively they are particular goods. And it must be remembered that man's rational appetite, or will, differs from his other appetites in that its object is not some particular good but good simply in general, or universal good. Consequently, no particular good, either alone or collectively, can satisfy man's unique appetite or will.

Ultimate objective Infinite Good If it is asked where such universal good is to be found, the answer is that it is found in *Infinite Good*. Of this good the goodness of creatures is but a reflection or participation. Man's rational appetite, or will, focuses his life upon no single particular good nor upon a collectivity of particular goods but upon the universal aspect of goodness. This it is which will satisfy all man's appetites and leave nothing further as an end of his rational activity. This Infinite Goodness is God.

Nothing finite can satisfy fully Nothing else can satisfy the human will fully. For just as soon as some finite object is chosen, others necessarily are left aside. Yet these too are good and the legitimate object of man's desire. Every choice involves the renunciation of some good, the privation of something which would make the choice more complete and satisfying. In other words, the choice of any finite good is imperfect, leaves something further to be desired and so cannot be the ultimate good which must give complete satisfaction. Saint Augustine (354–430) echoed the universal cry of the human heart in his declaration that God has made us for Himself and our hearts are restless until they rest in Him.[4]

No contra- This is not to say that the natural object of a *diction* finite faculty is the perfect possession of the infinite. This would be a contradiction in terms. The will of man is finite and remains finite; God, or the Infinite Good, remains infinite. When Infinite Good is said to be the ultimate objective end of man, this is not to confound the finite with the infinite nor to step out of the natural order. It means that the adequate objective of man's existence is Infinite Good. It does not imply that man ever can embrace it completely but only in the finite measure of his powers.

3. ULTIMATE SUBJECTIVE GOOD

Infinite Good Man's *subjective end* means man's goal viewed *as possessed* as possessed, the happiness or satisfaction which is anticipated in attaining to the objective final end. In so far as the objective end is real so too is the subjective. The example of the boy going home for dinner indicates how the subjective final end really exists. The dinner is not something merely pictured in his imagination or anticipated in his appetite. It is at home, waiting for him. But his enjoyment of the dinner, that exists only in his anticipated pleasure of sitting down and enjoying his meal. So with man's subjective ultimate end. It is Infinite Good really existing. Towards it as a real thing man's rational desires urge him. But his anticipated happiness of possessing it, this exists in his thinking processes, in the intentional order, or order of thought.

Nature of To the question about the sort of pleasure or *the happiness* happiness man will find in attaining his ultimate objective goal, it may be replied that it will be of an

[4] *Confessions*, I, 1, tr. by F. J. Sheed: (New York, Sheed and Ward, 1943).

intellectual sort. Obviously it could not be hemmed in by
the satisfaction of the senses. Nor is it the exercise of the
will. For if the will is taken as rational desire, then it means
the object is not yet possessed. And if it is will viewed as
delight or satisfaction, it must be said that delight and satisfaction are consequences, not causes, of something possessed.
Delight follows upon having the object which causes it.
The subjective final end of man, then, is an act of his intelligence, an act of contemplation, an act of the soul according to the best and most perfect virtue. It will be his
knowledge of the Infinite with the happiness which accompanies such knowledge.

Perfect hap-   It need not be stressed, that man's perfect
piness not in   happiness is not had in this life. There is too
this life   much evidence in every person's existence
against it. Life's happinesses, for the most part, are few and
quickly passing. If, then, man's destined happiness is not
enjoyed in this world, then where? Here ethics must lean
upon its companion philosophical sciences.

In the next   Natural theology proves man to be the product
life   of God's creative act and providential care.
On this ground it must be supposed that if man has the
natural tendency for perfect happiness it must be fulfilled
eventually somewhere—if not in this life then in the next.
Otherwise he would suffer a frustration, planned and willed
by his Creator, which is unthinkable. It contradicts the
very essence of God's love and wisdom.

Objective   This survey of man's destiny brings out that
goal and   happiness is not man's ultimate objective goal.
happiness   His eventual happiness is not excluded; for if
he attains to his objective ultimate goal, his happiness as-
suredly follows. But this view differs radically from conceiving happiness itself as man's ultimate destiny. Leaning
somewhat upon natural theology Christian ethics holds that
man as a creature of God cannot have in the last analysis

any destiny other than God Himself. For God in creating man could only have made him for Himself. As far as God's action is concerned any other goal would be beneath Him.

4. HUMAN HAPPINESS THEORIES

In general Opposed to the view which sets Infinite Good as man's objective and ultimate goal is *Hedonism*. Not a new theory, it maintains that happiness is the end-all and the be-all of life. It has no use for pain and refuses to consider human conduct in itself as either good or bad, right or wrong. The happiness proposed may be personal happiness, and then the Hedonism is *Egoistic*— or it may be viewed as the universal condition of men, and then *Utilitarianism* describes the doctrine.

Egoistic Some Hedonists accept the existence of God
Hedonism and place man's goal of happiness in the next life. This as well as other doctrines of theirs suggests a similarity to Christian ethics, but the underlying chasm must be remembered. Hedonists in general, however, do not set human destiny in the happiness of another life. It is here on this earth, in the present construction of space and time and circumstances. They deny God's existence and man's immortality and translate happiness into making pleasure dominate pain as much as possible. Whatever gives pleasure and so far as it gives pleasure ought to be desired and enjoyed. Whatever causes pain, first try to avoid it and, this failing, bear it without emotion.

Rejected An obvious objection to Egoistic Hedonism is the difficulty of setting the standard of happiness. Just as soon as a determinant of man's happiness is looked for, happiness itself is renounced as the ultimate standard. But granted this inconsistency, the question still stands: What is going to be the quality of man's happiness? Is it to be the happiness of the gourmand with food, of the musician with music, the thinker with science, the painter with his art, the saint with holiness or the sinner with vice? It seems every man can seek the pleasure which means most to him, which he wants most to have. "This sort of Egoistic Hedonism which puts before the individual his own personal and uttermost pleasure in this life as his supreme rule of conduct appears logically to justify, at least to men of coarse character and passionate impulse, a complete disregard for the ordinary laws of morality. This sweeps away every barrier against passion. It loosens every curb on animal impulse. It makes the desire of the brute the only standard of human reason. Wherefore . . . this system is a sheer denial of moral worth."[5]

Altruistic   Even in ancient times Hedonism widened
Hedonism   pleasure to embrace life as an entirety rather than just its isolated pleasures. Modern Hedonism inherited this tendency, which advanced its objective from individual happiness to the happiness of society and made the latter the goal of all living. From the premise of pleasure's supremacy, it seemed logical to conclude that if necessary one ought to sacrifice himself for the total happiness of mankind. Thus altruistic Hedonism prepared the ground for *Utilitarianism*. Prominent among its champions were Jeremy Bentham (1748–1832), James Mill (1773–1836) and his son John Stuart Mill (1806–1873).

Utilitarianism   *Utilitarianism* lays down *Utility* or the *Greatest Happiness Principle* as the ultimate criterion of morality. Accordingly the supreme objective of life is an existence exempt as far as possible from pain and as rich as possible in enjoyments, both in point of quantity and quality. Human conduct becomes right if it promotes happiness, wrong if it produces unhappiness. Happiness means pleasure and the absence of pain; unhappiness is identified with pain and the privation of pleasure. Pleasure and free-

[5] Kane, Robert: *Worth* (New York, Longmans, Green & Co.' 1920), p. 43.

dom from pain, John Stuart Mill insists, are the only things
desirable as ends.

J. S. Mill's   John Stuart Mill clung to happiness as the test
doctrine   of all rules of conduct and the end of life, but
interpreted happiness in terms of multiplying it among men
in the light of their social nature. "The social state," he
declared,[6] "is at once so natural, and so necessary, and so
habitual to man, that except in some unusual circumstances
or by an effort of voluntary abstraction, he never conceives
himself otherwise than as a member of a body; . . . Any
condition, therefore, which is essential to a state of society,
becomes more and more an inseparable part of every
person's conception of the state of things which he is born
into, and which is the destiny of a human being. Now, society between human beings, except in the relation of
master and slave, is manifestly impossible on any other foot-
ing than that the interests of all are to be consulted. . . . .
In this way people grow up unable to conceive as possible
to them a state of total disregard of other people's interests.
They are under a necessity of conceiving themselves as at
least abstaining from all the grosser injuries, and (if only for
their own protection) living in a state of constant protest
against them. They are also familiar with the fact of cooperating with others, and proposing to themselves a
collective, not an individual, interest, as the aim (at least
for the time being) of their actions. So long as they are
cooperating, their ends are identified with those of others;
there is at least a temporary feeling that the interests of the
others are their own interests." Every one thus "comes, as
though instinctively, to be conscious of himself as a being
who *of course* pays regard to others. The good of others becomes to him a thing naturally and necessarily to be at-
tended to. . . . ."

    [6] Mill, J. S.: *Utilitarianism* (New York, Belford, Clarke Co.,
1888), pp. 75–77.

J. S. Mill's   Thus did J. S. Mill strike out against the de-
doctrine   basing individualism of his day and widen
inadequate   happiness to include the greatest number. At
first glance this may appear admirable—as indeed it was
in many ways. Its inadequacies, however, should not be
overlooked. Yet there is no need in pointing them out to
stint praise for Mill's sincerity and the lofty moral character
of his life.

Pleasures   One of the chief weaknesses of Mill's doctrine
differ   concerns the standard of the greatest happiness.
Mill thought it quite compatible with the principle of
utility to recognize that some kinds of pleasure are more
desirable and more valuable than others. He said it would
be absurd to consider quantity and quality in estimating
other things but to think of quantity alone in regard to
pleasure. Without hesitation he declared that it is better to
be a human being dissatisfied than a pig satisfied—better to
be Socrates dissatisfied than a fool satisfied. And if the fool,
or the pig, is of a different opinion, it is because they only
know their own side of the question.

The ultimate   Now what is going to decide the relative de-
standard?   sirability of pleasures? Merely to ask the question implies that pleasure itself is not ultimate; for any
answer given will be pleasure's determinant and more
ultimate than pleasure. Nevertheless Mill suggested a test:
Let qualified persons who have experienced the pleasures
decide. But suppose those who have experienced them
differ. Is the majority opinion to prevail? If so, why should
the majority be thought to have a power of discrimination
superior to the minority? It may well be that the minority
is a minority because of its more refined and cultivated
powers of appreciation. Mill's theory fails, on this score, not
because it has no worth but because it limps as an ultimate
standard.

What is for man's happiness? The same weakness appears from Utilitarianism's goal of bringing men together to work for the common welfare. How can one know what will make other men happy? This raises the objection considered in the last paragraph. But more devastating to Mill's system is the principle that a man ought to sacrifice himself for the happiness of others. Why? Why should a person suffer to make some one else happy? How can that be his supreme goal in life and why is happiness the supreme good of others?

Happiness itself an empty objective Mill's failure to face these questions and give them satisfactory answers justifies Barrett's conclusion. "The most valuable life will probably be a life which increases human happiness, but it is not most valuable because it increases that happiness. It increases happiness because it is most valuable, and its various values, well integrated in a harmonious unity of action, are the source of happiness. To argue otherwise would leave the Utilitarian standard an empty formula. We must do what will increase human happiness —but what will do this? In itself this is no standard of *action*, for we can apply it practically only when we know what kinds of action are of a nature to give happiness. Happiness itself is an empty objective."[7]

Mill's own admission As a matter of fact Mill himself seems to admit this in his *Autobiography*—[8] "I never, indeed, wavered in the conviction that happiness is the test of all rules of conduct, and the end of life. But I now thought that this end was only to be attained by not making it the direct end. Those only are happy (I thought) who have their minds fixed on some object other than their own happiness;

[7] Barrett, C. L.: *Ethics* (New York, Harper and Brothers, 1933), p. 206.
[8] Mill, J. S.: *Autobiography* (London, Longmans, Green, Reader, and Dyer, 4th ed., 1874), p. 142.

on the happiness of others, on the improvement of mankind, even on some art or pursuit, followed not as a means, but as itself an ideal end."

Estimate of   Dr. Bruehl's[9] estimate of Utilitarianism and
Utilitarianism its dangers is clear and just. It "is not a selfish doctrine. It stresses the essentially social nature of man and recognizes the sympathetic impulse in man as a natural endowment. It urges the individual to live not for himself but for the greatest happiness of the greatest number. It is democratic in its general tendency and aims at setting up a community in which all have equal rights and none enjoy special privileges to the disadvantage of the rest. Both Bentham and J. Stuart Mill were noted social reformers of their day and they framed their utilitarian ethics to serve as an effective instrument of social reform. The system may be used to render valuable service in this respect but it is liable also to fearful abuse. Its possibilities for abuse spring from the fact that it fails to give clear expression to the rights of the individual. The danger of abuse is increased by its confusion of the social and political with the ethical end of life, a confusion which has culminated in the Totalitarianism of our days."

5. TOTALITARIANISM—STATE ABSOLUTISM

Totalitarianism primarily is a political philosophy. Yet in making the State absolute and man its mere instrument, it raises challenging and dangerous ethical issues. The State becomes man's ultimate goal and the standard of all worth and morality—if morality has any meaning in a system which repudiates it.

Origin   The term Totalitarianism seems to have been
                   used first in an article on Fascism by Mussolini, who may have gotten it from Georg Wilhelm Friedrich

[9] Bruehl, C. P.: *This Way Happiness* (Milwaukee, Bruce Publishing Co., 1941), pp. 82–83.

Hegel's (1770–1831) *Philosophy of Law*. It has other names—such as Economic Determinism, Dialectical Materialism, Historical Materialism. But most deservedly it is called Marxism after Karl Marx (1818–1883), whose Hegelian inspired doctrines Lenin (1870–1924) cultivated and applied to Russia. Marx worked in close association with Friedrich Engels (1820–1895), and both drew upon Hegel, Ludwig Feuerbach and Pierre Joseph Proudhon.

Communism typical   Since *Communism* alone continues officially to exist, it may be viewed concretely as a picture of Totalitarianism. It differs in detail from Germany's National Socialism and from Italy's Fascism. Still its conception of the State as well as its attitude towards other vitally important ethical issues is fundamentally typical of State absolutism in general.

Conception of the State —one party   Theoretically *Communism* repudiates the State, considering it a necessary evil for the time but eventually to be eliminated. But as a fact the Communistic State exists—an artificial organization under strict hierarchical leadership. There is only one party, one ruling class. It came into power on a wave of national crises and used, and uses, every possible administrative and political mechanism and institution to stay in power. Organized with minutest care, intolerant of criticism and opposition, based on authority, discipline and subordination, it demands absolute obedience and service from its members. They are rigorously tested and are liable to expulsion, or worse, for the slightest disloyalty.

All powerful   The *Totalitarian State* recognizes no organized limitation upon its power. There is no realm in which its power does not intervene or at least could not intervene. All religious and ethical basis of politics is rejected. Power politics is the ultimate end of the State's existence. Not only is the State a perfect society as being self-sufficient in its own order; it is absolutely and in every order the perfect society. The State, or the movement bearing the State, is the present god. It alone and exclusively decides what the common good is. It determines the aims of education and of marriage. It turns politics into a religion and the Church into its tool.

Ultimate moral criterion Of the more specifically ethical issues there is, first, the doctrine of Totalitarianism that all rights come from the State. Citizens have only duties—or at best only the rights which the State graciously grants. Without qualification the State can do no wrong. Its simple and ultimate criterion of morality is easily grasped: Whatever helps the Proletarian Revolution is ethical. Thus morality becomes a class weapon, the instrument and justification of the proletarian or exploited classes. It must be used to support the *new order*, in the interest of a more effective and more equitable mode of production and distribution. From such premises frightful inferences follow with inescapable logic. Forced labor is justified. Confiscation of property, lying propaganda, imprisonment, "liquidation" of undesirables, all is ethical by the standard of morality in the absolute State.

Its concept of man The Totalitarian State knows human beings only as instruments of the State. They are completely submerged in the national or social community. Totalitarianism makes the State superior to all persons and groups no matter what they are. It completely subjugates the individual man and the family. It denies all claims of personality and personal rights, intelligence, freedom and democracy. The conviction that the State exists for the citizens is reversed; citizens exist for the State. Man's spiritual side is rejected. The aim is to remake man by dehumanizing him. He is regarded as an atom in the universe, insignificant, without freedom and creative capacities, a creature of only one plane, having everything from, and owing everything to, the State.

Education   Education and all possible means to influence the people are taken over by the Totalitarian State. It inflates education to include anything that can be used to sway the masses—from religious life to sports, from the most unpretentious club to the largest factory. The halter of "education" is put on the citizens not only during working hours but also for their hours of leisure and recreation. They never escape from it.

Freedom   In the Totalitarian society there is no freedom, no liberty of speech, press, assembly or opinion. To keep in power the dictatorship deprives the people of all means of voicing their opinion and of learning the truth of current events. Every channel of communication is censored. Freedom of conscience is limited to the service of the State. All man's freedoms are upheld only in the interests of the toilers and for the strengthening of the social order.

Law   By Totalitarian standards law is a technical term. It is a means to organize power. It is not subject to criticism before the tribunal of reason and the natural law. For the consideration of the objective worth of legislation, Totalitarianism substitutes simply an appeal to authority. The leader's decision proves itself by his very decision. If he ordered it, it is right—a doctrine which evokes the brutal view of Thomas Hobbes (1588–1679), that authority and not truth makes law.

Criticism—   Totalitarianism is best refuted in those parts
discredits the of this work which emphasize man's nature,
person and   his personality, his inherent rights and duties,
the family   and which sketch the nature of the State with its relations to man and other societies. But even now it should be clear that Totalitarianism, in theory and in practice, not only destroys the personal nature of man, but condemns him to an existence fraught with insecurity and danger. To propose the State as the absolute goal of human

existence and morality contradicts man's nature and
destiny. As a unit he is naturally free. He exists before the
State. He has a destiny beyond the State. It is the State's
duty to help him achieve it. The State has no right to limit
personal freedom except in so far as it is needed by the
State's true purpose of promoting the common good. The
family also is a natural unit, with its own natural end, duties
and rights. Totalitarianism denies these essential rights and
dissolves the family in itself.

Atheistic   Waldemar Gurian has forcibly expressed the
atheistic character of Totalitarianism.[10] It
either replaces God by the closed and self-sufficient being
called society, or it misuses the famous sentence of the
New Testament: "Render to Caesar the things that are
Caesar's and to God the things that are God's." "The
totalitarian Caesar decides what can be given to God. God
is no longer the aim of the political unity but its means. He
is, as its mythical expression, its servant and instrument. The
society is not reflecting God; God is the reflection of the
society. The totalitarian regime adores the god produced
by itself. Thus, in the last instance, if it uses the name of
God, it adores its own image deifying itself."

6. SUMMARY

Totalitarianism has definite, if dangerous, attractions.
What has been said about it should suffice to show that
whatever may be offered in its favor must be weighed
against its basic errors. Likewise human happiness theories
hold out bright promises. But conceived in error they cannot
escape their unfortunate parentage. Man's destiny must
harmonize with his true and complete human nature. It
points to the conclusion that man has an ultimate goal, that
his goal is, objectively, Infinite Goodness and, subjectively,

[10] "The Totalitarian State," in *Proceedings of The American
Catholic Philosophical Association*, vol. xv (1939), p. 66.

the satisfaction and happiness which his finite possession of It can give.

READINGS

Thomas Aquinas: *Summa Theologica*, Part I–II, qq. 1 to 3.

Aristotle: *Nicomachean Ethics*, Bk. i.

Michael Cronin: *The Science of Ethics*, i, chapters iii and x.

Walter Farrell: *A Companion to the Summa*, ii, ch. 1.

Waldemar Gurian: "The Philosophy of the Totalitarian State," in *The Proceedings of the American Catholic Philosophical Association*, vol. xv, 1939, pp. 50–65.

Thomas V. Moore: *Principles of Ethics*, chapters xxv, xxvi and xxvii.

Chapter 4

GUIDE TO THE GOAL—THE NATURAL MORAL LAW

1. LAW IN GENERAL

The rôle of law The complex creature called man has a definite goal to reach. It is God Himself, if goal is taken as the objective ultimate destiny. If man's subjective destiny is meant, it is the happiness which attainment of the objective end will bring. *The moral "ought" springs from this relation.* For, granted the goal and man's power of reaching it, man must under threat of frustration strive towards it. In terms of ultimates, man's life-work spreads out before him, with the prophecy of inevitable struggle. He must travel from what he is to what he must become—an arduous journey, long and dangerous and laden with eternal consequences. To bring the pilgrim through safe God helps him by His grace and by law.

The super-natural order *Grace* means a special gift of God, in no way due to men. By it they enjoy a new mode of existence and acquire a destiny essentially loftier than the merely natural destiny which ethics reveals. Without losing his natural worth man moves into a higher order, above and beyond the natural. Hence the new order is called *super-natural* (*super*, above or beyond). Knowledge about the supernatural order does not come from the natural light of human reason. It comes from God Himself and constitutes supernatural or revealed theology.

Law defined *Law,* on the other hand, falls into the field of man's natural knowledge. It is the legitimate

58

object of philosophical investigation. Thomas Aquinas (1225–1274) defined law as a (1) reasonable command, (2) made and promulgated by legally constituted authority, (3) for the welfare of the community, or, as is usually said, for the common good.

An act of reason Law primarily is an *act of reason*. Acts of the will or arbitrary pronouncements of legitimate authority do not constitute the essence of law. If legislation is unreasonable, no matter what else may be right about it, it is not law and cannot claim observance.

Will not excluded Yet the *will is not excluded*. For law cannot be entirely divorced from the determination of the authority to enact the law and provide for having it made known and observed. Thus when rationality is stressed as fundamental, it is a matter not of excluding will but of giving due precedence to intelligence.

Twofold function Law has a twofold function: *to guide and to bind*. Law offers a plan of action, that is its characteristic note; but it is not just a plan. The legislator wants the plan carried into action. He commands its observance. As a plan or guide, law pertains to the intelligence. As an obligation laid upon subjects, law springs from the legislator's exercised will. Thus the reason and the will combine in the constitution of valid law.

Legitimate authority Law must come from *legitimate authority*. This may be a single person or a group of men, as the Congress of the United States of America. The point is that the originating source of law, for its enactment to be authentic law, must be the proper authority, functioning by the rights it enjoys and the procedures imposed upon it.

Promulgation *Promulgation*, or making laws known, does not belong to the nature of law. Yet unless the legislator brings a law to the notice of those it proposes to guide and bind, they can neither profit from it nor be bound by it. The right of promulgation as well as the duty of defining how it is to be done rest upon the law-making body. The Church has done this for ecclesiastical law, whose promulgation consists in publishing the law in the Vatican's official journal, the *Acta Apostolicae Sedis*. Unfortunately, civil authorities sometimes neglect to define procedures of promulgation, with consequent confusion and even injustice.

Purpose of law   The third important phrase of the definition of law stresses its purpose. *Laws exist for the welfare of the community, for the common good.* Any legislation which favors a chosen group, no matter its size, at the expense of the common welfare by that very fact forfeits all claim to be considered authentic law.

What the common good is not   The common good is *not* the sum-total or aggregate of the private goods of the members of society. This would mean merely the collectivity of the citizen's individual good. Again, and contrary to widely held opinion, the common good is not "the greatest good of the greatest number." It is not, as nineteenth century Utilitarians claimed, convertible with the good of the majority.

Adam Smith's view rejected   Of earlier origin is the view of Adam Smith (1723–1790), who considered the common good as something that would follow automatically if everyone sought his own private good to the highest degree. This was the odious theory of "free enterprise" and "harmony of interests," which introduced the tragedies of extreme individualism. It still claims some champions among capitalists and industrialists.

Single party systems   But more cataclysmic for the present time than any of these errors is the treacherous use of the phrase "common good" in the single party systems of Fascism and Nazism and Communism. While professing utter devotion to the social group, in reality they work only to benefit their own tyrannical exploiting cliques.

Common good defined The *common good* is defined as the totality of material and moral conditions which are practically necessary for members of society to achieve their due perfection. (pp. 17 ff.) Man's attainment of his ultimate goal is a personal achievement and will ever remain so. But being of a social nature he must look to organized society to help him. Those helps considered collectively are the common good (see p. 409).

In more detail The maintenance of law and order pertains to the common good as does the right of collecting such money as is required for the activities of organized society or, in other words, of the State. Protection against outside enemies also is a function of the common good. In behalf of the common good may be claimed all the facilities and services which citizens need to help them to their due perfection of body and soul as well as to other external goods but which they singly cannot furnish. Naturally, then, the common good is composed of many and varied goods. Yet it is not the common *goods* but the common *good*. It is really the collectivity of all those secondary goods from whose organization comes the state.[1]

[1] Cf. J. F. Cox, *A Thomistic Analysis of the Social Order*, p. 55. ". . . the only created good which can be considered for this commonness of existence is the human separate type of good. This can exist as an actual perfection for many persons, because it is not as such a perfection of any one of them. It is a good which can be loved and desired by many persons, but enjoyed or possessed as such by no one of them exclusively. It therefore has a common existence as a good for each and all of those desiring and loving it. Such a common good is the state, since as a unity of order resulting from the concerted action of its many citizens acting for a common end, it has an existence separate from any one of its citizens; hence it can act as the common good to be desired and loved by all. (*Sum. Theol.* I–II, q. 1, a. 2). The state community, therefore, is the existentially common good. This separate common good either as desired or achieved we shall call the objective common good (bonum publicum), or simply and unqualifiedly *the* common good."

Private and common good   Misconceptions about the relations between man's private good and the common good have wrecked lives and echoed in the cries of oppressed and miserable multitudes. Recall the injustices of the eighteenth century's *laissez-faire* and the nineteenth and twentieth century's Marxian socialism as prime examples of what can happen when man's social good is divorced from his private good. *Laissez-faire* championed an exaggerated individualism. Marxian socialism went to the opposite extreme and dissolved personal worth in the sovereignty of the social, or common, good. Both extremes had dire consequences. History proves that without paying terrible penalties, man cannot reject either the private good or the common good. Both must be considered and reconciled in the good life.

Man's ultimate goal the same   It should be clear that the ultimate goal of man in the social group is not different from the ultimate goal of citizens taken singly. The common good must help the individual citizen to the *good life*. Otherwise it is indefensible and obnoxious. Man's ultimate good, in terms of the adequate object of his rational nature, is of supreme importance. No true law can really conflict with man's highest good. But in behalf of the common good lesser goods of health and freedom and wealth and property can be curtailed and sacrificed. Yet the privations need not, indeed should not, imply the loss of man's highest destiny. Rather the sacrifice of the lesser goods should be stepping stones towards human perfection. In this way, far from conflicting with man's ultimate good, any sacrifice made for the common good promotes human welfare and advances man on the road towards perfection and his ultimate goal of Infinite Goodness.

Precedence of common good over private good   The precedence of the common good over the private good *exists only in the social order*. This superiority does not debase the individual person nor submerge him in some mythical collectivity called Society or the State. Man's greatest good remains personal, an individual good, synonymous with his ultimate perfection, for which he must strive. The common good exists for man, to help him—not man for the common good. To reverse this and have man exist absolutely for the sake of the common good degrades him to the level of a tool. His personal worth and rights evaporate. He becomes a cog in a vast machine or, at best, a cell in a living but monstrous organism.[2]

Kinds of law   Law as just explained covers the enactments of national, state and civic governments, and of other legislative groups. But human law is not the only law there is. There are, for example, the eternal law and the natural law, the moral law and the law God gave to Moses. Evidently these are not exactly the same. Law coming from God in direct commandment certainly differs from a decree of human authority. On the other hand, they are not totally dissimilar. How law can have meanings which are different yet partly alike may appear from a sketch of the origin and manifestations of law.

2. THE ETERNAL LAW

The universe   To seek the basis of law requires a widened
causal not   view of the universe in all its complexity of
casual   living and non-living things, of men and ani-

[2] For a logical, if revolting, application of this theory see *Time* (May 7, 1945, p. 35), where a Dr. Schuebbe, of the notorious Nazi Annihilation Institute at Kiev, cooly admitted that he had killed 21,000 people. He explained how the physicians at Kiev were ". . . aware of the importance of this job. Aside from certain devious phases of this action I still maintain that, just as one prunes a tree—by removing old, undesirable branches in the spring, so for its own interest a certain hygienical supervision of the body of a people is necessary from time to time." In nine months the Institute "pruned" between 110,000 to 140,000 "persons unworthy to live." They were epileptics, schizophrenics, Jews, foreigners, and gypsies.

mals and plants and elements. This totality did not produce itself; nor does it keep itself in being. Its origin and its existence flow from God, Who created it and sustains it. As divine, God's action manifests intelligence. It is *causal* not *casual*. It involves action and production with a purpose, with a goal, and this implies an arrangement of things to achieve that goal.

Definition   In a word, God's creation of the world corresponds to a pattern, which existing in God from all eternity is the *eternal law*. It is defined as the plan in the mind of God, according to which all things are directed to their proper ends. But in so far as the eternal law resides in God it lacks promulgation, and for this reason is not law strictly speaking.

3. THE NATURAL LAW

Definition   When, however, God created the universe, the divine plan passed into the actual existence of plants and animals and men and minerals. To every creature He gave an inherent drive, or nature, in virtue of which it would tend by His design toward its own perfection and join with everything else to perfect the universe of natures or simply nature. Creatures, individually and collectively, exemplify the divine plan and share in it. They bear, each one of them, its stamp upon their innermost being. They reflect in their concrete existence the eternal law. This participation of all things in God's plan is the *natural law*.

Natural law   Although the natural law embraces all crea-
and plants   tion, it does not apply in the same way to every-
and minerals   thing. With regard to non-sentient things of the plant and mineral kingdoms the natural law is blindly compelling. They cannot escape from it nor of themselves act contrary to it. Utterly without knowledge of any sort they follow inner drives of which they have no awareness whatsoever.

Natural law and animals On the other hand when the natural law and brute animals are considered, it is evident that, while they are subject to it, there is more than blind submission. Animals have sensory knowledge and appetites, modes of awareness and desire which plants and minerals do not have. Animals not only pursue the good, but they know the good as something sensible, concrete and desirable. Even as plants and minerals, animals are determined to the good, which they cannot reject. Unlike men, when animals perceive the good they cannot turn away from it.

Promulgation Thus minerals, physical bodies, plants, brute animals all exemplify God's eternal law not just by existing but even more so by manifesting definite properties and modes of behavior. Their inherent drives, or specific natures, which urge them to individual and collective perfection can be considered the promulgation of the natural law in their regard.

Physical laws conditional Although every creature falls under the eternal law, things without intelligence lack law's essential characteristic of rationality. To these sub-human material bodies and living things law applies in an imperfect way. The principles governing them might better be called laws of nature or physical laws to distinguish them from natural law as applied to rational beings. Physical law guides but does not command. Its necessity, though real, is *not absolute*, since it supposes that conditions remain the same and that there be no outside interference. Hence physical law is conditionally or hypothetically or physically necessary.

4. THE NATURAL MORAL LAW

Natural law and rational creatures Natural law strictly applies only to rational creatures, who fall under divine providence in the most excellent way. The light of natural reason, which leads men to discern what is good and what is evil, is the imprint of divine light upon them. They share in the Eternal Reason, whereby they have a natural inclination to their proper destiny and perfection. More exactly, then, natural law ought to be defined as *the participation by rational creatures in the eternal law*. To keep this meaning of natural law clear from law as governing non-intelligent things it is sometimes called the natural *moral* law. But it is, frequently referred to simply as the natural law.

Physical, non-rational acts   The addition of the word *moral* to the natural law needs careful analysis. Man cannot be divorced from the laws of nature governing the elemental and plant and animal kingdoms. He is related to them all. As any material body he conforms to the laws of mechanics. As a living sentient being he responds to a baffling array of biological needs and activities falling under their respective laws.

Human rational acts   Yet there comes a division when man's strictly human activity begins, an activity which while supposing everything lower soars immeasurably higher. Man knows suprasensory immaterial abstract truth. His desire outstrips the concrete forms of the good and reaches toward the absolute. Here man's rational nature must be kept in mind in order to understand his uniquely human activity. It may be that a man's daily non-rational acts (*acts of the man*) are numerous. Still the fact remains that some of his acts do bear the character of rationality, of intelligence and will and freedom. These are *human acts*. How often they occur is not the point. It is their difference from merely physical acts which needs stressing.

Man's freedom of choice   Man is not free to choose or reject the abstract or universal good. But of concrete goods he can make a choice. And that is why he is free—*not free to turn away from good*, but *free to make a selection among goods*.

Unlike animals man is not determined to this or that particular good, but he is determined to good in general. This general good the intellect can perceive in a variety of concrete goods. And these it can consider and evaluate on the basis of good in general.

Freedom and human acts Because man can choose among concrete goods, he escapes blind necessitating subjugation to external rule and enjoys freedom. And because he is free he can be the subject not only of acts which lack intelligence and freedom (acts of the man) but also of acts which manifest rational knowledge and freedom (human acts).

Human acts and the moral law Acts which lack intelligence or freedom do not directly concern ethics. Only those acts which bear the recognizable stamp of humanity, those *human acts* which spring from man's knowledge and will, these only deserve the name moral and furnish the proper material of the natural moral law.

Primary precept This law in its most simple, (irrevocable, ineradicable and immutable) precept states *that good must be done and evil must be avoided*. Where does this principle come from? It originates similarly to its counterpart, the principle of contradiction: that the same thing, at the same time and under the same aspect cannot be and not be. Both result from an intuition of being. Both are self-evident propositions. The principle of contradiction comes from joining the simple concept *being* with its negative *non-being* and constitutes the first principle of all speculative reasoning. Likewise, the primary precept of the natural moral law is indemonstrable and ultimate.

The moral ought However, the principle does not belong to the speculative reason, whose object is the true, but to the practical reason, whose object is the good. The practical intellect's first positive idea is of the good, which is what everything seeks. When joined to its negative, that evil is what everything avoids, it gives the first principle of all practical thinking, that good must be done and evil must be avoided. The same act which reveals the good, reveals also that it ought to be done.

Primary precept immutable, ineradicable The primary precept of the natural law, that good must be done and evil must be avoided, is beyond all change and cannot be erased from man's mind. This follows from the relation of the natural law to the eternal law, which is God's immutable plan for the universe and man's part in it. His principal purpose cannot change, and neither can the law binding him to it change.

Cannot be abrogated It is equally certain that God cannot abrogate the primary precept. For Him to do so would imply an irrational tampering with the pattern of His own designing. Recall that the question here regards only the primary precept of the natural law, that good must be done and evil must be avoided. This, it is maintained, suffers no change.

A difficulty At first glance, this may seem a gross exaggeration. Adverse examples come to mind from ethnologists, who relate how some tribes condone stealing and what amounts to cold-blooded murder.

Reply Such apparent exceptions do not conflict with the immutability of the natural law's *primary precept*. For even men of the lowest moral standards do what seems to them good. Their judgment about a particular good may err grievously, as the evidence shows. But this evidence, shocking as it is sometimes, proves that men are fallible in their judgments about the good. In no way does it prove that they are mistaken about the precept or that, corrupted as they may be, they are ignorant of it.

Applying the primary precept It is quite a different matter in making applications of the primary precept to the multiplicity of human needs and desires. These exist in the real, objective order. By God's plan there are definite patterns of satisfaction which men ought to follow. No matter what a man thinks, these patterns remain what they are, and so too does man's obligation to know them and act according to them.

Mistakes possible But for any number of reasons a man can and does make mistakes. From his knowledge of the primary precept, that good must be done and evil avoided, and from his knowledge of human good, a man makes his decisions. But his judgments about objective fact can be wrong; so too can his judgments about objective moral values be wrong. But his error does not change reality, though it can indeed help to establish a debased ethical code.

An example Some peoples still allow concubinage. But their error no more makes it right than a person's thinking the sun moves around the earth makes his judgment true. The objective facts remain just what they are. Thus the nautral law on this secondary level, that is with regard to deductions made directly from the primary precept and human good, is objectively immutable but subjectively liable to change.

Third level Nor does the difficulty of applying the natural law end here. There is still another class of precepts to examine, on what might be called the third level. From the primary precept that good must be done and from his knowledge of human good a man passes to the secondary precept that he must give to every man his due. Applying this secondary precept to the matter of human life a third deduction is possible, that it is wrong to injure a human being. For example, it is wrong to run an automobile into pedestrians. That seems self-evident, and so it is. But a difficulty appears. Think of a policeman pursuing a murderer. The natural law obliges him to do his duty, to stop the killer even with a bullet if necessary. That same natural law obliges him not to hurt human beings. Apparently the law contradicts itself. But notice how the matter of this judgment, the killing of a human being, changes according as it concerns pedestrians or murderers. The ethical judgment also shifts: that it is wrong to injure pedestrians, but right for the policeman to shoot the fleeing murderer. In more technical language it may be stated that in this third level of the natural law, the law varies objectively and subjectively to meet the varying needs of specific instances.

Summary   What, in a more concrete way, belongs to the natural law? A summary may be given on the basis of man's inclinations to good. First of all, man has an inclination towards good which he shares with all substances. They all strive to keep themselves in existence. In virtue of this tendency everything then which preserves human life and protects it pertains to the natural law. Again, human beings share with animals inclinations for sexual intercourse and for educating their offspring and such other appetites as nature gives to all animals. These too belong to the natural law. Finally, man has tendencies toward good which are uniquely his. Thus he has a natural inclination to know the truth about God, to live in society, to shun ignorance, to avoid offending those about him. Such matters as these fall under the natural law. Though the goods man seeks are various, yet he has only one nature. Man is a rational animal, and so he must tend not just to the goods which he has in common with substances and with animals but to the goods which befit him as a human being. Those goods have been set by nature. The mode of reaching them, however, rests with him. He must use his practical judgment. The rightfulness or wrongfulness of an act will be determined by whether or not it helps or hinders him in his advance towards the proper objects of his natural human appetites. Whatever prevents or jeopardizes or makes it harder for him to get the good violates the natural law.

Inadequacy of If a person stops with general principles, the
natural law application of the natural law seems rather
easy. But when it is brought down to the details of life and the
wide differences of the three levels of its application are recalled then some of its difficulties appear. Thomas Aquinas
recognized that in matters of action and in regard to details, truth or practical rectitude is not the same for all, but
only as to the general principles, and that the greater the
number of conditions added, the greater the number of
ways in which the principle may fail. It must be realized
how hazardous it is to apply the primary precept, how much
care and honesty and intelligence and investigation and
time and training a man must have to build up a sound
ethics for himself. In the light of the difficulties and human
weaknesses, it well may be asked whether men generally
could be expected to construct a completely satisfactory code
of ethics on the basis of the natural law and live by it alone.
The answer is that they most certainly could not. That is
why God gave men the undeserved blessing of revealed
religion.

5. HUMAN LAW

Men need Thomas Aquinas wrote that man is naturally
laws endowed with reason to guide him through
life. Were he designed to live alone he would need no other
directive. Then, under God, every man would be a king
unto himself. But human beings are not so designed. They
naturally gravitate into social groups, generating the need
of man-made laws.

Men selfish, Men are so fundamentally self-centered that
problem unless some unifying element prevails, the
complex group will break up, social functions will cease
and the commonweal will suffer. Another reason for human
law springs from the complexity of social problems which
arise and which must be solved. Leadership and control
are needed. For if every man is left to make his own decisions, chaos will result.

Inequalities among men   Human beings are as imperfect as they are unequal, and these inequalities must not be forgotten: inequalities of natural endowment and temperament and environment, of education and training, of interest and opportunity for reflection, of generosity and civic-mindedness. Neither must human selfishness be forgotten and passion and prejudice and low ideals. As long as human beings remain human, society without law is impossible.

Leadership   From the evident inequalities among citizens comes another reason for human law. Some members of the group are better equipped for leadership than others. Their wisdom and experience form a natural resource which ought to be turned to the benefit of the group in wise laws. Again, unless there exists an authority to decide what shall be done, there can easily arise differences of opinion to block needed action.

Good of society   The good of society demands that there be a legislative authority to break such impasses. Finally, there is need of sanction. Directives are not enough. There must be a power to insure observance and punish violations. For law not only guides; it obliges and coerces.

Human and natural law   Although human law differs from natural law, *they are not independent.* Human law echoes the natural law, gets its worth from it, obliges because of it, and cannot go counter to it. All human law is derived from the natural law and exists to promote the common good. The common good cannot oppose human good. So neither can human law. For legislation to serve society, then, it must further the human good or bear upon matter which has no opposition to moral good. Law enacted by human authority is truly law to the extent that it is derived from the law of nature. If it violates that law, it is a perversion of law. Thus from the natural law by way of the common good, human law gets its worth and its form. If men are to lead human lives they must live as social beings. This means submission to social order and to the laws which bind that order together.

Human law   The field of human law covers the needs of
and social   the social order, of the common good, and
peace   applies only to exterior acts. Whatever is for
the common good is proper material for man-made legislation. Consequently legislation must reckon with changes of time and place and a variety of persons and things and situations. Human law covers, then, everything which keeps the unity or peace of society.

Citizen's   Secondly, human legislation embraces any-
welfare   thing that helps citizens to lead good lives. For
the lawgiver's intention is directed chiefly to the common good and then to the order of justice and virtue, whereby the common good is attained.

Necessities   Thirdly, human law concerns itself with pro-
of proper   viding the necessities for proper living. Notice
living   how inadequate the view is, that human law
pertains only to material or physical or temporal goods— that its business is to keep citizens well and happy and safe and prosperous. It should do all of this; but not stop there. By definition human laws should help men *be virtuous and in so doing bring them to their ultimate goal.* To this extent it reaches beyond time into eternity.

Qualities   The qualities of human law are obvious. It
in general   must not conflict with the natural law. It must
be *reasonable, originate from competent authority, further the common good and be promulgated.* It must bear equitably upon all its subjects and be possible of obedience—not only absolutely but relatively. Its fulfilment ought not to be unreasonably difficult.

More in   Man-made legislation ought to foster religion,
particular   and thus be in accord with the divine law. It
ought to foster discipline, by harmonizing with the natural

law. This implies that the law should accord with right
reason and be possible of fulfilment by its subjects. It should
take into consideration the customs of the country and be
adapted to the time and place of its enactment. Thirdly,
it should foster the common welfare, that is, it should serve
mankind. The law ought to be needed either to remove some
evil or to secure some good. Its wording should be clear and
leave nothing obscure. Otherwise, the law itself becomes
a source of dispute and public unrest. It ought to be for the
benefit of no private citizen but for the good of the community in general.

Estimate of   In a given instance it may be difficult to be
law at times   sure whether a certain law has or has not these
difficult   necessary qualities. The National Prohibition
Law roused heated controversy. Some maintained that it
was contrary to the natural law, while others just as stren-
uously championed it.

Not just will   This analysis reveals how human law is not
of authority   just authority speaking its will in a given case.
Human law sinks deep roots into the being of things and
into the vast complexity of God's creation. It is not a temporary, shifting, stop-gap to a pressing problem: "Try it out;
see if it works and judge it accordingly."

Law's basis   The philosophy of human law presented here
in objective   takes law out of the subjective, empirical,
world   positivistic and opportunistic field and places
it squarely in the objectivity of a very real world. Law's
objectivity is the objectivity of that world, created, governed and pursuing its destiny according to a divine plan.

Dangers   Man's efforts to formulate laws in accord with
                  that plan may sometimes fail miserably. But
his efforts and failings cannot wipe out the objectivity of the
world and of man's place in it. Neither should they lead him
to surrender the struggle and submit to the arbitrary pronouncements even of legitimate authority. Just as surely as

he allows human law to break from its anchorage in the natural law, his freedom will evaporate and his precious rights perish.

Just laws bind   The question of a law's being just or unjust determines a man's obligation to obey it. If the law is just it obliges observance just as the eternal law from which it ultimately comes. Laws are just when they have in view the common good, do not exceed the legislator's powers, and when they lay proportionate burdens upon the subjects. On the other hand, unjust laws do not bind.

Example   For example, a legislator may go beyond his authority or make laws for his own gain and renown. Or he may single out some group to bear the heavy weight of his legislative hand while favoring his friends. Such laws are unjust. For the burden of furthering the common good is proportionately the same for all citizens. Laws are also unjust which conflict with divine laws. In short, so-called laws which violate the natural law or the divine law are not laws at all. They are acts of violence.

6. POSITIVE DIVINE LAW

Definition   More than once mention has been made of the *divine law*. This signifies God's pronouncements in the Law of the Old Testament, given to Moses, and in the Law of the New Testament, proclaimed by Jesus Christ.

Need   That men need such a direct and positive indication of how they ought to live should be beyond dispute after what has been said of natural and human law. Adequate as these might be theoretically, their practical inadequacies are evident. Consider the laws men make for men—how contrary, vague, variously interpreted, erring and confusing they are! Consider also the practical handicaps men face when they try to work out moral codes for themselves. That they might know with ease and certitude what to do and what to avoid, *men need the guide of God-given law.*

Control of interior acts   For quite another reason men need positive divine law. Human law extends only to external actions. But man cannot judge interior movements; he is competent only in what he can observe. Yet for men to be truly virtuous their interior as well as exterior acts must conform to the norms of right conduct. A man can hate without physically hurting his enemy. Human law could not adequately curb and direct such interior acts. But God's positive law can, since His jurisdiction and judgment cover man's thoughts as well as his actions.

And the natural law   However, the positive divine law does not wipe out or conflict with the natural law. It presupposes the natural law—even if it goes way beyond that law to point out man's obligations and his way through life.

READINGS

Thomas Aquinas: *Summa Theologica*, Part I–II, qq. 90 to 97.

John F. Cox: *Thomistic Analysis of the Social Order*, pp. 52–63.

Michael Cronin: *The Science of Ethics*, i, ch. xix.

Walter Farrell: *A Companion to the Summa*, ii, ch. xviii.

Karl Kreilkamp: *Metaphysical Foundations of Thomistic Jurisprudence*, pp. 38–73.

J. F. Leibell: *Readings in Ethics*, pp. 301–340.

Thomas V. Moore: *Principles of Ethics*, ch. ii.

John A. Ryan and M. F. X. Millar: *The State and the Church*, ch. xii., "The Moral Obligations of Civil Law."

Chapter 5

MORAL CRITERIA

1. CRITERION IN GENERAL

Need of criterion   The natural law is man's guide to right conduct. But for it to be useful he has to know the law not merely in a vague way but as applied to actual problems. What exactly does it command and forbid? Answers to the question do not come easily and with equal clarity. Some ethical principles are self-evident. Others result from simple analysis and reasoning. Still others need long and technical investigation, and even then are not always perfectly satisfactory. But whatever be the difficulty, when problems of conduct arise a criterion is needed to reveal how the action agrees with the natural law.

Criterion defined   *Criterion* means a test or a standard for judging something. The criterion of sportsmanship is the rules of the game. The criterion of an acid is whether or not it turns litmus paper red. Criteria of measurement are the yardstick and the time at Greenwich. The north-seeking tip of a magnet is a criterion of direction. Criterion is a familiar term. But its purpose in ethics needs explanation, because of morality's double aspect: the subjective, or formal, aspect, and the objective, or material, aspect.

Subjective and objective morality   Of primary interest here is the criterion of objective morality. The question is not whether or not a person is *guilty* of good or evil acts (subjective, or formal, morality) but whether the action itself is good or evil (objective, or material, morality). *Objective morality* belongs to the action itself, apart from circumstances or personal considerations of knowledge and freedom and will. Thus, when a man speaks contrary to what he holds to be true, objective morality focuses not upon whether or not he is *guilty* of lying but upon the goodness or evil of the act of *lying itself*. The same, for example, with helping the poor. Objective morality passes over the motives of the philanthropist to examine the nature of the act itself of giving away money. This distinction between objective and subjective morality, frequently ignored or at times hopelessly muddled, must always be considered in dealing with ethical problems. Objective morality is one thing. *Subjective, or formal, morality* is another. Though distinct they should not be opposed. For the criterion which indicates objective morality points out the direction formal morality ought to take. The ethical character of conduct must be thought of as a union of the two: the subjective, or formal, and the objective, or material. Ignorance about the objective evil character of an act can excuse from responsibility of evil-doing. But the action itself remains unbecoming and evil—even though the offender may be guiltless.

2. PRIMARY MORAL CRITERION

The appetites and their objects good Preceding chapters dealt with the nature of man. Here they find essential application. For the analysis of human nature disclosed manifold appetites. Man well deserves the title of microcosm, or little universe. He shares plain existence with the elements, life with plants, sensibility with brute animals and beyond this has rational faculties of knowing and willing. On the basis of these appetites the principle was accepted that the object of every appetite is good relative to that appetite. *The primary moral criterion* The appetites and their proper objects give the key to the question of the primary criterion of moral goodness. *That is morally good and right in itself which is the natural object of a natural appetite.* To satisfy an appetite by seeking its object and enjoying it is good and right in itself. To use an appetite in such a way that its natural object or exercise is frustrated is to abuse that appetite and constitutes moral evil. For being destined to an ultimate goal, man must use the means to attain it. The means are human acts, whose inspiration comes from human nature. True, the objects of these tendencies are only proximate ends, but in pursuing them man is working towards his ultimate natural goal and perfection.

Conflict among the appetites   At first sight this principle seems simple. Actually it is far from being simple when the complexity of man's needs and desires is recalled along with the fact that being on different planes they can conflict. The satisfaction of one may require the sacrifice of another. Diabetics must give up many pleasures of eating. Men surrender any number of pleasure-giving luxuries for the sake of accumulating money. Love of God and of country frequently involve heroic renunciation. Yet warriors do not choose death because they like to die. Martyrs do not prefer execution because they think life evil. They are making choices of things legitimate and good in themselves, honor to life, God to creatures, which tragic circumstances, not nature, have brought into conflict. Thus within human beings as presently constituted there are the seeds of discord. There is a struggle of the higher appetites over the so-called lower appetites. The good life becomes a struggle of establishing harmony and order among the appetites. It is the price of man's integrity.

Subordination of the appetites   Although man has many appetites, they are not in themselves all truly human, specifically belonging to man, and so of equal dignity. The responsibility of living morally begets the responsibility of living in a way to insure the domination of those appetites which perfect man as man, which contribute to his development not just as a plant or a brute animal but as a human and social being. The lower exists for the higher. Each part of an organism has its own proper rôle to play·and its own proper object and action. Yet its perfection must coincide with service to the entire being of which it is a part. So it is with man's appetites. Each has its proper object. But proper satisfaction cannot be divorced from the over-all perfection of man. Rather every appetite must co-operate in man's due development and welfare.

Human perfection the key — Man has been shown to have an ultimate goal. He is born into this world with a destiny that transcends it. As a result, the organization of his appetites, his choices among their impetuous prompt-ings, must regard his *human dignity* and his social obligations. Thus eating is certainly good in itself. It insures man's physical well-being. But when a man allows the craving for food to dominate his life, when instead of eating to live he lives to eat, such eating becomes evil. It violates the order which ought to exist between eating and human perfection. Note carefully that eating in itself is not evil. It is the abuse of it, the disregard of human perfection which makes glut-tony wrong. On the other hand consider lying. Men have the power of exchanging ideas. Speech exists for this com-munication. But what happens when men speak contrary to what they hold to be true? Speech then serves only to mislead and to falsify. The very purpose of speech suffers frustration. Lying thus appears evil—something intrin-sically wrong.

Man's social perfection — The criterion of morality as *the natural object of a natural appetite* is not restricted to the appe-tites regarding the individual person. It applies also to the appetites which spring from man's social nature and per-tain to the social good. Marriage and having a family cor-respond to appetites which concern the good of the person but even more so the good of society. Again, there is lying.

Its morality must be weighed both from the person's individual point of view and as a wilful frustration of a faculty bearing upon the common good. Thus objective or natural morality must reckon with man both as a personal individual being and as a member of society. The appetite in both orders must be considered.

Primary criterion basic but not complete The statement that the criterion of morality is *the natural object of a natural appetite* needs careful attention. It does *not* assert that because something corresponds to a natural appetite it is good without qualification. It means that objects and actions when they correspond to natural appetites are good in themselves and not intrinsically evil. Whether they are legitimate for a certain person under particular circumstances involves another question. *How do they fit into the general picture of man's appetites and nature?* And this introduces further questions about the over-all determinants of morality. The importance of the criterion of objective morality is this. If an object or an action is good in itself then it *may be* legitimate and moral when viewed in the totality of the circumstances and man's dignity and destiny. But if an object or an action is not good in itself, it can never be right, can never be moral. It is intrinsically evil and never allowable.

Appetite must be natural It also should be pointed out that the appetite in question must be natural. It must belong to human nature as such. A person may acquire an "appetite" for caviar or black olives or hundred-year-old cognac or rare tobaccos. But no one would claim they belong to human nature as such. They may not be opposed to it and may not be evil; but that does not make them natural in the present use of the word.

Must be normal Again, a natural appetite means a normal appetite—not one verging on the pathological. The desire for money or its equivalent corresponds to a

natural appetite. But it is not a natural appetite which
hounds the miser. The criterion of morality involving the
natural objects of natural appetites applies, therefore, to
man's natural and normal appetites with their proper
objects.

Secondary   Finally, in regard to this criterion it should be
criteria   stressed that it is the *primary* criterion. There
are others, shortly to be considered, called secondary or
derivative criteria. The secondary criteria are valid and
useful as far as they go; but they are not ultimates. They
depend eventually on the principle of the natural objects of
natural appetites. However, sometimes it happens that a
direct appeal cannot be made to the primary criterion.
Then one must do his best with the *secondary moral criteria*.

3. SECONDARY MORAL CRITERIA

Of unequal   The secondary moral criteria are not of equal
value   value. Some of them approach the primary
criterion and share its worth. But others at best give only a
degree of probability.

General   The secondary criterion which most closely
injury with   resembles the primary criterion is the principle
general   of *general injury with general observance*. That act
observance
                is evil which if considered as a universal mode
of human behavior would prove generally harmful: on the
contrary that act is good which when so universalized
proves helpful. This secondary, or derivative, criterion of
general injury postulates the principle of the primary
natural criterion but furnishes a test for knowing what the
natural is. The essence of nature is progress towards perfection. Any action which can frustrate this perfection-
seeking impulse is certainly opposed to that nature and
evil for it. Consequently, if by raising a questioned form of
conduct to the universal level and abstracting from particular circumstances it is found harmful to the human race,
then it is unnatural and morally evil.

Kant's Categorical Imperative   The derivative criterion of *general injury with general observance* suggests one of Immanuel Kant's (1724–1804) statements of his *Categorical Imperative*.[1] "Act always on such a maxim as thou canst at the same time will to be a universal law." The difference between Kant's *Categorical Imperative* and the principle of *general injury with general observance* is that the *Imperative* is offered as ultimate. It rests on nothing else, is self-sufficient and self-evident, universally known and perfectly adequate as the basis of morality. The principle of *general injury* is not ultimate but, as explained, is derived from the primary criterion, upon which it is based and from which it gets its worth.

Conditions for use   The application of the principle of *general injury with general observance* requires that the effect result from the action itself and not from some determination of free will or from the excess or failure of the action or from the lack of something which the action involves. Unless these requirements be observed, startling conclusions follow. Thus it can be argued, quite falsely, that being a physician is intrinsically wrong. For if everybody turned to medicine, society would disintegrate. Here, the error comes by drawing the conclusion from what is displaced and not from the act itself of being a physician. Again it might be argued that if everybody constantly used morphine, universal injury certainly would follow. But the injury arises not from the normal but from the excessive use of the drug. It might be inferred, and again erroneously, that men and women being together in factories is unnatural, because grave social injuries would inevitably follow. Again the criterion is misused. For the social evils would result not from the act itself of men and women

[1] Kant, I.: *Fundamental Principles of the Metaphysics of Morals* (New York, Longmans, Green, and Co., 1927, translated by T. K. Abbott, 6th ed.), p. 55.

working together but from the evil advantages they chose to take of the situation. As an example of the proper use of this criterion, think of stealing. A thief may take a few dollars from a wealthy man. Little harm seems done. But suppose theft became universal. No property would be secure and the social fabric would crumble. Notice how the effect in the last instance follows from the act of stealing itself. It does not come from too much or too little of the act. It is not caused by a special turn of the will or by the lack of something arising from the act. The general social harm comes from the act itself as being this particular kind of act. Thus this criterion of *general injury with general observance* is one of the ways to prove stealing is unnatural and intrinsically evil.

Indicative of morality   Although this criterion of *general injury with general observance* plays an important rôle in solving moral questions, it is merely an indication of morality. It does not constitute morality, any more than a compass constitutes a traveler's direction. It points the way. That is the function of any criterion. Consequently, this moral criterion of *general injury* faithfully points out the way to ethical conduct even when no evil follows in a particular instance. As Michael Cronin says,[2] "*An act which, if raised to a general line of conduct, would work evil for the race is bad, not merely when it is generally adopted and when it does actually work evil but in each particular case in which it is performed, and whether evil effects actually follow in the particular case or do not.*" The reason for this is that an act is bad not because it results in evil but because at its very roots it is against human nature. The criterion functions to expose its basic unnaturalness. This remains irrespective of the actual consequences of the act in a particular instance. This may seem rather strange, but it has a familiar counterpart in drugs. A certain drug is known

[2] Cronin, M.: *The Science of Ethics* (Dublin, M. H. Gill and Son, 1930), i, 145.

to be poisonous in certain quantities. It keeps its deadly sting even if a particular person should happen not to die of it.

Human convictions Another secondary, or derivative, criterion is *common human convictions*. The human race is old and in many ways wise with the experience of ages. This criterion rests upon the fruit of that experience. It appeals to convictions about good and evil which men have extensively held over long stretches of time. Circumstances of special cultures and historical moments pass with the centuries. A residue remains—the collected, universal wisdom which humanity has managed to distil out of its struggle for survival and progress. This criterion ties in with the primary criterion of natural appetites and objects. For an ethical principle which has been held by all men at all times indicates that men have learned in this instance what best conforms to human nature.

Value However, it has not the value of the criterion of *general injury with general observance;* it can be dangerously subjective. Further, it is a relation between convictions and human nature, whereas the former secondary criterion represented a relation between human nature itself and the good of humanity. Another weakness springs from the practical difficulty of finding ethical convictions which have the required universality. One such criterion concerns marriage as opposed to promiscuity. But it has been only after long and arduous investigations and controversies that this attitude of men universally towards the marital union has been generally admitted.

Moral feelings Of still less worth among secondary criteria are *the moral feelings*. They are so undefinable and fluctuating and subjective that at best they can never be fully trusted and at worst ought to be mistrusted entirely. The person who says that something is right or wrong because he "feels" it to be that way really puts the question outside rational discussion. Still, *the moral feelings* do have some worth. For there are multitudes of people who abstain from evil and do good for the simple reason that that is the way they feel about it. Any further questioning about their motives or their conception of good and evil is futile. However, the simplicity of their position is illusory. They quite easily confuse right and wrong with questions of etiquette or delicacy or even unadulterated prejudice, and in complicated matters fail utterly to find truth.

4. OBJECTIVE MORALITY AND CIRCUMSTANCES

Criteria *valuable but* *imperfect* The survey of the primary and secondary moral criteria indicates that when used properly they are valuable, but that their use is difficult and liable to error. Here again is evidence that for men to know right and wrong with ease and certitude they must have something beyond human reason. To concede this does not lessen the real worth of natural morality. To admit the imperfection of the criteria does not deny their value. Their importance in the natural order as tests of objective morality cannot be overestimated. For man's insight into the objective nature of an action must be the first step in determining the morality of any action. If an action is objectively right man can proceed to ask whether under *these particular circumstances* it remains right. But if it is against human nature, it is intrinsically bad and further inquiry is useless. No circumstances can change its evil character and make it right. In any problem of ethics, therefore, the first question to be asked and answered concerns objective morality.

Circumstances However, since circumstances can *change the* *the morality of human acts* even to the extent of making an objectively good act evil, they deserve further consideration. Circumstance means anything related to an event. It embraces all those facts and things which surround an action, which place it detail by detail in a definite pattern. Such items as who the person is, where and when the action took place, what were the means used, how it was done and what was the motive—these are circumstances which can affect morality. For a man wilfully and unjustly to kill a human being is murder. But murdering one's mother is matricide—a crime worse than murder. For it violates filial love as well as justice. It is even more unnatural than murder. To relieve a poor man's poverty is right; but giving him money to have him help with a crime is wrong. The evil intention makes an objectively good action actually evil.

Morality of circumstances The circumstances which involve morality are those which the agent *can control*. Suppose a mother gives her child candy which, though she thinks it is pure, happens to be poisonous. Tragic as the circumstance is, it does not make her a murderess. On the other hand, intentionally to give the child poisoned candy would make her a criminal. Regarding, then, the circumstances over which the agent has control, the following principles must be considered.

First principle First, *all circumstances necessary for an act to achieve its due object must be present.* Wilfully to remove one makes an action bad. Think of a physician's order, that a patient be given a certain medicine and that the circumstance of time is critically important. The nurse who intentionally gives the medication at some other time is guilty of immoral conduct and is responsible for any harm which follows.

Second principle Second, for an act to have its complete moral goodness *there must be no evil circumstance whatsoever.* For even if an act is objectively good a bad circumstance destroys its moral integrity. Gambling at bridge is not intrinsically wrong. But if a man uses money which his family needs, his gambling becomes evil.

5. THE END DOES NOT JUSTIFY THE MEANS

The principle   Of all the circumstances which can modify an action's morality, none probably has received more attention than the purpose or motive of the agent, the end or goal he has in mind. This is the circumstance which answers the question *why* an action is done. Its familiar expression is that *the end does not justify the means.*

It does not mean   There is a perfectly just meaning of the principle which is not questioned here. It does not deny that when a man wants to do something he must choose means suitable to his purpose. If he wants to make a journey in the speediest way possible, he will go by airplane. His purpose, the end he has in view, makes his choice of the airplane reasonable and justifies it. If a young musician wants to become an artist, he will go to a competent teacher. Again, the end or purpose in view makes the choice of means reasonable and justifies them. With all of this the principle that *the end does not justify the means* conflicts in no way.

It is an ethical principle   *The end does not justify the means* is an ethical principle. The meaning of "end" is probably already clear. Purpose, motive, goal, intention, objective are synonyms commonly used for the more philosophical term "end." What has the agent in mind to accomplish by his act? That is the "end" as here understood. The word "means" also scarcely needs explanation. Money is a means for paying bills. Strikes are a means for wage earners to improve working and living conditions. Ether is a means for relieving pain. An appendectomy is a means for saving life. The ethical principle that *the end does not justify the means* lays down the rule that no matter how good the intention or motive or purpose or "end" of the agent may be, it cannot make a bad means good.

Examples   A pretty and young Lady Robin Hood stole from her employer to pay for her father's operation.

She also used his money to pay medical bills for her mother and to help unfortunate people. Her total theft amounted to $35,000. Apparently her only motive or "end" was to help people—a motive deserving praise and beyond criticism. But the means she used to help them was theft, and theft is intrinsically evil. Applied to this case, the principle that *the end does not justify the means* affirms that good as the girl's motive or "end" was, it did not change the evil character of her deed. Taking her employer's money was theft. Theft it remains in spite of her good intentions, and so deserves to be condemned. Take another instance. Fire breaks out in a theatre. The manager fears a panic if he tells the straight truth. He tells a lie to get the people out safe. His action is evil, not because of bad intentions but because he used the evil means of lying, which his laudable purpose does not rectify.

Principle rejected by some
Mostly on the plea of helping others, some deny that *the end does not justify the means* and hold that the end *can* justify the means. It is right, they say, under certain circumstances to do evil to accomplish good. "It's plain common sense to do a little wrong for the sake of a great good or to avoid a greater evil." "A person has to be practical in this life." "What's the use of making a sacrifice for an abstract theory!" "It's just being too good for this world." This attitude is far from being purely theoretical. It enters profoundly into daily life—and especially into the views of those who pride themselves on being practical and efficient. If there is fear that telling a patient the truth may upset him, tell him a lie; it is the easiest way out. A physician saves the mother by killing her unborn baby. Her health, the needs of her family, the tragedy of her untimely death, her usefulness to society, these are the physician's pleas to justify murder to save a life. But such pleas do not justify the crime, even though tragic effects may result.

Rejection destroys morality   Unfortunately instances do arise where the principle that *the end does not justify the means* involves tragedy. Simply throwing it over-board seems the easiest way out. But before jettisoning the principle it might be well to pause and consider. Rejecting the principle or disregarding it spells the end of any rational system of morality. For if good intentions can make evil means right, then the action's morality is coming not from some objective consideration but from the agent's inten-tion. Then there will be as many "moralities" as there are intentions. Every man will be a moral law to himself and different moral laws at different times—depending upon circumstances.

Morality not determined entirely by intention   Before morality is tied up simply with inten-tions, consider first how subjective, how changing, how contradictory, how open to whim and passion and prejudice and self-seeking people's intentions are! Above all, to accept the principle that at times the end does justify the means is equivalent, at least tacitly, to rejecting man's nature and place and purpose in life. Man has a destiny and his actions must lead him to it. Those that do are good. Those that de-flect him are evil. This is morality's objective basis, which disappears when morality follows intentions.

6. SUMMARY

In the totality of any human act, naturally the agent's intention must be considered. But morality lodges first in *objective action*, in considerations distinct and separate from man's thinking. As in the world of physical things, man's awareness does not create them; so in the world of moral being. Actions have their own worth, their own due reality and truth in the very nature of man's world and his place in the totality of the world. Man's duty is to discover that reality and truth and try to live by it. His conduct must conform to objective morality, not create it. His intention can disfigure goodness, but it cannot make evil good.

READINGS

Michael Cronin: *The Science of Ethics*, i, ch. v.
Walter Farrell: *A Companion to the Summa*, ii, 28–38; 65–82.
E. F. Garesché: *Ethics and the Art of Conduct for Nurses*, ch. vii, Part I.
Paul J. Glenn: *Ethics*, pp. 97–119.
Charles C. Miltner: *The Elements of Ethics*, ch. xii.

Chapter 6

HUMAN ACTS AND THE EMOTIONS

The ultimate objective norm of morality is the *natural moral law;* the proximate subjective or manifestative norm is *conscience.* The natural law gives the *principles* of right and wrong. Conscience makes the application of these principles to particular *human acts.*

1. ACTS OF HUMAN BEINGS IN GENERAL

Responsibility unequal Any man's life shows a complex pattern of actions, which neither human beings nor human law puts on the same plane. Some distinctions are and must be made. There is a difference between blinking and winking. There is a difference between unintentional homicide and murder. There is a difference between the heart's beating and a calculated lie. There is a difference between a man's speaking falsely about the truth and speaking truthfully about the false. There is a difference between shooting a gun known to be loaded and doing damage with a weapon that was not known to be loaded. In many ways man's actions differ, but for ethical purposes they fall into two divisions: There are actions for which the agent is responsible and others for which he is not responsible.

Acts of the man The actions of which man is the agent but for which he is not responsible are *non-voluntary acts.* They miss the required measure of responsibility. They cannot be attributed to the agent as being under his control. He is their cause but not their rationally responsible cause. They are simply *acts of the man.*

Human acts   On the other hand actions which come under a man's control and for which he is rightly held responsible are *voluntary*. The marks of humanity are reason and will and freedom. When an act comes from a man as its intelligent and free and willing agent it is truly a *human act*— not just an act of the man. A kleptomaniac is not a thief but a mentally ill person. No one blames him. His action is non-voluntary, an act of the man. If, however, the police catch a thief, he pays the penalty, because he is responsible for his evil action. It is a human act.

Requirements of a human act   For man's action to be a human act, an act for which he must take full responsibility, he must know what he is doing, be free to do it and will to do it. *Knowledge, freedom* and *voluntariness* are the characteristics of a human act. To the extent that any one of them is missing a man's action lacks human quality and becomes according to the deficiency an *act of the man*, an act for which the agent is only partially responsible.

Knowledge necessary for willing   For a person to be credited with an action, good or bad, he has to *know* what he wills. In itself the will is blind. It is the faculty of desire, and a man cannot desire what he does not know. It is the faculty of consent, but a man cannot consent to the unknown. There may be a starving family right next door and neighbors perfectly able to help them, but the neighbors are not guilty of neglect unless they know the need and refuse help. A nurse through no neglect on her part gives a patient the wrong medicine and serious complications follow. It is sad and regrettable. But the nurse is not responsible or blameworthy. *Nothing is willed that is not known* is an important ethical principle.

Importance of knowledge   This is why, although morality lodges in the will, *knowledge* is so important to the good life. To act properly men must know what is right and wrong. Yet knowledge of itself does not guarantee proper conduct.

A man may know what is right and even prefer it to its opposite. But human perversity is such that he may still go ahead and do the evil thing. This does not minimize the importance of knowledge. It merely shows, against Socrates (469–399 B.C.) and similar thinkers, that knowledge is not all sufficient to insure proper conduct.

Freedom   *Freedom* is the second requirement of a human act. It is not enough that a person choose something. His choice must be free. It must follow the self-determined act of the will. The will must be its cause. An act which the will itself does not produce is not free. This may happen when the will has action forced upon it from within the human composite itself, for example by a quick and irresistible upsurge of passion. Or the compulsion may come from without, as happens in the instance of physical force. On either supposition the man's action is not under the control of his will and is not a human act.

Examples   The night watchman who opens the door to thieves rather than be shot is psychologically free, but not culpable. The robbery is not attributable to him. Likewise, when violence is used to force a person to sign a contract, he is exercising his psychological liberty yet the civil law is correct in declaring such a contract invalid. The signing was not a human act, and morally cannot be imputed to the man.

Will   Thirdly, an act to be human must be willed, must be *voluntary*. Many actions are below the level of rational choice. For example, the processes of growth, digestion, respiration, assimilation, purely reflex acts, do not fall directly under the control of the will. A simple but clear example is the difference between winking and blinking. The latter is non-voluntary; the former is voluntary. To the extent that actions do not spring from the will, they are *acts of the man*—not *human acts*. For unless man's conduct proceeds in some way from the will it is not truly human, not imputable to him. He is not responsible for it.

2. KINDS OF WILL

Perfect and imperfect will   The fact that there are various ways in which actions can be willed complicates volition. Volition itself does not have degrees: a person either wills or does not will. But the will depends upon knowledge and knowledge can vary widely—from perfection down to something just short of ignorance. On the basis of the clarity with which a man knows what he is willing, the act of the will itself is *perfect* or *imperfect*—perfect when knowledge is complete, imperfect when it is not complete. A student agrees that lying is wrong, yet in order to get out of a difficulty deliberately tells what he knows is a downright falsehood. His volition is perfect. On the other hand, suppose that in a state of anger he speaks harshly and even untruly. Afterwards he acknowledges that he did not know what he was saying. In this instance volition was imperfect.

Positive and negative will   From another point of view volition is *positive* and *negative*. In a sense all acts of the will are positive. Volition is by its very nature the operation of the will—not the absence of operation. If there is no action there is no willing. However, a person can will to do or will *not* to do. When he wills to do something, it is called a positive act of the will. When he wills not to do something, to refrain from action, it is called a negative act of the will. A revengeful employee may will to damage a valuable machine by pouring sand into the oil cups. Or he may will to ruin the machine by not oiling it. In both instances he wills, and in both instances evil follows. But his volition in the first instance is *positive:* he wills to do. In the second instance it is *negative*, because he wills not to do.

Actual will   The distinction of volition as actual, virtual, habitual and interpretative offers a little more difficulty than the will as perfect and imperfect, positive and negative. *Actual will or intention* means just that. A person consents or wills something at the very moment he is faced with it. The organ grinder holds out his battered hat for a donation. Deciding his music was worth it, a bystander gives him something. The action comes from an actual intention, from the will at the time of making the contribution. The doctor looks at a boil, decides it needs lancing and proceeds to open it. His volition or intention is *actual*.

Virtual will   *Virtual intention or will* signifies an act of the will which *produces* action but the agent while performing the act does not think of his intention. A young woman decides to be a nurse and presents herself to the superintendent. So far her intention or will is actual. But now follows the long process of training, day after day a long succession of duties. Before each and every one of them she does not say solemnly to herself, "I will to be a nurse, therefore I'll do this." Sometimes she may do this very thing; but more often she will do her work with not a thought about intending to be a nurse. Yet the fact that she is in the hospital, in training, and is receiving and obeying orders, all spring from that original actual intention which still endures, which still influences her conduct. But because she does not advert to it at the moment, it is no longer actual but *virtual*.

Habitual will   As with the virtual intention, the *habitual will* or *intention* starts off by being actual. A person makes up his mind to do something but, though never retracting the intention, forgets all about it. So far the habitual and virtual intentions agree. But there is an important difference. When something is willed virtually, the agent at the moment does not think of the intention, but the action nevertheless follows as a *result* of the former unretracted but forgotten decision. When the intention is *habitual* the action does not *come as the result* of that former unretracted intention but *from something else*.

Example   Suppose a person begins the day with the resolution to be kind even to his most disliked associate. Later in the day he discovers his most disliked classmate in need of help. Without in the least adverting to his morning's resolution but simply out of pity he does what he can. In no way does the morning resolution cause the kindness. The act springs from the emotions of the moment. With reference to this act the intention of the morning is called habitual. It was made, never retracted, forgotten and the assistance given was not its effect.

Value of habitual intention   At first glance the value of the habitual intention may seem questionable. Since it does not result in action, what importance has it? In many ways it does not rank high in the order of voluntary activity. Still it has some worth-while applications. Take the instance just given. A resolution to be kind, made in the morning, is quickly forgotten though not withdrawn. Suppose the kind deed to be purely emotional and in no way voluntary. Can the agent be held responsible for the good act if he did not will it at all? The reply must be that an act not coming from the will is not a human act and so cannot be attributed to the agent as its responsible cause. However, the habitual intention preserves something of a voluntary character in the act. The man resolved to be kind, forgot about it and did a kindness out of pure pity. There is no will in it at the moment. Yet the morning's resolution endures until it is withdrawn. And since it was not withdrawn, it perseveres and gives a complexion of volition to conduct which otherwise might fall below the human level.

Example   Another application of the *habitual intention* may help to show its worth. Many persons start the day by offering it and all its worthy actions to God. The little prayer is as quickly forgotten as said. The day begins and the person takes things as they come, with perhaps never a thought of God or of his morning's offering. He goes from one thing to another, acting on the motivation of the moment. What is the influence of the morning's dedication? Was it an empty useless formula? Are the day's activities consecrated to God or are they lost through lack of actual will? Certainly actual will and intention are missing, and there is no question of virtual intention. But on the basis of *habitual intention* the day does not escape the influence of the morning's dedication and all its activities which can be dedicated are dedicated to God.

Interpretative A fourth sort of will or intention is called *in-*
will *terpretative*. Unlike the virtual and habitual intention or will the *interpretative intention* does not imply an actual will in the background. As a matter of fact there is no act of the will at all, no intention. The *interpretative intention* means that there would be an act of the will, there would be an intention towards the object or act, *if the act or the object or their necessity were known.*

Importance   Since the interpretative intention involves no act of the person's will, it may be asked what is its importance. The answer may be seen in an application. For an operation to be ethical the surgeon must have the consent of the patient or of someone with authority to speak in his name. Of himself the surgeon has no right whatsoever over the patient's body. But suppose the patient is brought in unconscious. Speed is of the essence of saving his life. It would be hopeless if the surgeon had to wait for consciousness to return. Instead without delay he does what seems best. He has not the patient's explicit consent for the indicated amputation. Yet he acts ethically if he proceeds with the operation. He interprets the intention, or will, of the helpless patient: If he knew the limb had to be taken off to save his life, he would will the operation.

Actual will From many points of view actual intention dif-
the best fers from virtual and habitual and interpretative. The last is certainly the weakest; habitual is useful,

virtual approaches the actual, but not one of the three completely substitutes for the actual intention or will. They lack the vitality of the actual will. Nothing can really take its place. It alone puts the human being with all his higher faculties squarely behind what he is doing and hopes to achieve. It gives concentration; it implies understanding. It springs from intelligent dedication and love. It most accords with human nature and human activity. If men want to live intelligently, if they want to be masters of their actions and destiny and preserve themselves from life's dehumanizing influences, they must cultivate the habit of planning their conduct, understanding their choices, and making the right ones. They must know what to will and then will what they know and want. Knowledge and actual will must be brought into daily activities. Only then in the highest degree can men claim them as their own.

3 INDIRECT VOLUNTARY

Direct will Another and very practical distinction of volition considers will as *direct* and *indirect*. It is *direct* when a person wills something itself, either for itself as an end or as a means to an end. A patient wills to have good health. Happiness, knowledge, success, reputation, money are not infrequently the objects of human desire and will. Again something may be willed directly as a means. A person wills to eat certain things to stay well. A man wills to work hard to support his family. Another man steals in order to get the money he needs.

Indirect will The will is *indirect* when a person wills not the thing itself but something of which it is a consequence. Because of its importance the indirect will or, as it is often called, the *indirect voluntary* deserves careful attention.

Examples Take a concrete instance. A man wants to go to the movies but foresees that it will make him late for an appointment. If he decides to go, he wills to see the movies directly but indirectly he wills to be late. He knew that this unwanted effect would follow from going to the movies. Nevertheless he went and consequently cannot free himself of blame for being late. Suppose a nurse knows that some instruments have not been sterilized and foresees harm if they are used. Still she gives them to the surgeon. Her action is gravely wrong and she is responsible for the harm which follows. Even if there be no actual harm, she is guilty. For in willing to use the instruments and in foreseeing the evil effects, she willed the bad effects when she willed to use the instruments.

The principle The principle regarding the responsibility of such indirectly willed consequences is clear. To the extent that the consequences of actions willed indirectly are foreseen and a person is free to act or not to act he is responsible for the consequences.

Morality of The question arises about the morality of con-
indirect sequences willed indirectly. There is no problem
voluntary when the indirect object of the will is good. The problem concerns those occasions when the object willed indirectly is not good. For instance, a general foresees when he orders an attack that some of his men will be wounded and killed. The direct object of his will is his country's welfare; indirectly he has to will the casualties and assume responsibility for them. May he order the attack in spite of the casualties? Take another instance. The surgeon wills directly the health of his patient. But he foresees that the remedy indicated, namely amputation, means the loss of a limb— certainly an evil effect. May he go ahead in spite of the bad effect which cannot be divorced from the operation? A pregnant mother develops an acute case of appendicitis. The physician foresees that an operation will mean an abortion. If he operates he wills directly the mother's health, but indirectly he wills an abortion. May he go ahead?

Double effect defined An analysis of these cases reveals that the actions had two effects, one good and one evil. The general's attack has the double effect of victory and casualties. The surgeon's operation has its double effect of health and the loss of a limb, or, with the pregnant mother, the effects of health and the loss of her child. Thus the indirect voluntary involves an action which has several effects, and this is why the ethical principle of the indirect voluntary is often called the *principle of the double effect*.

Conditions for using the indirect voluntary When a person faces an action whose foreseen results include some that are good and desirable and others which are bad and unwanted, may he at any time will to do the action in spite of the bad effects? The answer is yes. But note the four conditions of the principle most carefully. An action which has double and opposite effects may be done provided—

1. that the action which is done is in itself good or at least not bad.
2. that the agent wills and desires the good effect. It is never right to will or desire the evil effect. It can be permitted or tolerated but never willed.
3. that there be a sufficient reason for allowing the evil effect. If good and bad effects are to follow, obviously the good must be such as to outweigh the evil.
4. that the good and the bad effects be coordinate. They must stem from a common cause—not the good effect from the bad effect. Otherwise evil would be the cause of good, which is never permissible (p. 88). This point is delicate but most important. Consider the appendectomy on the pregnant mother. From the operation come the two effects of health and the loss of the child. Notice that the health does not come from the abortion but that it as well as the good effect of health both come from the operation. No action in which the good, however great it may be, is produced by an evil cause can be ethical. Thus the New York girl (p. 89) who stole her employer's money to help the poor did wrong. The money and the assistance it gave were not coordinate but

subordinate effects: theft produced stolen money and the money provided some good things.

Application   If these four conditions are applied to the surgeon's problem of the appendectomy, it is evident that he could perform the operation even if an abortion should certainly follow. His action in performing the operation is not evil in itself, condition one. He wills the good effect, the mother's health, condition two. The good effect of saving the woman's life balances the bad effect of losing her child, condition three. Condition four is fulfilled, since the good effect is not produced through the evil effect.

Cooperating in evil   The indirect voluntary or the principle of the double effect has great practical value in the problem of *cooperating in another's evil deed*. Suppose a nurse in the course of an operation discovers that it is unethical. To stay means she takes part in an immoral action. To leave means she endangers the patient's life. What must she do? She should stay and the morality of her conduct stands vindicated on the principle of the double effect. Her normal services are not evil in themselves. Her will rests in the good effect of the patient's well-being, not in the evil effect of the unethical operation. There is a just balance between the good and bad effects. And finally the good effect of her services, to help the patient, is not the result of the bad effect. For the same reason the conduct of the night watchman (p. 94) was not wrong. His action of handing over the keys was not evil in itself. He willed the good effect of his own safety. The good effect more than outweighed the bad effect and was not the result of the evil effect of the theft.

Principles   The instances just given of cooperating in another's evil act presuppose that the cooperator does not will the evil act (material cooperation). If he wills it (formal cooperation), then he intends it and shares responsibility for it. To will evil is always wrong and such formal (voluntary, intentional) cooperation is never lawful. When the problem of cooperating in another's wrong doing arises, a person's first thought should be to avoid the situation if possible. This is especially true if he knows beforehand that he is going to be implicated.[1]

4. IMPEDIMENTS TO VOLUNTARY ACTIVITY

Voluntariness   For an act to be *human* and one for which the person is *responsible*, he must know what he is doing, be free and will the act. These three characteristics often are summed up in the one word *voluntary*. That act is termed voluntary which has the necessary characteristics of knowledge, freedom and volition. *Voluntary act* and *human act* mean exactly the same thing. Anything which interferes with knowledge, freedom or volition makes an act less human or voluntary. Such interference may arise from ignorance, habit, violence, the passions in general and particularly fear. These impediments frequently diminish, sometimes even destroy, the voluntary or human quality of man's actions and consequently affect his responsibility. This is why they must be examined carefully.

Ignorance defined   *Ignorance* means the absence of due knowledge. That seems simple until the various kinds of ignorance are remembered. Then the problem gets a little complicated.

Invincible ignorance   In the first place the ignorance may not be the person's fault in any way. He has exercised due care but without success. The absence of the knowledge he ought to have simply cannot be helped. He is not responsible. Ignorance for which a person is not accountable is called *invincible*, meaning that it cannot be overcome through

[1] Cf. for some practical applications to nurses, Moore, T. V.: *Principles of Ethics* (Philadelphia, J. B. Lippincott Co., 1943, 4th ed.), pp. 157–158.

ordinary means. A nurse does not know whether a certain medication ought to be given. She makes every effort to find out but gets no satisfaction. Her ignorance is invincible and she is not responsible for it.

Vincible ignorance Ignorance may be the person's fault. It could have been removed, but directly or indirectly he willed to stay ignorant. He is responsible for it. This is called *vincible ignorance,* because it could be overcome through ordinary means.

Affected ignorance When the agent wills this ignorance directly by making an effort to keep it, it is called *affected ignorance.* A person may say, "Don't tell me what the rule is. Then I'll know it and be responsible for keeping it." Or go back to the example of the nurse and the medication she did not know whether or not to give. Suppose she purposely made no effort to find out but deliberately took pains to remain ignorant. Her ignorance would be *affected.* She would be responsible for it.

Crass ignorance On the other hand, vincible ignorance when willed indirectly is called *crass ignorance.* The agent does not make the proper effort to dispel it. He does not actually will to be ignorant; he simply does not exert himself to learn. Thus a nurse in her student days may have preferred dozing to being alert in class. Lazily she turned away from her books to lighter reading or perhaps allowed recreations to monopolize her time and attention. She may manage to graduate, but is almost certain to lack the knowledge she should have. This ignorance was not directly willed. She may not have thought about it at all. She simply took the path of least resistance. Indirectly she is guilty of it; but not in the same way as a person is guilty of affected ignorance, which is willed directly.

Ignorance and responsibility The various kinds of ignorance bear differently upon the agent's responsibility. *Invincible ignorance* takes away responsibility, so that the agent is not accountable for the bad effects, if any follow. *Crass vincible ignorance* diminishes guilt but does not take it away entirely. For the ignorance itself was not willed, though things leading to it were. And this is why the person does not escape all responsibility. *Affected vincible ignorance* impairs the voluntariness of conduct to some extent, since it implies the absence of due knowledge. Yet in the light of the way this ignorance is cultivated directly and intentionally, it may be said to increase voluntariness. *Affected ignorance*, "being deliberately fostered to serve as an excuse for sin against the law, shows the strength of the will's determination to persist in such sins. It is thus said to increase the voluntariness of an act, or, more accurately, to indicate an increased voluntariness in the act that comes from it."[2]

Habit　　　　If an action is repeated often enough over a period of time, it becomes almost automatic. A man given to profanity may curse and swear and realize it only if someone reminds him. Lack of advertence or of will in conduct arising from habit raises the question of how habit affects responsibility.

Habit and　　A person is not *directly* responsible for the
responsibility　actions themselves which spring from habit. By definition they escape either his knowledge or his will or both. But in so far as he knows he has the habit and wills to keep it, to that extent and *indirectly* he wills what results from it. *Habits for which a person is voluntarily responsible do not take away responsibility for actions which come from them. Habits for which a person is not voluntarily responsible take away responsibility.* This principle applies equally to good and bad habits and to the voluntary character of their good or evil products.

Examples　　If a man drinks too much, knows he has the habit and realizes it is wrong but does nothing

[2] Glenn, P. J.: *Ethics* (St. Louis, B. Herder Book Co., 1938), p. 35.

about it, he is guilty of intemperance. It is voluntary. On the contrary, take the tragedy of adults getting a child drunk in order to laugh at him. The child grows up burdened with the habit of drunkenness. But realizing its evil, he wills to get rid of it. He does what he can to shake it off, but occasionally falls. In so far as the falls result from the habit which he does not want his responsibility is lessened. For the habit of drunkenness does not suppress *all* psychological liberty and responsibility except when it produces such a fit of frenzy that the man drinks automatically. When the habit in question produces good actions, a person is similarly responsible for them. Thus a man who has struggled hard to be gentle and polite loses none of the credit if kindness becomes habitual with him. It was voluntarily acquired, voluntarily kept. It is his and so are its good effects.

Violence   For acts to be truly human or voluntary, they must have the background of knowledge and will and freedom. Ignorance and habit can be impediments. So too can *violence* and *passion*. Violence here means external force which one person exercises upon another to make him act against his will. Naturally the interrelation of will and body is intimate and mutual. However, it is not the body which gives conduct its essential moral character. The will does that. And external violence cannot directly touch the will. The body, however, it can touch. If the body is forced to act against the will and with the due resistance of the agent, such actions are not the agent's. They are not voluntary but merely the *acts of the man*, non-voluntary.

Two aspects   Two aspects of the problem of violence need to be kept separate. First, a person must give due resistance to the violence. Often this is hard to gauge. For the resistance may be merely a token resistance, involving some cooperation. Then the action would not be entirely due to violence but might be partly voluntary.

Second, there may be due resistance to the violence, but the will nevertheless consents. In spite of the violence such an action would not cease to be voluntary.

Violence and These considerations of external resistance and *responsibility* internal consent are basic to the principle that *violence to which proper resistance is made and no consent is given destroys responsibility.* Actions which result from it are not attributable to the agent. Granted that the victim of a criminal assault resists and gives no internal consent, she escapes all responsibility. The action is simply not hers and in no way imputable.

5. THE PASSIONS

Definition It is easier to name than to define the passions. Love and hate, joy and grief, desire and hope, despair, horror and aversion, courage, rage and fear are familiar names. To define *passion* as a *strong emotion* may be helpful if some explanation of emotion is given.

Rauth and Sheehy[3] stress the importance of *meaning* in emotion. A surgeon's emotional reaction to his first operation is not going to be the same as to his hundred and first. The existence as well as the kind of emotion depends upon its meaning for the particular person under the particular circumstances. It is meaning in emotion which marks off emotions from mere feeling. Another important distinction is that along with emotions appear very complex and significant physiological changes. Some of them are increased heart rate (pulse), redistribution of blood, change in rate and depth of respiration, improved muscular contraction, rapid restoration of fatigued muscles, inhibition of certain glands and smooth muscles. It should be noticed also that the experiencing of an emotion in a given situation is not subject to conscious control. But the responses which are due to voluntary muscles do fall under the control of the will.

[3] *Principles of Psychology* (Milwaukee, Bruce Publishing Co., 1945), pp. 92 ff.

Emotion,   At times, however, the volitional control breaks
passion and   down and the emotional expression is uncontrolled.
will   Such strong emotions are often called passions. The
extent of a person's control over his passions depends in
part upon his physical make-up but above all upon his
training.

Passion and   The relationship between passions and a per-
responsibility   son's control of them raises the question of how
they alter *responsibility*. As with ignorance, so with the
passions. The question of responsibility for actions done in
passion becomes a question of a man's responsibility for the
passion. Has he willed or consented to the passion? If he
has, then he is responsible for the passion and cannot dis-
own its consequences. On this basis men have passions that
are willed and are voluntary and those which are not willed
and are non-voluntary.

Non-volun-   Passions are *non-voluntary* when the person
tary passion   does not cause them, does not try to keep or
stimulate them, when he does not will and consent to them.
In short he is not responsible for them. How do passions of
this sort affect responsibility for actions done under their
influence?

And   If the passion is so violent as to take away
responsibility   knowledge or the person's control of his conduct, then the action is simply an *act of the man*, a non-
voluntary act, an act for which the person is not accountable. And since he is not responsible for the passion which
produced the action, then he is not responsible for the
action. This, however, is an extreme case. Most often passion of the non-voluntary sort is not so violent. At the most
it interferes with the proper functioning of intelligence or
will. *To the extent that it does impede a man's knowing and willing,*
to that extent passion lessens responsibility for actions which
follow upon it. Still, it seldom takes away all responsibility.
For even while experiencing such passion, a person may

understand what he is doing and, though passion may make it more difficult, still he can resist it. Suppose a nurse, publicly and most unjustly rebuked, gets violently angry. She vents her wrath upon her patient by ungentle treatment, negligence and acrimony. The anger lessens, but does not absolve her from responsibility for the cruelty.

Voluntary passion   Passions are *voluntary* when they are willed and this is done either by intentionally arousing the passion or by consenting to the passion after it has been aroused. In these instances the person is responsible for the passion and is therefore responsible for its effects. The principle is that *voluntary passion does not lessen responsibility.*

Example   A neighbor's dog night after night has kept a crabbed old man awake. He dislikes killing the dog and knows he should not. But he proceeds to work himself into a rage, so that he will not realize what he is doing. He thinks over how he has been wronged, the injustice of it, his loss of sleep and his dwindling good health and shattered nerves, the cruelty of his thoughtless neighbor, his rights as a decent citizen. When he actually shoots the dog he is violently angry. But the whole thing has been directly willed. He willed to kill the dog and willed the anger as a means. He is fully responsible.

Another example   Think again of the nurse who thought herself grievously wronged. She is aware of her anger and foresees that harm may come of it if she does not restrain it. Nevertheless, she does not oppose it. Rather she encourages it, with the result that the foreseen evil occurs. Though originally she may not have been responsible for the passion, yet she consented to it and to the evil which might come from it. She is responsible, therefore, both for the passion, which she willed directly, and for its evil effects, which she willed indirectly.

Fear defined   Because *fear* is one of the passions which frequently enters into the problem of moral responsibility, it deserves special attention. Fear is a recoil of the mind, a shrinking back from impending evil, accompanied by physical and mental agitation, which may be slight or reach the climax of panic. When fear robs a person of the use of his faculties and self-control, he is not responsible for his actions. The cry of "fire" in a theatre has been enough to turn people into wild animals. Such occasions are not typical of the moral problem of fear; for in such instances there is no question of responsibility.

Typical   A more typical situation is signing a contract
situation   from fear. The contracting party knows perfectly well what he is doing and wills to do it. But he is doing it only out of fear. If he were not afraid he would not sign it. That is the peculiar difficulty of fear. It induces people to do something which, except for fear, they would not will to do. But when they do it, they do it knowingly and willingly.

Fear and   Consequently, fear does not dissolve responsi-
responsibility bility. The principle is that *fear, be it ever so grave, does not destroy responsibility but lessens it*. If this is so, it may be asked, why does positive law invalidate contracts made from fear? The answer is that such legislation is for the common good. If these contracts were considered valid, grave injustices would quickly follow and contracts would be worthless. In general, for a contract to be invalidated by fear, the fear must be caused directly and wrongfully and for the express purpose of obtaining consent to the proposed act.

Application   Dr. Moore's[4] application of the moral principle
                  about fear to the nurse's problems merits quotation. "Fear is the emotion which most often clouds consciousness and diminishes guilt. It must be borne in mind, however, that merely being threatened with consequences, no matter how serious, does not in itself do away

          [4] Moore, T. V.: *Principles of Ethics*, pp. 34–35.

with responsibility. In the days of the martyrs those who coolly denied the faith in order to save their lives were guilty of a grievous sin. And in our own days a nurse who acts against her religious or moral convictions to secure or maintain a position, or for any other reason, is grievously culpable."

6. SUMMARY

Principles   Theoretically the requirements for an act to be human or voluntary are simple. The agent must know what he is doing, be free and will it. Anything which interferes with these conditions, which impedes freedom or knowledge or will, lessens the voluntary character of the act and makes it less human. Ignorance, habit, violence and the passions, especially fear, can affect human responsibility. The principles governing the moral aspects of these obstacles to voluntary activity have been given.

Practice   But in practice their application is often difficult. The question of personal guilt is always delicate, sometimes clear but very often next to impossible to define. What a person did may be perfectly plain. That is objective. It can be analyzed and brought under the proper ethical principles. But gauging the person's responsibility or guilt is a difficult matter. The deviousness of human behavior should be a warning to go slow in judging. So too should this brief exposition about the obstacles which can lessen and sometimes even remove responsibility. Likewise, natural kindness and Christian love ought to encourage people to withhold judgment.

Judging others   The action may be judged and condemned. Condemnation of the agent does not necessarily follow. These two aspects of morality should be kept apart: the objective and the subjective. With every right men should concern themselves with the principles of good and evil and strive to apply those principles to their lives. They also should encourage others to know what is right and live by it. But when the problem of weighing the guilt of human beings arises, ordinarily the question is best left aside. If duty forces a person to pass judgment, he should be as careful and honest and well-informed and unprejudiced as possible.

READINGS

Michael Cronin: *The Science of Ethics*, i, ch. ii.

Paul J. Glenn: *Ethics*, ch. i.

Charles F. McFadden: *Medical Ethics for Nurses*, pp. 26–44, 255–265.

Charles E. Miltner: *The Elements of Ethics*, ch. x.

Thomas V. Moore: *Principles of Ethics*, chapters iii and xiv.

J. E. Rauth and Sr. M. M. Sheehy: *Principles of Psychology*, pp. 92ff.

Chapter 7

CONSCIENCE—MANIFESTIVE NORM OF MORALITY

1. INTRODUCTION

Applying the law and criteria The natural moral law and the criteria, primary and secondary, which reveal the law's practical application have been examined. But to be guides to good and evil, the law and its criteria must be focused upon actual concrete moral problems. The process of applying moral principles is something personal, intimate. It belongs to a human subject, and in this sense is subjective, as uniquely as any other process of thought and reasoning. And it is this process and the ethical judgment which results from it that characterize conscience.

Importance of conscience Conscience comes closest to man's final and practical decision about good and evil. It is the court of last appeal. It is the proximate, irrefutable, subjective, manifestative norm of morality. Yet conscience is not automatic. It is not a machine which operates at the push of a button. Rather it pertains to human beings as any other intellectual function, in equal need of education and training. The decisiveness of conscience, its fallibility, its critical necessity for the good life, the frequent but vague and even meaningless use of the word urge the need of knowing what conscience is and of cultivating a correct one.

True conscience needed The nurse who resigns a good position, because it is against her *conscience* to assist at immoral operations; the surgeon who turns down a good proposition, because fee-splitting conflicts with his

113

conscience; men and women who respect and follow *conscience* owe it to themselves to understand the reality behind the word. Only in that way can they deal intelligently with moral issues. For it is not enough to obey conscience. The issues at stake are often too critical for thoughtless, blind or unreasoned decisions. A man must follow his conscience, certainly. But with equal certainty he is obliged to make sure his conscience is true.

2. CONSCIENCE DEFINED

Not   The fog surrounding conscience partly arises
inexplicable from the way it often is referred to. "The voice of God," "God within you," "the still small voice of conscience," "the faculty of conscience," "the interior voice," are only some of the epithets. Each of them has an aspect of truth; but the truth rather fades in the false impressions they create. To clarify the notion of conscience a person must be willing to make the effort. The first step is to reject the notion that conscience is something mysterious, something separate from human intelligence and reason, something mystical and inexplicable.

Not ethical   Knowledge of the natural law and of the cri-
principles   teria for understanding its application leads to principles of right conduct. Some of these principles are self-evident. Others depend upon analysis and involved reasoning. Then there are other principles which come from positive law. But however obtained these moral principles belong to the class in general of theoretical ethical truths. They are more speculative than practical. Although indispensable to conscience they are not conscience. Conscience is an act of the practical reason which uses these principles. It applies them to *individual* problems of conduct, to decide whether a particular act is good, and so to be done, or evil, and so to be avoided.

Conscience a   *Conscience is an act of human reason.* That is the
judgment   fundamental notion to grasp. Men reason

about many things, and the judgment which results takes its name from the sphere which engages their attention. In the mathematical order, a man may reason to the conclusion that the square of the hypotenuse of a right angled triangle is equal to the sum of the squares of the other two sides. Or the judgment may concern fact, that hydrogen and oxygen combine to form water. Notice that although these judgments involve different spheres, they do not propose obligatory action. They belong to the realm of knowledge simply. They are speculative. And human reason as producing them is called the *speculative reason*.

Of practical reason   On the other hand, man formulates judgments which bear upon action, which declare that something is right and must be done, or that something is wrong and must be avoided. In these judgments it is man's reason which is functioning—but not the same as with speculative judgments. These pertain to truth as such. The judgments of right and wrong conduct pertain to action, to the obligation of *doing* or *not doing* something. Hence they are called *practical* judgments and human reason in forming them is called the *practical reason*. To this category belong the judgments of conscience, which is partially defined as *an act of the practical reason*.

Definition   Although conscience can refer to the entire process of applying the proper ethical principle to a particular concrete and immediate instance, it most often refers simply to the judgment which ends the process. Thus conscience is defined as *a practical judgment of human reason bearing upon the good or evil character of an action to be done here and now*. Regarding past actions conscience can also pass judgment of approval or disapproval. But conscience bears chiefly upon contemplated action.

Example   Suppose a hard-up student finds he can get some money by stealing. Theft seems an easy way out, but he thinks over the situation: I know theft is unlawful. I need this money all right, yet it's stealing to take it. I can't do it. He may say that conscience *spoke* to him or refer in some other vague way to the decision. But the plain fact is that he reasoned about taking the money. He laid down the general principle: Theft is unlawful. He applied his contemplated act to it: This is theft, and he concluded: This act is unlawful. That conclusion is conscience.

Objection   A person may recall making many judgments about what he should or should not do, but never remembers going through such a process. The conclusion or decision seemed to come automatically, spontaneously. Quite possibly he did not advert to the reasoning process. But that in itself does not prove he did not reason. It may indicate that he reasoned so swiftly and accurately and unhesitantly and easily that the whole thing was over and done with before he knew it. It may also indicate his wholesome moral training, that when good and evil were proposed he made the right decision practically from habit. Still when important questions arise, when the issues are complex and serious, the rational activity of conscience often becomes, as indeed it should become, explicit. Then a man clearly and purposely reasons his way from moral principles to what he should do in the particular, concrete instance confronting him. This is called *forming* one's conscience.

3. KINDS OF CONSCIENCE

Basis of   It has been pointed out that conscience is not
division   automatic. It is a judgment of the practical reason, essentially a function of the intelligence and so open to all the obstacles and dangers which plague man in his pursuit of truth. According as conscience does or does not certainly correspond to truth, that is to objective morality, it is true or false, certain or doubtful, lax or scrupulous.

True and false conscience   Conscience is *right*, or *true* or *correct*, when its judgment corresponds to objective moral truth. To do this, the ethical principle on which the judgment of conscience rests must be true. For a wrong principle produces a wrong conclusion. Likewise a mistake about the nature of the proposed act can falsify the conclusion. When either of these happens conscience is false or *erroneous*. Its judgment does not reflect objective ethical reality. Suppose a person begins to *form* his conscience on the principle that all gambling is unlawful. He reasons from this principle that, since playing bridge for money is gambling, he cannot play bridge with his friends for money. He has reasoned rightly to a false conclusion—because he started with an untrue principle. Again conscience can be erroneous because a mistake is made about the character of the contemplated action. Think again of the bridge player. This time he is considering a slight infraction of the rules. Cheating, he condemns as wrong. But he does not consider his little deception cheating—whereas it actually is. He concludes, erroneously, that the deception is not wrong. He started with a valid principle and reasoned cogently, but ended in error because he erred about the action he wanted to do.

Invincibly erroneous   When conscience is false, or erroneous, the person may or may not be responsible for it. If through no fault of his own a man with the best of intentions makes a mistake about the morality of a proposed act, he is without blame and not responsible. His conscience is *invincibly erroneous*.

Application   This may be exemplified in the practice which some Arctic Eskimos have of abandoning their useless old people to freeze to death.[1] "I took the old woman out on the ice today," was the way an Eskimo broke the

[1] De Ponsins, G.: *Kabloona* (New York, Reynal and Hitchock, Inc., 1941), quoted from *The Reader's Digest*, June 1941, p. 158.

news. The woman was the man's own mother. "He was fond of her . . . . He had always been kind to her. But she was helplessly blind and so old she was no longer good for anything. So, the whole family agreeing, he had led her out on the frozen sea and left her there alone to die." The horrible act considered in itself was murder. But neither the man nor his people thought of it that way. Granted the lack of knowledge and the false conscience were not the man's fault, his conscience was then invincibly erroneous. This does not make the atrocity right; but it takes away the personal guilt of the crime.

Vincibly On the contrary, when the mistake which
erroneous results in a false judgment of conscience is through the person's own fault, reasonably could have been avoided or was due to lack of good will or to bad intentions, he is blameworthy and his conscience is *culpably*, or *vincibly erroneous*.

Application A nurse who wilfully neglects to learn the ethical principles of her profession becomes responsible for the mistakes in conscience which may result. Suppose she has been under the impression that therapeutic abortions are ethical. A friend explains that she is mistaken, that they are gravely immoral and that she can verify this from the professor of ethics. Instead of looking into the question, she insists that she is right and refuses to take any chances of having her mind changed. Such ignorance is vincible and culpable. The nurse is responsible for her false conscience and for the errors which may follow.

Certain and In the same way that judgments in general
doubtful are certain or doubtful, so can the judgment
conscience of conscience be *certain* or *doubtful*. Conscience is *certain* when the person is sure he is right. There is no fear or hesitation. The issues appear clear and he rests in a firm, unwavering decision about the action's morality. On the contrary, he may not see the situation clearly enough for

a sure judgment. He fluctuates between its being right and wrong. He cannot make up his mind. He is in doubt. His conscience is *doubtful*.

The certitude   The certitude of conscience about right and
of conscience   wrong is not the same as the certitude men
have about the laws of magnetism or about the principle that whatever happens has a cause. Conscience is a practical judgment. Its certitude is neither physical, as with the magnet, nor metaphysical, as with the principle of causality. The certainty of conscience is *moral certitude*. This means that the possibility of error has not been excluded absolutely, but that a man reasonably has tried to avoid error and is certain beyond any prudent doubt that his judgment is true.

4. SCRUPULOUS AND LAX CONSCIENCE

Both are false   *Lax* and *scrupulous consciences* are both erroneous.
But they differ from the simply false conscience. Any time conscience errs, it is erroneous, or false. With the scrupulous and lax conscience, however, it is more than a misjudgment. It is an ingrained disposition or predisposition to judge too severely or too lightly. It is not merely a mistake. It is rather a complexion of the entire personality. The lax conscience errs in judging evil actions good; the scrupulous conscience errs in judging innocent and good things evil. Both are opposed to proper moral conduct. Both involve grave dangers and sometimes have tragic results. It is pointless to ask which is worse. They are both bad because both are false.

Definition of   A *lax conscience* is a false conscience. The person
lax conscience   consistently minimizes evil, justifies real moral
faults and in general favors an easy interpretation of law and its obligations. On little or no ground he regularly judges things to be moral and legitimate which really are not. An employee, for example, defends his petty thievery

as being all right, because his employer does not feel the loss—or an alcoholic defends his drinking, because it hurts only himself.

Causes   The *causes* of a lax conscience, or, as it is sometimes called, a hardened conscience, are varied. It may be due to ignorance, vincible or invincible (p. 103 ff.), or false moral principles. Environment of low moral standards can also play a part. So too can disdain of good advice. Education, the home, associates, false ideals of life and good living, these likewise can produce a lax conscience. But there remains another cause which deserves special attention. A person may have everything which good moral education, environment, home and church, and associates can furnish. He may know perfectly well how to discriminate between right and wrong. But little by little he eases away from good and leans toward evil choices. He sees where right is but disregards it. From being able to distinguish clearly between right and wrong he comes to confuse them and gradually ceases to know what is right. The phenomenon finds a parallel in the sensory order. By shutting off the alarm every morning and turning over for an extra few minutes sleep, a person is conditioning himself not to hear the alarm at all. If a person habitually disregards what he knows is right and chooses to do wrong, the time will come when he will not only do wrong but transform it into right by the alchemy of a lax and hardened conscience.

Curing the   The cause of a lax conscience suggests the *cure*,
lax conscience though in practice the cure may be very difficult. Education in correct ethical principles, training in right thought, moral living, healthy environment, and eagerness to seek and follow the advice of informed and good-living people, these will help a person to recover a true conscience. But in addition he must cultivate a readiness to do right when he sees it. Delay, postponement, reluctance,

compromise will thwart his efforts if they are allowed to interfere. They are obstacles as great as ignorance or spurious reasoning and perhaps are even harder to overcome. Yet the effort must be made. No normal human being can reconcile himself happily to a false conscience. He must avail himself of every reasonable means to avoid laxity and restore his conscience to moral truth and vigor.

Scrupulous   The *scrupulous conscience* reverses the judgments
conscience   of the lax conscience. It sees evil everywhere.
defined
A scrupulous person tortures himself first with the ordeal of making up his mind whether something is right or wrong. Then when the decision is made, he torments himself with fear that it is wrong. And finally when the act is done, he worries and frets about it. There is no peace of soul for the scrupulous. His thoughts are a ferment of anxiety and remorse. He lives under a pall and every aspect of his life suffers.

Causes   Some of the *causes* of a scrupulous conscience
                  are the same as for the lax conscience. The
person may be ignorant of ethical principles. He may fail to seek proper advice or refuse to follow it. His home and environment may contribute. Parents and religious leaders may be responsible, because of their perverted views of goodness and their erroneously strict views of life. The person's own weak attitude towards making any decision carries over into the judgments of conscience. Extreme nervous tension, illness, superstition, pride, religiosity, almost a neurotic fear of God's wrath and vengeance, gross lack of confidence in God's love and mercy, intensely morbid fear of eternal damnation, these are some of the ingredients which produce a scrupulous conscience and can ruin a man's life.

Curing the   *Curing* a scrupulous conscience is a delicate
scrupulous   task. The cause must be sought by every pos-
conscience   sible means. If it is bad health, nervous dis-

orders, a remedy must be sought for them. If it is ignorance, the cure is information—a matter not nearly so difficult as, when there is need, of helping a person to greater strength and skill in formulating correct judgments. Perhaps the most practical suggestion to be made is to stress the value of an intelligent and experienced counselor. A scrupulous person needs sympathy and help. He cannot be his own physician. He must submit without reserve to a trusted adviser and follow his instructions. The road to recovery may prove shockingly slow and painful, but that is the price he must pay. What he is seeking is well worth it. For rectifying a scrupulous conscience not only restores moral health but makes him capable, perhaps for the first time, of real inner peace and happiness. He sometimes becomes a new person with undreamed of capacities for work and success.

5. PRINCIPLES IN FORMING CONSCIENCE

States of conscience   In formulating the principles of right conscientious behavior these various states of conscience must be considered. Conscience is either certain or doubtful, true or vincibly or invincibly erroneous.

Vincibly erroneous   Obviously it is *never right* to follow a conscience which is culpably, or vincibly, erroneous. This would amount to doing evil intentionally.

Certain conscience when true   The second principle is that *a certain conscience must be followed, both when it is true and when it is invincibly erroneous.* That good must be done and evil avoided is an ultimate ethical principle; yet the final decision about what is good or evil rests with conscience. To act against conscience, when it is certain, is to act wilfully against what is held to be right. Such ethical suicide can never be lawful.

When false   To act against conscience cannot be right when conscience is true. Just as certainly it is not right when conscience is unavoidably false, that is, when it is invincibly erroneous. The person is not responsible for the error, he does not know about it, he thinks he is right. No alternative remains. He must do right as he sees it and avoid evil as he understands it. His judgment does not correspond to objective fact, but it does correspond to moral truth as known and does preserve a man's moral integrity. Any other course amounts to doing what is held to be wrong or not doing what is considered right.

The certain conscience should be true   The obligation of following conscience when it is *certain* reveals why it is so important to have conscience *true*. The more sincere and honest and courageous and sacrificing persons are, the more fatal are their mistakes when they act on false ethical principles. Horrors of all sorts have been perpetrated in the name of righteousness. Men and women need true ethical principles in order to conform their conduct to the objective pattern of human conduct and destiny. An invincibly erroneous but certain conscience saves a person from moral turpitude, but it does not obliterate the tragedy, sorrow, injustice and other evils which can follow from sincere but false ethical thinking, from unsound principles or from prejudices. In the broad, over-all picture of man's personal and social destiny, it is not enough for his judgments to be free of doubt. They must be true, just as his judgments in the physical or metaphysical sphere must be true—not because he thinks they are true but because they correspond to objective fact. Man's conscience, as any other intellectual faculty, must be educated. His ethical principles and application must be valid. Surely a *certain* conscience must be followed, but men are bound to use reasonable means to make their certain conscience true.

Doubtful conscience   The third principle about conscience states that an *uncertain or doubtful conscience can never be followed. Doubt must be removed and conscience made certain.* The reason behind the principle is evident. Doubt means uncertainty. Uncertainty may be about an action's being right or wrong (practical doubt) or about the existence or meaning of a law (speculative doubt). In either instance men face alternatives of right and wrong and are not sure which is which. To proceed in such a state of mind would show indifference to right moral conduct. For if a man says that something may be right or may be wrong but that he is willing to do it anyway, he is really prepared to do the action even if it is wrong. This is equivalent to choosing evil. It proves readiness to transgress the moral law, and this can never be right.

Solving   The principle about an uncertain, or doubt-
doubtful   ful, conscience requires that *before acting a man*
conscience   *must solve the doubt and make his conscience certain.*
One way is to ask advice. An appeal is made to somebody who reasonably can be supposed to know the answer and his guidance is accepted. Or the person may grapple with the situation himself, recalling the pertinent ethical principles, analyzing the problem and carefully applying the principles with due regard for circumstances. This second way is not the easiest, but when the doubt cannot be solved by getting advice it may have to be relied upon. A third way is to follow what is called the safer course. Suppose the doubt concerns a law's existence. By assuming that it does exist a man is sure he will not make a mistake. He chooses the safer course and acts on the supposition that the law exists and applies to him. The fourth way of solving the uncertainty of conscience involves the moral principle that a doubtful law does not bind. Helpful as this rule may be, it must be understood and applied with great care.

Doubtful laws   The principle that *doubtful laws do not bind*
                   comes into operation, first, when there is no question of an obligatory end to be obtained, and second when the doubt cannot be solved directly, either by seeking advice or by reasoning it out. In practice the principle is

used most safely when the doubt concerns positive human law or doubtful obligations of justice. Law may be doubtful either as regards its existence or its application. As long as there is a prudent reason for supposing a law's non-existence or non-applicability and there is no question of a goal which must be secured, this principle, often called *probabilism*, may be used for solving the doubts of conscience.

Application Such doubts frequently arise in matters of tax laws. A man is not sure whether or not a certain deduction in his income tax is allowable. Inquiries bring only further confusion. May he take the deduction or not? Since the law's meaning is doubtful, so too is its binding force. The principle that a doubtful law does not bind solves the man's doubt and makes his conscience certain about the morality of taking the deduction. In this instance the doubt rested on the meaning or application of the law. When doubts arise about a law's existence they are handled in the same way. A physician, for instance, has a patient with an unusual disease. Is there a law obliging him to report it? He looks into the matter himself, seeks advice, does his best to solve the doubt; but it remains. The law's existence is doubtful. Following the principle of doubtful laws, he refrains from reporting the disease. Again, according to this principle, the obligations of justice must be certain; otherwise they do not bind. The nurse who is honestly doubtful whether or not she damaged some equipment need not assume blame or hold herself liable for replacing it. Her doubtful obligation frees her of responsibility.

The safer course There are situations, however, where the principle that doubtful laws do not bind may *not* be used, where probabilism would be immoral, where the *safer course must be followed* in settling the doubt of an uncertain conscience. This happens when the action involves an object or end which must be realized. For example, a nurse is doubtful about the contents of a medicine bottle. It may be the right drug; she thinks it probably is. But she is not sure. May she go ahead and use it? Her profession obliges her to do what she reasonably can for the patient's welfare and to avoid what might injure him. This is a goal which she must strive to secure. As long as she is a nurse she cannot reject it. Morally, therefore, she cannot jeopardize her patient's recovery. She must follow the safer course and refrain from using the questionable drug until she is sure about it.

Application   Similarly, a hunter may be uncertain about an object he sees. He thinks it probably is a deer but admits it may be another hunter. May he risk a shot? Again, look at the situation. Natural law obliges him not to destroy human life unjustly. To risk a shot while he thinks it might be a man amounts to being willing to commit murder. No matter the probabilities that it is a deer, as long as some reason remains that it might be a man he cannot shoot. He must follow the safer course and hold his fire, because he is obliged without choice to respect human life. When situations are faced in which certain objectives must be secured probabilism cannot be followed. The safer course must be chosen, the course which will most certainly achieve the goal which the agent is bound to secure.

6. CONSCIENCE INFALLIBLE AND REFORMABLE

Infallibility   There are two terms, *infallibility* and *reforma-*
and   *bility* of conscience, which are rather confusing.
reformability   They may be understood in a perfectly correct
sense. But they may also be taken in a way that has danger-ous implications. For this reason they merit a brief explana-tion.

Infallibility   *Infallibility* in general means exemption from error. In so far as conscience is a judgment of human reason, it enjoys no more infallibility than any other judgment. That conscience can be erroneous, lax, scrupulous, indicates its fallibility. Conscience has, however, an aspect of infallibility—not in so far as it is a human judgment, but in so far as the true conscience incorporates and reflects God's law. That law, be it natural or positive moral law, enjoys the infallibility of its Maker. And conscience as truly indicating conduct on its basis certainly cannot be erroneous.

Reformability   *Reformability* of conscience occasionally signifies a change of view on moral matters. If this means that people ought to correct an erroneous or lax or scrupulous conscience, it is highly desirable. Again, that people deepen their ethical insights and become more sensitive to right and wrong is also a fact. And if this is what changing means, this too is admirable. But if "change of view of moral matters" means that principles change in the sense that there are no fixed unalterable principles, but that basic moral principles under social and economic pressure must alter to meet new needs, this conflicts with the nature of the natural moral law. This law rests ultimately in the Creator's design for man and all other creatures and enjoys the immutability of its Founder. Man's appreciation or understanding of moral principles can indeed undergo change, for better or for worse. But to suppose that those primary principles themselves change objectively and apart from man's thinking about them leads inevitably to the doctrine of the evolutionary character of morality. And this doctrine in practice eventually results simply in the rejection of morals as a coherent and coercive system.

7. SUMMARY

Forming conscience is no simple matter. In the first place the intellectual character of conscience must be appreciated. It is a judgment, liable to all the usual difficulties and dangers of human reasoning. Cogent and true thinking implies consistency and must rest on true moral principles. Hence, for conscience to be true, a man must begin with true ethical principles. But it is not enough that they be true and be known. They must be applied to the particular situation with due regard for all the circumstances bearing on its morality. In estimating the moral issues a man must strive for truth, avoiding as carefully as he can the laxity which is blind to evil no less than the scrupulosity which sees evil everywhere. But once a man has formed his conscience, done what he could to make it true and certain, then he must follow it. In this sense conscience is autonomous and supreme.

READINGS

Horace J. Bridges: *Humanity on Trial*, pp. 89ff.

Michael Cronin: *The Science of Ethics*, i, chapters xiv, xv, xvi.

Horatio W. Dresser: *Ethics in Theory and Application*, ch. xv.

Edward F. Garesché: *Ethics and the Art of Conduct for Nurses*, ch. xiv, Part I.

Charles J. McFadden: *Medical Ethics for Nurses*, pp. 18–26.

Michael Maher: *Psychology*, pp. 334–344.

Chapter 8

VIRTUE IN GENERAL

1. VIRTUE DEFINED

The good is
man's destiny
The aim of morality is to orientate a man toward the good. The natural law and its criteria are extrinsic guides. Conscience is his intrinsic guide. The journey involves action and specifically the sort of action which manifests intelligence and will and is called voluntary. These notions have been dealt with in the chapters on human nature and man's ultimate goal, on the natural moral law and the moral criteria, on human acts and on conscience. From this it appears that man's destiny is not merely to do an occasional good deed but at all times to pursue the good, in other words, to be virtuous. By nature that is his calling.

Habit and
virtue
To live means to act and living means doing the same thing many times over. Conduct which in the beginning was difficult often by repetition becomes less difficult. A facility is acquired, a certain temper of mind and will and even physical predispositions. The result is a new power or tendency for a specified mode of behavior, which, good or bad, becomes comparatively easy. This acquired facility is called *habit*. Morally good habits are virtues. Morally bad habits are vices.

Habit defined
Habit in general is a "tendency, established by voluntary practice, to act in one way rather than in another out of various possibilities."[1] The voluntary aspect needs emphasis. For habit does not involve physical or mechanical necessity. It always implies some action of

[1] Moore, T. V.: *Principles of Ethics*, p. 41.

the will. It produces a tendency or inclination to a certain mode of behavior but not a compulsion. Think of habit in terms of power which can be exercised in various channels. Of all the possible channels, habit gradually reduces the number and confines the exercise of the power to one. This does not abrogate freedom nor prevent a person from acting contrary to that channelled mode of behavior. Even with a habit firmly acquired, man remains free to act or not to act according to it. Habit never becomes a purely mechanical thing like the contraction of the pupil of the eye exposed to light.

Virtue   A morally good habit is virtue. *Virtue* denotes perfection of power. And a being's perfection, let it not be forgotten, follows chiefly upon the measure in which it fulfills its purpose. Human virtue is a habit, then, which bearing upon action, merits being called an operative habit, a habit productive of good works. It may be defined as *a good habit of the soul, whereby men live righteously.* What was said of habit not being simply a mechanical reaction should be applied also to virtue. It is not a sort of compulsion imposed by some external stimulus. Virtue develops from "internal initiative, from truly human conduct involving intellectual insight and voluntary choice."[2]

2. ARISTOTLE AND VIRTUE

Aristotle's   Aristotle defined virtue as a "state of character
definition   concerned with choice, lying in a mean, i.e.,
the mean relative to us, this being determined by a rational principle, and by that principle by which the man of practical wisdom would determine it."[3]

Aristotle's   The notion of the *golden mean* as virtue's es-
golden mean   sential characteristic marked the best of

[2] Moore, T. V.: *Principles of Ethics*, p. 42.
[3] Aristotle: *Nicomachean Ethics* (trans. by W. D. Ross, London, Oxford University Press, 1931), II, 6. 1107 a 1.

ancient non-Christian thought. It is the nature of things' Aristotle wrote, "to be destroyed by defect and excess, as we see in the case of strength and of health . . . .; both excessive and defective exercise destroys the strength, and similarly drink or food which is above or below a certain amount destroys the health, while that which is proportionate both produces and increases and preserves it. So too is it, then, in the case of temperance and courage and the other virtues. For the man who flies from and fears everything and does not stand his ground against anything becomes a coward, and the man who fears nothing at all but goes to meet every danger becomes rash; and similarly the man who indulges in every pleasure and abstains from none becomes self-indulgent, while the man who shuns every pleasure, as boors do, becomes in a way insensible; temperance and courage, then, are destroyed by excess and defect, and preserved by the mean."[4]

Lippmann's commentary   Aristotle's thought seems clear enough, but it may help to have Walter Lippmann's commentary.[5] Aristotle, he says, "expounded the theory that happiness is due to virtue, and that virtue is a mean between two extremes. There must, he said, be neither defect nor excess of any quality. We must, in brief, go so far but no further in obedience to our impulses. Thus between rashness and cowardice the mean is courage; between prodigality and niggardliness it is liberality; between incontinence and total abstinence it is temperateness; between ostentation and meanness it is magnificence; between empty boasting and little-mindedness it is magnanimity; between flattery and moroseness it is friendliness; between bashfulness and impudence it is modesty; between arrogance and false modesty, it is truthfulness."

[4] *Nicomachean Ethics*, II, 2. 1104 a 10.
[5] Lippmann, Walter: *A Preface to Morals* (London, George Allen and Unwin, 1929), pp. 166–167.

The golden   Aristotle's *golden mean* is not an absolute or
mean relative mathematical mean. It must be interpreted
relatively to the person concerned. "If ten pounds," he explained, "are too much for a particular person to eat and
two too little, it does not follow that the trainer will order
six pounds; for this also is perhaps too much for the person
who is to take it, or too little—too little for Milo, too much
for the beginner in athletic exercises. The same is true of
running and wrestling. Thus a master of any art avoids excess and defect, but seeks the intermediate and chooses
this—the intermediate not in the object but relatively
to us."[6]

Mean difficult Yet Aristotle, as well as anybody who tries to
to determine   apply the standard of the golden mean, faced
the difficulty of establishing it. "For in everything,"
Aristotle admits, "It is no easy task to find the middle . . . .
any one can get angry—that is easy—or give or spend
money; but to do this to the right person, to the right
extent, at the right time, with the right motive and in the
right way, *that* is not for every one, nor is it easy; wherefore
goodness is both rare and laudable and noble."[7]

Not all   While the golden mean is difficult to determine
actions have a in practice, some actions do not have it at all.
golden mean   For, as Aristotle explained, spite, shamelessness, envy, adultery, theft, murder, and suchlike imply that
they are themselves bad, and not the excesses or deficiencies
of them."It is not possible, then, ever to be right with
regard to them; one must always be wrong . . . . simply
to do any of them is to go wrong. It would be equally absurd, then, to expect that in unjust, cowardly, and volup-
tuous action there should be a mean, an excess, and a deficiency . . . . But as there is no excess and deficiency of
temperance and courage . . . . so too of the actions we have

[6] Aristotle, *Nicomachean Ethics*, II, 6. 1106 b 1.

[7] *Ibid.*, II, 7. 1109 a 25.

mentioned there is no mean nor any excess and deficiency, but however they are done they are wrong."[8]

The golden mean leans toward an extreme Finally in Aristotle's conception of virtue it should be noticed that in some instances the golden mean favors the side of excess and in other instances deficiency. Rashness is the excess of boldness; cowardice is its deficiency; but cowardice is more opposed to courage than rashness. In other words, courage leans more towards rashness then it does towards cowardice. Again, self-indulgence, which is excessive pleasure-seeking, is more opposed to the virtue of temperance than insensibility, which is the want of proper enjoyment of pleasure. "We describe as contrary to the mean, then, rather the directions in which we more often go to great lengths; and therefore self-indulgence, which is an excess, is the more contrary to temperance . . . . The moral virtue is a mean, then . . . . between two vices, the one involving excess the other deficiency, and . . . . it is such because its character is to aim at what is intermediate in passions and in actions . . . . Hence also it is no easy task to be good . . . . Hence he who aims at the intermediate must first depart from what is the more contrary to it, as Calypso advises—Hold the ship out beyond that surf and spray. For of the extremes one is more erroneous, one less so; therefore, since to hit the mean is hard in the extreme, we must as a second best, as people say, take the least of the evils. . . . ."[9]

3. THOMAS AQUINAS AND VIRTUE

Aristotle and Aquinas Aristotle's conception of virtue had, and still has, wide acceptance and influence. Thomas Aquinas used it, as he did so much of Aristotle's teaching, as a nucleus of his own philosophy of moral values.

[8] *Nicomachean Ethics*, II, 7, 1107 a 10.
[9] *Ibid.*, II, 9. 1109 a 15ff.

Aristotle's   Virtue perfects the will. But the will's perfec-
golden mean   tion follows from its harmony with the natural
accepted   law, and thus virtue, likewise, takes its character from that law. Aquinas, as Aristotle did, pointed out
that law suffers violation either by failure to live up to its
demands or by exaggerating them. Neither extreme is
virtuous. For right moral action seeks the happy or golden
medium. Gluttony and starvation are evil. Between the two
is the virtue of temperance.

The golden   Aquinas agreed with Aristotle in insisting that
mean of   the golden mean is *not absolute.* It is the mean
reason   set by reason. To estimate it justly reason
must consider the circumstances and character of the person
involved, for these vary not only with persons but also with
the same person at different times. Aquinas summed up the
matter in saying that the golden mean of the moral virtues
is *determined in relation to men, as set by human reason under the
guidance of law.* The mean of virtue, therefore, does not
spring from things considered in themselves and absolutely
apart from the persons and circumstances involved, but is
relative.

The golden   Yet there is one virtue whose golden mean is
mean and   found in the nature of things, without con-
justice   sideration for personal circumstances or emotions and passions. This is the virtue of justice. For it the
golden mean or standard is universally the same. When
something is owed, there is no question of a middle course
between underpayment and overpayment. The only
golden mean here is the debt. The view of justice is single,
impersonal, unemotional, objective. It concerns the return
of something definitely owed and precisely defined. Anything short of that is not justice. Anything in excess of it is
not justice. This is why it is said that in the virtue of justice
the golden mean of reason coincides with the medium of
objective reality.

4. CULTIVATING VIRTUE

Its necessity   Before some suggestions are made for cultivating virtue, a word should be said about its
necessity. For unless a person knows he ought to acquire
good moral habits, he is not likely to trouble himself about
the ways of doing it. William James (1842–1910) argued
vigorously in behalf of forming good characters. "The hell
to be endured hereafter," he wrote,[10] "of which theology
tells, is no worse than the hell we make for ourselves in this
world by habitually fashioning our characters in the wrong
way. Could the young but realize how soon they will become
mere walking bundles of habits, they would give more heed
to their conduct while in the plastic state. We are spinning
our own fates, good or evil, and never to be undone. Every
smallest stroke of virtue or of vice leaves its never so little
scar." Good moral habits spell the difference between happiness and misery even in this world. And if a man looks
beyond this life to his ultimate goal, the case for virtue
becomes infinitely stronger. Virtue is the perfection man
must seek, not merely because it will make him happy but
because *he must seek Infinite Goodness as his ultimate goal*, and
virtue is the absolutely necessary means to that end. He
may miss many things in life; but a man cannot reject
virtue without damning himself to unnatural frustration.
Virtue, by insuring man's prompt, unfaltering, steadfast
and more facile adherence to right moral conduct furnishes
the best guarantee that he will reach his destiny.

Virtue   Virtue becomes a second nature, not in the
corrects   sense that it rubs out humanity but in the
character   sense that it perfects it. Human virtue answers
to the perfect idea of virtue, which requires the right use of
the appetites. Most people find their appetites need control.
Virtue furnishes it and thus helps men surmount personal

[10] *Psychology* (New York, Henry Holt & Co., 1893), pp. 149–
150.

defects and weaknesses. The miserly man can become
generous. The proud and suspicious and envious and cring-
ing can remedy their defects, if they really want to. The
cure is to cultivate the opposite virtue. Laziness gives way
to industry, self-indulgence to restraint, gluttony and drunkenness to temperance, selfishness to love of one's fellow man.
Human character can be molded and virtue plays a vital
part, but naturally it involves a struggle. Self-conquest perhaps describes it better. Good moral habits can be cultivated
and can be made to transform the weak, defective person
into a better human being.

When begin training in virtue When it is recalled that virtue implies loyalty
to one's convictions about duty and unselfish
devotion to the good and that it involves the
educating of the will to prompt obedience, it is clear that
training in virtue cannot begin too early. Dr. Moore advises that all attempts to develop true virtue, to stimulate
the child to lay down his own lines of conduct in obedience
to moral ideals, should be made as soon as the child begins
to understand the spoken word. "Unless an adolescent,"
Dr. Moore writes, "takes himself in hand, the parents or
teachers will not get far with an attempt to control conduct
by rewards and punishments."[11]

Cultivating virtue— motive In cultivating virtue due consideration must
be given to such practical helps as William
James suggests as well as to the powerful influence of environment. But these presuppose *motive*. The
reason for this is simple. Habit is not a mechanical process.
Neither is virtue, which is a good moral habit. Virtue is the
result of man's deliberate choice. Since choice follows upon
understanding, a man must have a strong, stable, appealing
motive.

Motive important Too often *the need of motive and of associating
it with the desired habit* is minimized or for-

[11] *Principles of Ethics*, p. 42.

gotten in favor of mere repetition, and training the will follows the pattern of training a prizefighter or weight-lifter. The analogy is unfortunate. Muscle is one thing. Human will is quite another. The right kind of exercise does indeed strengthen muscle. But it does not follow that exercise for the sake of exercise likewise strengthens the will. Will is a spiritual faculty. Likewise it is a blind faculty, dependent upon the intellect for direction. On this basis the need for appropriate, attractive motive cannot be questioned. Motive is stressed not to the disparagement of will-training but to emphasize that such training, to be human and psychological, presupposes motive.[12]

Environment   *Environment* is a second potent factor in cultivating virtue. By environment is meant the things about a man—his physical surroundings, his friends, his books, his work, his pleasures, any and every external thing which can bring its influence to bear upon him. Environment plays a major rôle in any discussion about character or crime. In some instances its importance is so magnified that free will and personal self-determination pass out of sight or are categorically denied. It is not to fall into that error to stress the part environment, good and bad, plays in developing good and bad moral habits. Man keeps his free will. He can and often does revolt against his environment. But it likewise remains generally true that environment powerfully draws a man to itself and slowly makes him one with it.

A wholesome   Cultivating a wholesome environment is an
environment   elementary but necessary step towards cultivating virtue. This means wise choice of associates and friends. It involves a critical attitude towards reading and movies and the theatre and social gatherings. It means deliberation about the use of leisure. It means planning to use

[12] Cf. Lindworsky, J.: *The Training of the Will* (Milwaukee, Bruce Publishing Co., 1929), pp. 69–111.

time and not to "kill time" in aimless lethargy. It means that a man will make his life purposeful, alert, rich in worthwhile attachments and pursuits and occupations. He will not be at the mercy of circumstances but bend circumstances to the enriching of his life. Such a program has its difficulties; but they are the obstacles which make the enterprise all the more rewarding. Dedication implies renunciation. But the renunciations demanded by the culture of virtue will leave no void which the possession of virtue will not more than fill.

Practical   What has been said about motive and en-
maxims   vironment may seem theoretical in contrast to
more practical suggestions often made for cultivating good habits. Yet *environment* and *motive* are fundamental. Only if they are given due weight in theory and in practice will the maxims of William James have the results they should have. James' doctrine[13] is not new, but it has stood the test of time and kept much of its value.

                     The first maxim: *Launch yourself with the*
Maxim one   *strongest and most resolute initiative possible. A*
person should gather about him everything which can support his good resolution. He should put himself in conditions which encourage his new way of life, take a public pledge if he can, and make engagements incompatible with his former behavior. He must back up his good resolution with every available aid. This gives the good resolution such momentum that the temptation to break down will not occur as soon as it otherwise might. Every day without a break adds to the chances of its not occurring at all.

                     The second maxim: *Do not let an exception*
Maxim two   *occur till the new habit is securely rooted in your*
life. Each lapse is like dropping a neat ball of string. A single slip undoes much tedious work. The important thing

[13] James, W.: *Psychology, Briefer Course* (New York, Henry Holt and Company, 1893), pp. 145 ff.

is not to lose a battle. Every gain on the wrong side undoes
the effect of long and hard-won conquests on the right. A
man should aim at a series of uninterrupted successes, until
repetition has fortified his new habit to such an extent that
he will be able to cope with any opposition under any circumstances.

"Tapering- The principle of never allowing an exception
off" conflicts with the technique of "tapering-off"
such habits as the excessive use of alcohol and narcotics. On
this question there is a legitimate difference of opinion; but
James' view seems reasonable. "In the main . . . all expert
opinion would agree that abrupt acquisition of the new
habit is the best way, *if there be a real possibility of carrying it
out.* We must be careful not to give the will so stiff a task as
to insure its defeat at the very outset; but, *provided one can
stand it,* a sharp period of suffering, and then a free time, is
the best thing to aim at, whether in giving up a habit like
that of opium, or in simply changing one's hours of rising
or work. It is suprising how soon a desire will die of inan-
ition if it be *never* fed."[14]

Maxim three Third maxim: *As soon as you possibly can, act on
every resolution you make and on every emotional
prompting you experience in the direction of the desired habit.*
Maxims, sentiments, feelings, devout wishes and exalted
emotions, no matter their number or strength, unless they
end in action are illusory. Worse than that, they can be
downright harmful. When a man lets resolves and fine
feelings evaporate without bearing fruit, it is worse than
a lost opportunity. A positive obstacle has been raised
against future resolutions and emotions taking their normal
path. James thinks there is no more contemptible type of
human character than that of the sentimentalist and
dreamer who spends his life in a sea of sensibility and
emotions but who never gets down to carrying out his

[14] James, W.: *Psychology*, p. 146.

dreams in manly vigorous action. A man should not allow himself an emotion towards a good habit without giving it some concrete expression.

Maxim four   The fourth maxim: *Keep the spirit of effort alive by a little gratuitous exercise every day.* By this James meant that a man should do something every day for no other reason than that he would rather not do it. A man, James thought, who has daily inured himself to habits of concentrated attention, energetic volition, and self-denial in unnecessary things will stand like a tower when everything rocks around him and his softer fellow-mortals disappear like chaff in the blast.

Criticism   This doctrine is not entirely acceptable. It needs to be supplemented with what has been said about strong, compelling motives. To do things simply because they are against the will is irrational. Why sacrifice anything for the sake of sacrifice alone! And furthermore where is the proof that the will can be strengthened in this way? It has been pointed out (p. 137) that this view rests upon an analogy with physical powers. But the will is not a physical faculty. Its training cannot be identified with the training of an athlete's biceps. The will takes its cue from the intelligence. And the strength of the cue will be the strength of the motive which the intelligence formulates and passes on to the will.

Need of motive   A man should first seize upon a worth-while, adequate, reasonable and appealing motive, and then put his renunciations into daily practice. No matter how slight the sacrifice may be, or what it may be, it will have meaning, and in turn buttress the motive. For the oftener a person thinks of the motive and makes it operative, the livelier it becomes. Then when the hour of dire need comes the man will stand firm. For the motive which has been functioning, which daily has been heeded, which has resulted in manifold expressions will stand firm.

And all the trifling, unnecessary but meaningful renunciations will pay rich dividends.

Summary   Harold Titus, while mentioning most of the points James made, notices as James did not the aid religion and prayer can give towards cultivating good moral habits. "In gaining control of some impulse or habit," he writes, "we should avail ourselves of the help which social convention, psychology, and religion can give us. After reviewing in our mind the dangers of the old ways, we should center our attention upon the new habit to be established. We must remove, where possible, any stimuli which lead to the old temptation, then make a beginning in the line of conduct we wish to cultivate. It will aid materially if we are able to associate with a group where the new conduct is lived and approved. We tend to cultivate those habits which are approved by the group of which we are a part. For many, prayer, faith, comradeship, and the loyalty to a great cause which religion is able to instil will be effective."[15]

5. VICE THE CONTRARY OF VIRTUE

Vice defined   Opposed to virtue is *vice*. Whereas virtue is a morally good operative habit *vice is a morally evil operative habit*. This aspect of vice as a habit should not be overlooked. A lapse from the moral law does not constitute vice. A man can commit sin and yet not be vicious. It is only when he contracts the habit of sin that he becomes vicious, and it is only a sinful habit which is called vice. Virtue stands between its opposites of defect and excess. The one ruins moral goodness by failing to measure up to it, as cowardice falls short of fortitude. The other ruins moral goodness by immoderately pushing a good thing beyond the bounds of reason, as gluttony exceeds temper-

[15] *Ethics For Today* (New York, American Book Co., 1936), p. 202.

ance in food. In either way moral goodness suffers. This
privation of the goodness voluntary conduct ought to have
constitutes the essence of moral evil. When a man's voluntary acts habitually manifest this privation, they deserve
to be called vicious and the evil habit a vice.

Seven capital   On the basis of vice as either an inordinate
vices and   pursuit of good or an unreasonable aversion
pride   from it can be enumerated the evil habits
which, because they are so fundamental, are called the
capital vices. The goods which chiefly attract the human
appetites are immaterial goods, such as reputation and
honor; bodily goods which pertain to preserving the individual person, such as food and drink; physical goods
which insure the continuance of the race, such as sexual
pleasures; and finally external goods, such as wealth and
possessions. When a man inordinately pursues honors and
reputation, he cultivates the vice of *vainglory*. When he
takes inordinate pleasure in food and drink, the vice is
gluttony. When he seeks sexual pleasures inordinately, the
vice is *lust*. And if he makes too much of wealth, he suc-
cumbs to *covetousness*. On the other hand a person may
turn away from goodness because of some unpleasantness
attached to it, either as regards himself or as regards somebody else. He may balk at the effort needed to acquire
virtue and yield to *sloth*, which means laziness and prone-
ness to avoid physical exertion. Regarding the good of
somebody else a man may view it with displeasure, as in
some way harmful to himself. When this displeasure is
accompanied with rage and an inclination to vengeance,
it is called *anger*. When rage and vengeance are absent, it
is called *envy*. These seven capital faults have been considered traditionally the roots of all human moral evil. It
may be noticed that pride does not appear. This is because
pride, which means an inordinate love of self, underlies
all the other vices. For in giving way to any vice a man is

inordinately pursuing his own selfish good, which is just
another way of declaring him guilty of pride.

Eliminating   To get rid of evil moral habits a man should
evil habits   practice the corresponding virtue. Against
pride he cultivates humility. Covetousness is met with generosity. Lust is opposed with purity in thought, word and
deed. Gluttony yields to temperance in eating and drinking.
But to eliminate any vice a man will have to struggle. If he
cannot counteract it with the opposite virtue, perhaps he
can weaken the undesirable habit by disuse. Or he can put
a penalty on himself, something unpleasant which he will
have to bear if he gives way to the bad habit. In regard to
developing the counter-habit, Rauth and Sheehy point out
that the substitution of the good for the evil habit is "made
easier by a frank discussion of the undesirable behavior, the
events which led up to it, and the consequences. In such a
discussion, the undesirable and unpleasant effects can be
contrasted with the desirable results of the counter-habit. In
attempting to develop a counter-habit, there must be no
exceptions. Every urge to indulge the old activity must be
made a stimulus for practicing the counter-habit."[16]

6. SUMMARY

All peoples have a conception of virtue, though its actual
expression varies considerably. Even today there are those
who would reject the traditional virtues and try to build
up systems on what they pretentiously call the "new
morality." Yet the doctrine of Aquinas stands, based on the
concept of man as a being of manifold appetites but with
one dominant and ultimate destiny. His way to it is by
realizing his perfections in their due order of value. This
takes the practical form of habitually doing good and avoiding evil, in other words practicing virtue and avoiding
vice. Aquinas' doctrine rests upon Aristotle, though he went

[16] Rauth and Sheehy: *Psychology*, p. 74.

beyond the ancient Greek in clarifying and applying the notion of the "golden mean." The pursuit of virtue has its difficulties but no one has ever claimed it to be easy. It needs intelligence and perseverance. Motivation must be stressed, a wholesome environment cultivated and the practical maxims followed. The good life means the elimination of vices; but more than that it must manifest the earnest pursuit of all the virtues, which the following chapters will take up in some detail.

READINGS

Thomas Aquinas: *Summa Theologica*, Part I–II, qq. 55–58.
Aristotle: *Nicomachean Ethics*, Bks. ii and iii.
Michael Cronin: *The Science of Ethics*, i, 593–616.
Walter G. Everett: *Moral Values*, pp. 286–290.
Walter Farrell: *A Companion to the Summa*, ii, ch. viii.
Johann Lindworsky: *The Training of the Will*, pp. 25–111.
Thomas V. Moore: *Principles of Ethics*, ch. iv.
J. E. Rauth and Sr. M. M. Sheehy: *Principles of Psychology*, pp. 70–75.
Harold H. Titus: *Ethics for Today*, ch. xiii.

Chapter 9

CARDINAL VIRTUES—PRUDENCE

1. CARDINAL VIRTUES IN GENERAL

Virtues reducible to four The problem of dealing with good moral habits in particular is simplified by an old fact, that they are reducible to four cardinal virtues. As Walter Lippmann puts it, "We may be sure that no quality is likely to have become esteemed as a virtue which did not somewhere and sometime produce at least the appearance of happiness. The virtues are grounded in experience; they are not idle suggestions inadvertently adopted because somebody took it into his head one fine day to proclaim a new ideal . . . the cardinal virtues correspond to an experience so long and so nearly universal among men of our civilization, that when they are understood they are seen to contain a deposited wisdom of the race."[1]

Derivation according to subject The conception of the basic virtues as *prudence, justice, fortitude* and *temperance* goes back at least to Plato (428–348 B.C.), the Greek philosopher who was Aristotle's master.[2] But neither he nor Aristotle, who likewise stressed them, offered to explain why they should be the four virtues from which all the others stemmed. Centuries later Thomas Aquinas showed how they corresponded to the human faculties. First there is the faculty or power which is rational in its essence, the practical

---

[1] Lippmann, W.: *A Preface to Morals* (London, George Allen and Unwin Ltd., 1929), p. 226.

[2] For a summary of Plato's and Aristotle's ethics, cf. Barrett, C. L.: *Ethics* (New York, Harper Bros., 1933), pp. 126–152.

reason itself. This is perfected by the virtue of *prudence*, which guides reason to modes of behavior leading to man's ultimate goal. Then there are the three powers which enjoy a measure of rationality in so far as they are under control of reason. The will is perfected by *justice*, which determines it to seek the good due to others on a basis of equality. The faculty which impels a man to seek pleasure, the concupiscible appetite, is perfected by the virtue of *temperance*, which restrains him in its pursuit. Finally there is the faculty of holding to the good as defined by reason, the irascible appetite. It is perfected by the virtue of *fortitude*, which gives a man heart to face danger. This explanation accounted for the four virtues in terms of their subjects or the four faculties of reason, will, and the concupiscible and irascible appetites.

According to object   Aquinas got the same result from an analysis of virtue's formal principle or object, which is the good revealed by reason. This good has a double aspect. It may exist among the acts of reason itself, and the virtue which directs reason to this good is *prudence*. Or this good may exist according as reason establishes order among man's outward actions and inner passions. The habit which establishes order in outward conduct is *justice*. The passions, however, have a twofold effect. They may incite man to do what reason forbids or they may restrain him from doing what reason commands. Those which incite him to do something against the good of reason need a curbing virtue, which is *temperance*. And those which hold him back from doing what reason commands suggest his need for a strengthening virtue, which is *fortitude*. Temperance moderates impetuous desires; fortitude inspires men to follow the hard path of duty.

Cardinal   The prominent place these four virtues have held points to their deep psychological origin and amply vindicates their right to be called *cardinal*. Unfortunately *cardinal* has swung so far from its root meaning that today it has little significance. *Cardinal*, from the Latin *cardo*, originally meant the pivot and socket upon which a door was made to swing.

Cardinal virtues pivotal As applied to the virtues of prudence, justice, fortitude and temperance *cardinal* indicates their pivotal relation to the good life. No door swings smoothly without its hinges. Likewise the virtuous life depends upon the cardinal, or hinge, virtues. For they are the general virtues, of which other virtues are divisions. Thus any virtue which produces good in the deliberations of reason falls under prudence. Every virtue which safeguards the good of what is owed pertains to justice. Every virtue which controls passion comes under temperance. And every virtue which strengthens man against passion can be called fortitude.

Their object important Again from the point of view of the importance of what they concern these virtues merit the title of cardinal or principal. For prudence is the virtue which commands. Temperance suppresses desires for the pleasures of touch. Justice prescribes what is due between equals. And fortitude fortifies a man against danger, especially against the fears of suffering and dying. In some ways other virtues may be called principal; but in respect to their formal principle of good and to their matter prudence, justice, fortitude and temperance are cardinal.

Cardinal virtues go together It is characteristic of the cardinal virtues that *they function together*. If a person practices one of them more earnestly than the others, they all share in the growth. For one of them alone cannot flourish without the other three. Similarly if one is neglected, the others share in the neglect. "The reason for this," as Garesché writes,[3] "is found in the very nature of these

[3] Garesché, E. F.: *Ethics and the Art of Conduct for Nurses* (Philadelphia, W. B. Saunders Co., 1944, 2d ed.), p. 69.

virtues, each one of which so perfects the human character as to draw the others in its train. Thus to give everyone his due, as justice requires, needs a high degree of prudence, temperance and fortitude. To judge correctly on all occasions what is the right way of acting, which is the characteristic of prudence, requires much justice, temperance and fortitude. In like manner the other cardinal virtues, temperance and fortitude, require each one for its perfect exercise the aid of the others in a high degree."

Cardinal   The cardinal virtues are so fundamental that
virtues merit *no life can be virtuous without them.* And unless a
study   man is virtuous he cannot reach his ultimate
goal, Infinite Goodness. This brings out the absolute necessity of the cardinal virtues and emphasizes the primary reason which should bring a person to study them and dominate any other motive. But virtue implies action. And unless a man's conviction about the necessity of the cardinal virtues is to be sterile, he must set about building a character rooted in them. Amidst the hardships of the task he can find encouragement in the testimony of the ages: that the virtuous life is the happy life. Nor should he forget that the happiness meant includes the present life. But it goes beyond that, to stretch into the future. The best insurance a man can have that he is pursuing his destiny and is in the way of reaching his ultimate goal of Infinite Goodness is a life dedicated to virtue. This inescapably commits him to cultivating the cardinal virtues.[4]

2. PRUDENCE

Definition   The first of the cardinal moral virtues is not
                 strictly a moral virtue, or a virtue belonging to

[4] This exposition of the cardinal virtues in particular is drawn largely from Thomas Aquinas, *Summa Theologica*, II–II, qq. 47–56, for prudence: qq. 57–122, for justice; qq. 123–140, for fortitude; and qq. 141–170, for temperance.

the will. *Prudence* is an intellectual virtue. As Aquinas says, it is the right reason of human conduct or behavior. It guides man to select and to use the means for attaining virtue's golden mean. This mean is the object of all virtue, but it is prudence that disposes and arranges things to secure it. Prudence signifies wisdom in human affairs. It joins the company of the moral virtues because, dealing properly with the means for achieving the goal of human good, it functions with the will, which carries these means into action. Prudence may be defined, then, as a virtue of the practical intellect which prompts a man in the midst of the particular, concrete and shifting circumstances of life to choose and use the best means to a good end.

First of the cardinal virtues This is why prudence holds *first place* among the cardinal virtues. It is the light which must shine upon them all if they are to have the due order of virtue. However, prudence does not determine the end of the moral virtues. That has been set in man's nature by his appetites. They owe nothing to prudence. But prudence does scrutinize and choose the best means for making the action of the appetites orderly and morally good.

Acts of prudence Prudence functions in a threefold way. It inclines a man to seek truth by advice and consultation. It helps him to weigh and pass judgment upon what he discovers. Thirdly, it leads to a command which puts the product of his inquiry and judgment into action. This act of command is most significant. If a man perceives the right means but fails to use them, he falls short of the virtue of prudence—likewise if he neglects to seek sound advice. The value of asking advice must be acknowledged. At the same time men should avoid being gullible. Aristotle advised them to be quick in carrying out advice once it has been accepted but slow in accepting it. Keep your critical sense alive. Recall St. Augustine's (354–430) statement that prudence keeps most careful watch and ward, lest a man be taken unawares and be deceived by evil counsel.

Prudence not selfish　　There is a tendency to think of prudence solely in terms of personal good. This would make it too selfish to be virtuous. Prudence does concern the self, as of necessity all the virtues do. For their purpose is to bring man to his natural perfection and ultimate goal. But self-fulfilment must not be confused with selfishness. No more and no less than other virtues, prudence tends to man's perfect self-fulfilment. But it goes beyond that, to find a proper place in his relations *with the family and the State*. In this way it transcends the individual person. Centuries ago Thomas Aquinas pointed out that since prudence rightly counsels, judges and commands concerning the means of obtaining a good end, prudence regards not only the private good of the individual but also the command good of the multitude.

Other virtues need prudence　　Prudence is *necessary* to all the other moral virtues. Their objective is man's ultimate end. Their office is to help him attain it. But it is prudence which guides a man to the means and urges him to use them. There is reason for prudence being needed. The essence of virtue is the golden mean between the extremes of defect and excess. But this mean is not absolute. Neither are circumstances always the same. This is why prudence is so necessary for the other virtues. For it is its special attribute to point out in the individual instance the correct path to virtue. And this path is the mean. Without prudence the other virtues would lose their orientation and run to imperfection by defect or excess.

Prudence needs other virtues　　On the other hand, prudence *needs the other moral virtues*. Without them it loses its meaning, since its sole concern evolves around the selection and use of means. It does not set the ends. Yet means have significance only in virtue of the ends for which they are used. The knowledge and desire of good ends flow from the other moral virtues. So that without them prudence would be nugatory. Consequently no man can pretend to be prudent *who does not have the other moral virtues.*

Associated virtues Here may be mentioned the noteworthy virtues connected with prudence. There is the habit of taking good counsel. Another associated virtue is the disposition to judge rightly about matters of every-day practical life. Then there is the habit of interpreting laws according to their spirit—as against the lifelessness of their words. This means that under exceptional circumstances a man can appeal to a higher principle than the law in question, even if it demands abrogating the law for the occasion.

3. DIVISIONS

False prudence The phrase *good end* in the definition suggests that there are various kinds of prudence corresponding to the objectives which men pursue. The thief plans ways to get his loot and escape. This seems a good end to him, and he is disposing things to secure it. His action has the appearance of prudence, just as its objective has the appearance of good, whereas both are evil and false. So is his prudence spurious. It is *false prudence*, since it pertains to an evil end.

Imperfect prudence There is a second kind of prudence which is true but *imperfect* in a twofold way. It may be that the good which it proposes as an end is not the ultimate objective of life but some particular good. Thus a person can be truly a prudent business man, a prudent navigator, a prudent physician, a prudent parent, a prudent nurse. Or the prudence may be imperfect because it fails to make the appropriate means to an end function as they should.

Perfect The third kind of prudence takes counsel, judges, commands rightly in respect of the ultimate end of man's life. It is not concerned directly with the particular goods of existence but with the ultimate good of man's destiny. This is the *true and perfect prudence*.

Personal,   Another division of prudence distinguishes
domestic,   prudence on the basis of individual good, the
political   good of the family and the good of the State.
prudence   These are different *good ends*, and so give rise
to different kinds of prudence. Personal prudence, or simply prudence, is directed to the individual person's good. Domestic prudence concerns the good of the home. Political prudence seeks to secure the common good of the State.

4. COMPONENTS OF PRUDENCE

Memory   It may help to understand prudence better if
     it is analyzed into its components. They are memory, reasoning, understanding, docility, shrewdness, foresight, circumspection and caution. In order to carry the valuable lessons of the past into the future a man must remember the past. Experience is heralded as the greatest teacher. But it can teach only if its lessons are remembered. This is *memory's* rôle.

Reasoning and   But the use of these lessons as well as the appli-
understanding   cation of principles to life involves *correct reasoning procedures*. Understanding moreover gives man the right to estimate about those primary principles which are so essential to prudential behavior.

Docility   Yet in spite of his best efforts to be prudent, he
     is going to fail unless he recognizes the need of *docility*, the need of being taught. Here the voices of two great thinkers should be heard. Prudence is concerned with matters of action, said Aquinas. But these matters are so various that no man can consider them all. And even for those he can consider a man needs time. All this emphasizes man's need to be taught—especially by older people who understand about practical matters. Aquinas was merely echoing Aristotle's statement that it is just as sensible to

accept the undemonstrated assertions and opinions of experienced, prudent and older persons as it is to accept their cogently reasoned demonstrations. No man therefore is entirely self-sufficient. He needs instruction and advice.

Shrewdness and foresight   Likewise he needs to be *shrewd*. Shrewdness does not mean being artful or sly. It means a facility for making up one's own mind in practical and speculative matters. Its connection with prudence is as obvious as the need of foresight. Of all the parts of prudence foresight rates highest. For whatever prudence needs is needed in order to guide a being to its destiny. The vision of an objective not yet realized characterizes foresight, which plainly is required whenever there is a question of selecting and using means. And this is the specific action of prudence, to choose means to ends.

Circumspection   But foresight of the end is not enough. All the circumstances of the particular situation must be reckoned with. This demands *circumspection*. For when men are dealing with a definite action, it can happen that a thing is good in itself and suitable to the end but nevertheless evil or unsuitable because of some combination of circumstances. Hence a man must be circumspect. He must compare the means proposed with the actual circumstances confronting him.

Caution   Finally there is *caution*. Need for it springs from the everyday fact that the false often is found with the true, and evil with the good. Good is frequently hindered by evil and evil goes about disguised as the good. For a man to tread his way prudently in such a maze he does indeed have to be cautious.

5. CULTIVATING PRUDENCE

Appetites set—means various   The component parts of prudence suggest that it has to be acquired. It is not from nature. The right ends of human life are indeed set. But the means to the end in human concerns are far from being fixed. They vary from person to person and from one set of circumstances to another. Natural inclinations are fixed, but the knowledge of appropriate means of realizing them is not fixed, is not in man naturally.

Ways of cultivating prudence However, in various degrees man can come to know the means and to use them. Such knowledge and use pertain to the virtue of prudence. Obviously therefore he must work to acquire it, and this he can do by cultivating memory, reasoning and understanding. He must swallow pride and strive to profit from the experience and advice of his elders. He must be shrewd and exercise foresight and circumspection and caution. He must be prepared for a long and difficult struggle. For since prudence is concerned with the particular aspects of action, and since these aspects are practically innumerable, he must steel himself to be patient. This is why Aquinas thinks there is little prudence among the young. Prudence comes from living. This implies a large measure of experience and time, and so it should be looked for in the aged.

6. IMPRUDENCE

Imprudence defined Opposed to prudence is *imprudence*, which signifies the lack of this virtue in persons who can and ought to have it. Imprudence frequently appears as precipitation, thoughtlessness, inconstancy and negligence. These do not resemble prudence in the least. But there are other vices which, because they resemble prudence, sometimes pass as its counterfeits. Such are worldly prudence, craftiness, guile, fraud and disquieting solicitude.

Precipitation and thoughtlessness *Precipitation* pictures a headlong plunge into decisions which have not been carefully formulated. Instead of calmly drawing upon experience and using his mind to understand the situation and taking a shrewd estimate of probable developments and seeking advice, a man rushes into action. He sacrifices prudence to impetuous passion and will. This of course ties up closely with thoughtlessness, whereby a man fails to judge correctly through neglecting the things which insure right reasoning.

Inconstancy and negligence Wrong judgment underlies *inconstancy*, which surrenders a good purpose to a rebellious appetite. A man gives up the good he ought to hold to, because he finds something more pleasant. Such weakness follows from a defect in reason, which rejects what it rightly had accepted. Reason can resist passion; when it does not and is inconstant, it reveals imperfection. As precipitation arises from want of counsel and thoughtlessness from lack of judgment, so inconstancy springs from failure in the act of command. For a person is inconstant when he fails to do what has been counselled and judged to be right. He is *negligent* when he omits something which ought to be done. He fails to use proper care, and since care belongs to prudence, his negligence proves him guilty of imprudence.

Counterfeits —worldly prudence Among the vices which masquerade as prudence mention may be made first of *worldly prudence*. This is the man's attitude who makes physical things the end of all living—the end of life itself. Such exclusive fixation on the physical has the disorder of vice. The lower exists for the higher, the body for the soul, physical things to help man to his ultimate goal. They deserve man's attention and love—but not as ends in themselves. They are means to contribute to man's perfection and to his progress toward Infinite Goodness. When a man makes the good things of the world the end of all his living, they do not cease to be good in themselves. But he injects evil by his inordinate and unlawful love. The habitual quality which prompts it far from meriting the title of prudence deserves condemnation as a vice.

Craftiness is another counterfeit of prudence. It
Craftiness uses means which are apparently right and
just, but which actually are not. The purpose in view may
be good or evil. But even if it be good, it does not justify
craftiness. Guile and fraud go along with this vice, abetting
it with false words and deeds.

Inordinate Finally there is *inordinate solicitude* about tem-
solicitude poral things. Naturally men must care for
them—but not with an anxiety which unsettles the mind.
Solicitude as prudence's counterfeit takes three forms. Temporal things may be sought as ends in themselves. This is just
as unreasonable as worldly prudence. Both confuse proximate
ends with ultimates and disorganize a man's life. Secondly,
solicitude may be inordinate because a man is too earnest
about temporal things. He does not seek them as ultimates
but cherishes them to such an extent that he grows cold to
spiritual things, which ought to be his chief interest. Thirdly,
a man may be unduly solicitous through fear that he will
lack the necessaries of life if he does what is right. In brief,
temporal goods exist not to be man's master but his servant.
Disorder, and vice, arise and virtue suffers when he pursues
them as ultimate objectives or becomes overly solicitous
about them.

Causes of With regard to the vices of imprudence,
imprudence Aquinas traces them to pleasure, which he
says, agreeing with Aristotle, is the great enemy of prudence.
He admits that forgetfulness can obstruct prudence and
that sorrow can pervert it. But it is pleasure, and above all
sexual pleasure, which leads people to imprudence.

Pleasure good The reason is not that pleasure is bad in itself.
but at times No pleasure is designed naturally to lead men
antagonistic astray. On the contrary by the Creator's plan
pleasure is one of *man's great motivations towards fulfilling his
duties*. But in man there are many and various pleasures
with their corresponding appetites. The good life implies

that man establishes due order among the higher and the lower. This is the office of reason and prudence. But because of the variety and vigor of pleasure and the way sensual satisfaction can becloud reason, man's appetites and pleasures can rebel against reason and be antagonistic to his general welfare.

Consequences   Often it is not easy to submit to the guidance of reason and prudence. The resulting struggle varies with the strength of the opposition. The greater the anticipated pleasure, the more intense the struggle—when this pleasure happens to be against man's good. And since sexual satisfaction ranks highest among sensual pleasures, it is to be expected that the battle to control it will be severest and failure for this cause most frequent.

READINGS

Thomas Aquinas: *Summa Theologica*, Part I–II, qq. 58–65, and Part II–II, qq. 47–56.
Clifford L. Barrett: *Ethics*, pp. 126–152.
Walter Farrell: *A Companion to the Summa*, ii, chapters 9 and 10; iii, ch. vi.
J. F. Leibell: *Readings in Ethics*, pp. 236–241.

Chapter 10

CARDINAL VIRTUES—JUSTICE

1. JUSTICE DEFINED

The term   As with other words of honorable histories, justice has acquired various meanings. Sometimes it signifies all the virtues taken collectively and is synonymous with holiness. Or it becomes identified with the good simply, as when Plato considered it the perfect harmony of all the soul's powers. However, as a distinct moral virtue with its own subject matter, justice has a narrower and more exact use.

Definition   *Justice*, according to Thomas Aquinas, is the moral habit by which a person constantly and perpetually wills to give every man what belongs to him. This definition closely resembles Aristotle's, that justice is a habit whereby a man is capable of doing just actions in accordance with his choice. Aristotle emphasized that justice concerns free actions, whereas Aquinas stressed the quality of will and the aspect of *otherness* which justice implies.

Perpetual,   If taken literally *perpetual* might be misleading.
constant will   In some meanings it can be applied only to God. But in the definition it indicates that the virtue of justice requires that a man wills to be just *always*. It does not satisfy the moral habit of justice for a person to be just merely on occasion in some particular matter. Justice requires a steadfast inclination, at all times and under all circumstances. That is why Aquinas added *constant*, to indicate the will's firm and unwavering adherence to giving everyone what belongs to him.

Otherness   *Otherness* is another aspect of justice which needs emphasis. Justice concerns external actions and things in so far as they bear upon one man's relations with another. Justice leaves the passions to other virtues, such as prudence and temperance. It leaves to art the right way of making and producing things. But it reserves to itself the problems of man's conduct and use of things in his dealings with other persons. Hence a man cannot exercise justice towards himself.

Object of   Justice deals with social relationships, and
justice   operates to keep men living harmoniously together. This general objective, however, has a double aspect. First, there is the *thing or action* which is owed another. Justice demands that he receive it. He is an honest man who pays his just debts. But what makes a debt just? This is the second aspect of justice. Why is something owed? What is the source of one man's obligation in justice to another? The answer is *right*. One man has an obligation, because another has a right. Since the object of justice, then, is the just, and the just is the same as right, right becomes clearly the object of justice and it belongs to justice to give everyone his right.

Positive and   The right or the just is something that is re-
natural rights   lated to another person according to some definite equality. Right is of two sorts, *natural right* and *positive right*. A man can have a right to something by the nature of the thing itself. Thus men have a *natural right* to food, to liberty, to be unmolested in their property, to have health and life respected. On the other hand a man may acquire rights to something by mutual consent. This establishes *positive right*. For example a man has no right to another man's property. But by agreement, or contract, one may consent to let the other have it upon payment of a certain sum of money. In this way men can will to establish rights, provided that what is concerned is not against the

natural law. For no agreement or contract can establish a right to something evil. Adultery is immoral and remains immoral even though all the parties concerned consent to it.

2. DIVISIONS OF JUSTICE

Justice is usually divided into legal, distributive and commutative. All three agree in having the common good as their objective. But whether this is enough to warrant their being considered strictly and univocally as parts of justice as defined has been questioned. Admittedly the division of justice offers some difficulties. But for practical purposes the usual plan can be followed. There is first *general*, or *legal*, justice. Opposed to this is particular justice, which has two divisions: *distributive* and *commutative*.

3. GENERAL, OR LEGAL, JUSTICE

Definition   General, or legal, justice signifies a *citizen's relation to the common good*, or to the State. Every virtue in so far as it aims at the common good is to that extent referable to it. Since the common good is properly the object of justice, it follows that all virtue can pertain in some degree to justice. Hence the justice binding men to the common good is called *general*, as involving all the virtues.

Legal   Its title of *legal* comes from similar considerations. Legal presupposes law. Law exists to establish and to preserve the common good. Since justice as here considered is a virtue which brings men into conformity with law and so directs them to the common good, legal fittingly describes it.

Embraces all virtues   But whether or not this relationship which citizens have with the State and its welfare is called legal, or general, justice, it embraces all the virtues in so far as any virtue contributes to the common welfare. From this point of view legal, or general, justice is identified with all the other virtues. They are merely viewed differently, as bearing more especially on a man's obligation to the State. Thus a citizen who pays his debts is just. At the same time his action promotes the common good, which rests on the mutual acknowledgment of rights and duties to respect personal property. From this social point of view his action may be said to belong to general, or legal, justice. Yet there is really no inherent difference between the virtue which prompts the man to pay his debts and the act considered as promoting the common good.

Not the same as virtue in general General, or legal, justice is not the same as virtue in general. For the virtue of a good man as such is not the same as the virtue of a good citizen. Citizenship adds definite commitments. It involves the responsibility of striving for the common good (p. 60). The virtue, then, of good citizenship deserves special title, and general, or legal, justice well describes it.

4. DISTRIBUTIVE JUSTICE

Particular justice General, or legal, justice deals with man's duties to the State. *Particular justice* concerns private persons, who, with reference to the State, may be conceived of as parts to the whole. This gives rise to the double order of part to part and of the whole to the parts. Considered as parts, men have duties to one another, which constitute the field of *commutative justice*. On the other hand the whole may be considered relative to the parts, that is, the State relative to the citizens. And this gives rise to *distributive justice*.

Definition Distributive justice is defined as the virtue which obliges the organized community, or the State, to share among its members according to their ability and merit the good things (as well as the burdens) which it controls. This justice is called distributive, because it essentially implies something being distributed by the State among the citizens. For what belongs to the community as a whole is due to its parts, to its citizens.

Equality of proportion　Yet it is not due them with absolute equality. They have equal rights to share in the common goods (and burdens) in proportion to their importance to the community. Consequently the mean of distributive justice is not arithmetical, not an exact equality of thing with thing. It is an equality of proportion. It is an equality between what one person receives and what another receives based on their relations to the community.

Examples　Thus when the community honors its heroes, a man twice as heroic as another ought to receive twice the recognition. Similarly, in collecting taxes, the burden should be spread on the basis of ability to pay. The result can be, with perfect legal justice, that some men may pay next to nothing while others will surrender a major portion of their incomes.

5. COMMUTATIVE JUSTICE

Definition　Justice simply, properly and strictly is *commutative justice*. It is defined as the moral habit by which a person constantly and perpetually wills to give every man what belongs to him. It evokes the picture of buying and selling, where the notion of commutative justice is familiarly exemplified. By commutative justice a man gives everyone his due and abstains from taking what belongs to another. Unlike distributive justice, which concerns the community's property, commutative justice involves personal property. Something is given to another as strictly owed.

Essential components　The obligation of commutative justice has three components, which should be noted. The obligation implies a relation *with another person*; for a man cannot be obliged in justice to himself. There must be something *strictly owed*. This means that what is involved be clearly defined and that a man have a strict and certain right to it. Finally the satisfaction of the obligation demands *exact equality*. No underpayment will dissolve the debt; and no overpayment can be demanded on the basis of the debt itself.

Arithmetical mean of commutative justice The equality demanded by commutative justice must be clearly understood. Commutative justice demands something *really and objectively equal to another man's right*. It seeks to make return in exact proportion to what is owed. Consequently the medium of justice proper is the same for everybody, regardless of time or manner or agent or other circumstances. The mean of commutative justice is an exact quantitative equality between external, objective thing and external, objective person. It demands that a person pay back to another just so much as he has grown richer out of the other man's property. The result is an *arithmetical equality*, or mean.

Different from other virtues In respect to its mean of strict mathematical or quantitative equality commutative justice differs from the other moral virtues. Their golden mean was seen to be proportionate and had to be weighed in the light of the persons concerned as well as of all the circumstances. This is disregarded in the mean of justice, which is strictly defined, unchanged by circumstances, arithmetical, the same for all men at all times. The real mean of justice proper meets the essential requirements of right rational order. It is also the rational mean. In this respect justice does not fall short of the other moral virtues.

Examples Thus temperance implies the mean of moderation—eating neither too much nor too little. But what is too much or too little? The amount must be determined not absolutely in terms of quantity but relative to the person, to his physical constitution, to his work and present situation. But in the matter of justice the mean is not relative. If a man owes another man $25, justice demands payment of exactly that amount—no more and no less. The mean is definite and absolute.

Restitution   The guilty violator of commutative justice is *bound to restitution*, which imposes the duty of returning what has been unjustly taken or possessed. Restitution reestablishes equality by giving back the exact amount involved. There is no obligation to restore more, nor is the obligation satisfied by repaying less. The whole of what has been gotten unjustly must be surrendered to its rightful owner. If this cannot be done, it must be disposed of in some other way. The unjust possessor cannot keep it. Originally restitution applied to external objects. But its scope has been widened to include unjust injury to another person's body or to his good name, in other words, to defamation.

Defamation   *Defamation* merits more than a passing word.
and   All too frequently people minimize its evil and
restitution   forget entirely the duty of restitution. When a person, as in a legal trial, justly testifies and tells the truth about the accused, he is not bound to repair the injury which may follow. On the contrary, if a man speaks both unjustly and falsely to injure another's good name, he is bound to restitution. A nurse who not only breaks her obligation of professional secrecy but at the same time lies about her patient is bound to repair the harm she causes. Finally a man is bound to restitution if he speaks the truth but unjustly. What a nurse reveals about her patient may well be true, but if she violates her professional obligations, her revelation is unjust and she is liable to restitution. It is no easy matter to repair the harm done by defamation. If the revelation is true, it is even more difficult. Yet the guilty person is bound to do what he can to compensate for the damage he has inflicted.

*The
equivalent
lacking*
Even if a person cannot give back the equivalent, the obligation of restitution remains. He must repay what he can, when he can. Compensation must be made as far as possible. If a man has unjustly suffered the loss of a limb, he deserves compensation in some way. Likewise, as regards a man's obligation to God and to his parents, he cannot give back the equivalent of what they have given him. Yet he is bound to repay them in so far as he can.

*Restitution
and
punishment*
When a man holds another person's property unjustly or has been guilty of unjust damage, two considerations arise. One is the damage or possession of the thing. The other is the act of injustice committed. The possession or damage is remedied by restitution, whereby the exact equivalent is returned. But there remains the moral fault, which demands that punishment be inflicted by legitimate authority. Consequently when the court orders a man to pay something over and beyond the amount of restitution, it is acting within its rights and the person is bound by its decision.

*Who are
bound to
restitution*
The person who commits a crime against commutative justice is bound to restitution. So also are his *accomplices*. This includes all those who in any way voluntarily caused or helped the person commit the crime, either by counselling or commanding or in any way whatsoever. Furthermore, as it is unjust to take away another's property, so also it is unjust to deprive a man of its use against his will. In either way he suffers unjust injury. A person, therefore, who unjustly withholds another person's property or deprives him of its use is bound to restitution just the same as the man who steals or injures another man.

*Apparent
exception*
There is, however, an apparent exception to the obligation of restitution, when restitution would threaten the rightful owner or somebody else with

serious injury. Under such circumstances the thing ought not be returned at once. For restitution is directed to the good of the person involved. When it would amount to injuring him or somebody else, it would be unreasonable and obviously wrong. Yet, whoever keeps the property in question cannot appropriate it. He must return it at an opportune time or entrust it to a competent person. A physician, for instance, might take away a hunting rifle from a mentally ill patient and not be obliged in the least to return it until the man had recovered. But if the patient failed to get well, the rifle would not become the physician's.

6. ASSOCIATED VIRTUES

Many virtues are associated with justice, which will be seen in more detail. Here some of the important ones may be simply enumerated. They fall into two groups. In the first group are virtues which do not come under justice strictly, because the debt owed cannot be paid with equality. They are: religion, piety, patriotism, reverence and love of God. In the second group are virtues which fall short of justice, because what is involved is not a strict debt. They are: truthfulness, gratitude, zeal for law, friendship, liberality, and the habit of following the spirit, rather than the dead letter, of a law when the situation demands it.

7. OPPOSED VICES

As with virtues associated with justice, so with some of the vices opposed to it—they will be seen later on in detail. For the present it may be noticed that justice is violated by murder, mutilation, theft and robbery. In the courtroom it suffers from unjust judgment, accusation and defense, from false witnesses and unjust legal procedure. Outside of the courtroom justice is opposed to reviling, backbiting, talebearing, lying, derision and cursing. Cheating and usury

have to do largely with injustices in commercial and
business transactions.

8. SUMMARY

Three sorts   All the moral virtues are social but justice
of justice   more than the others. It implies a background
of men organized into some sort of community. Thereby
arise three relationships: the State to the citizens, citizens
to citizens, and the citizens to the State. The differences
among these relationships are not to be minimized; still
basically they all involve the obligation of giving others
their due. The State has the obligation of giving citizens
their due, of taking all into equal consideration when it
dispenses benefits or imposes burdens. This is *distributive
justice*. On the other hand citizens are obliged to give the
State its due, of contributing to the common welfare in
service and in money and in general living. This is *legal*,
or *general*, *justice*. Finally, there are the obligations which
men have to give one another their due, and this is *commutative justice*.

Justice strictly   As mentioned in the beginning, it is question-
commutative   able whether justice can be applied in exactly
the same meaning to all three sorts. In its exemplary form
justice is commutative. This fits the definition perfectly. In
problems of commutative justice there is no doubt or vague-
ness about the persons or the obligation. The amount is
definite, the right is clear, and the debtor is just as certainly
known as the man collecting the debt.

Differences   When like standards are applied to distributive
    or legal justice, differences appear. Sometimes
the right may not be clear. But most often what is owed is
not definite. A citizen must pay his taxes. Legal justice demands it. But exactly how much? Or again, the State, by
distributive justice, is bound to allot positions equally
among the citizens. But which citizen specifically should

get which position? For these reasons justice most strictly means commutative justice and less exactly is legal and distributive justice. Yet these latter two show enough of the fundamental notion of justice, of owing something to someone, to merit being called justice, though their distinction from commutative justice should be remembered.

READINGS

Thomas Aquinas: *Summa Theologica*, Part II–II, qq. 56–122.
Clifford Barrett: *Ethics*, chapters x, xi and xii.
John F. Cox.: *A Thomistic Analysis of the Social Order*, chapters iv, v and vi.
Michael Cronin: *The Science of Ethics*, i, 621-632.
E. Stanislaus Duzy: *Philosophy of Social Change*, chapters iv and v.
Walter Farrell: *A Companion to the Summa*, iii, chapters vii to xiii.
William Ferree: *The Act of Social Justice*.

Chapter 11

CARDINAL VIRTUES—FORTITUDE

1. FORTITUDE

Virtue leads to the good and happy life and to man's ultimate goal by guiding his actions according to right reason. Inevitably this involves difficulties. Pleasure, for instance, is indeed good in itself, but must be carefully controlled lest its inordinate pursuit bring ruin. Its control comes from the virtue of *temperance*. Another obstacle to the good life is man's disinclination to grapple with the difficulties. He needs something to stir up his interest and to help him meet and conquer hardships. This is the office of the virtue of *fortitude*.

Fortitude taken broadly   *Fortitude* may be taken broadly as synonymous with firmness of mind. In this sense it is a general virtue, since all virtue must be firm and steadfast. Any virtue, then, which fortifies the mind against passion can be called fortitude.

Definition   But taken more narrowly, fortitude means *firmness in meeting difficulties*. It is defined as the virtue which for worthy ends braces the soul to meet danger courageously. It heartens a man to withstand bodily pain, even death itself, and to act reasonably under the threat and fear of grave injury. Fortitude belongs to the will, to the soul.

Not bravery   Fortitude is not merely brave action, which need not spring from fortitude. It can come from ignorance, as when a gardener picks up a coral snake because he thinks it harmless. Or again, what appears dangerous to one person may not seem so to another. Contrast the excitement of a man in his first battle with the veteran's coolness. Bravery may come also from passion. Sorrow or anger or melancholy or despair or hilarity can produce deeds of apparent courage which have little or nothing to do with fortitude.

Not renunci- Finally it is not uncommon for men to pay a
ation high price of suffering and sacrifice for honors, pleasures, money, position or to escape punishment or pain or some other kind of misfortune. Such conduct may resemble virtue, but unless it comes from the will and on behalf of real and not merely apparent good, it is not fortitude.

Allays fear Fortitude aims to *curb fear* and to *moderate daring*, but chiefly to allay fear since its principal act is endurance. It brings the will fearful of bodily injury to stand firm with the good of reason. Death is the most repugnant of bodily evils. So fortitude functions to steady the will especially in the face of death. But the virtuous man does not risk death for the sake of dying. He has some good purpose in view. And the fears which fortitude deals with are those arising from danger in behalf of a worthy cause. Thus fears arising, say from illness or a terrific storm at sea, may be met with courage but not necessarily with fortitude. There may be lacking the aim to accomplish some good.

Examples On the contrary, an heroic purpose stimulates a front-line soldier to overcome the fear of death. He is fighting for his country and his bravery is a tribute to fortitude. So too does fortitude cause a judge to overcome fear of revenge, when for the sake of justice he risks personal injury and perhaps death. Likewise a nurse or physician shows fortitude who, though fearful of contracting a patient's deadly disease, rises above his fears to care for him. Or think of an aviator on a dangerous rescue mission. He conquers his fear of a flight and a landing which may cost him his life. These are some of the fears which the virtue of fortitude steels a man to meet and surmount. Notice that they imply bodily danger and have in view a worthwhile good.

2. FORTITUDE AND PLEASURE

A question The soldier may meet the fear of death in battle, the aviator may conquer his fear of the hazardous flight, the doctor and nurse may dominate their fear of contagion, but will they enjoy their victories? Will they find pleasure in their heroism?

Pleasures differ In reply, the distinction among pleasures must be noted. There is the pleasure which the satisfaction of sensory appetites brings. It results from the material, bodily contact between the sense and its object. On the contrary there is a spiritual pleasure, proper to the soul. When, therefore, it is asked whether fortitude brings delight, the reply cannot be simple.

Spiritual pleasure On one side the brave man has something to make him happy. He has the spiritual pleasure which comes from an act of virtue and from the good which it achieves. On the other hand he has cause for both spiritual sorrow and physical pain in the prospect of suffering and dying. Furthermore, except by a special gift of God, sensible pain can dull or even blot out the spiritual delight of virtue. Yet the consolation of virtue can overcome sorrow, inasmuch as a man prefers the good of virtue to the less valuable life of the body.

Bodily pain It is true that spiritual sorrow at the prospect of suffering and death can be overcome by the delight of virtue. But it must be remembered that bodily pain is more sensible and keenly felt than spiritual pleasure. This often fades before intense pain.

Feeling no   In many ways virtue is its own reward. Yet a
test of virtue   man may show magnificent fortitude and feel
little, if any, happiness in the danger or sacrifice he may
have to suffer. After all, the test of virtue is not feeling but
conviction and action. In a word, as Aristotle remarked, it
is not necessary for a brave man to have conscious delight in
virtue; it is enough if he be not sad.

Virtues   Closely related to fortitude are the virtues of
related to   magnanimity, magnificence, patience and
fortitude   perseverance. Each may be considered briefly
with a note on the vices opposed to it.

3. MAGNANIMITY

Magnanimity   *Magnanimity* (literally, *great in soul*) agrees with
defined   fortitude in overcoming difficulties, but differs
in that its difficulties are less grave. Magnanimity means
the soul's longing for great things. Greatness may mark an
act done exceptionally well in a small matter. But simply
and absolutely an act is great when it evidences the best
use of the greatest thing. The greatest thing which comes to
man's use is honor. Man can offer it to God Himself.

The magnan-   *Magnanimity*, then, concerns honor of the
imous man   highest order and achievement. This is why
the practice of magnanimity does not belong to every
virtuous man but only to great men. The magnanimous
man thinks himself worthy of high as well as lower honors.
When they come to him he is not inflated and when they do
not he is not depressed. He is above honor and dishonor.
He takes pleasure in accepting favors only when he can
repay them with interest. His occupations conform to his
greatness of soul. He never says false and vile things about
himself nor denies praise when it is true. He shuns flattery
and hypocrisy as revealing a cribbed mind. With the great
as well as with the less he mingles as he ought. He prefers
the virtuous to the merely useful. He cultivates excellence

and shuns the vulgar. Kindliness, generosity, gratitude stamp his conduct. He values external goods but not to the extent of sacrificing virtue. Likewise he esteems honor, but not at the cost of lying. His goals are high, but when opposition and failure come he does not whine. The magnanimous man always seeks excellence. Even in practicing other virtues, he is satisfied with only the best.

Magnanimity and humility Magnanimity is no enemy of humility. These virtues *complement each other*. Magnanimity leads a man to think himself worthy of great things, because he appreciates God's gifts. If he is endowed with virtue, artistic or scientific talents, wealth or any other good, magnanimity urges him not to deny the gifts, not to bury them, not foolishly to deny he has them, not to accept mediocre standards. Magnanimity stimulates him to meet the obstacles in his way. Humility, on the other hand, brings a man to think little of himself in the light of his deficiencies and shortcomings. What he can most truly claim as his own too frequently furnishes him little cause for anything but regret. Again, magnanimity makes him think others as well as himself blameworthy for not living up to the gifts God has given them. But at the same time humility makes him honor and esteem people as better than himself for the admirable qualities they do have.

Magnanimity and external goods The magnanimous man scorns external goods in the sense *that he would not do moral evil to get them*. Actually he does not despise them but esteems them as often being very useful for doing good. Virtue can exist without external goods, without wealth and power and money and influential friends. But to function most successfully it needs them. They can help all the virtues—above all the virtue of magnanimity, which implies high achievements. The magnanimous man evaluates the goods of fortune, recognizes their utility and uses them as efficiently as he can. But neither their possession nor loss greatly affects him. It is with them as with honors. He is above them. They are not his goal in life but the instruments for helping him to the goal. With or without them he is not greatly disturbed.

Presumption   Opposed to magnanimity by excess or deficiency are the vices of presumption, ambition, vainglory and faint-heartedness. *Presumption* indicates that a person has too great a notion of what he can do. It is opposed to magnanimity by excess. It makes a man high-handed, proud, haughty, restless, bent on excelling in everything with no thought of virtue. However, what a man can do with the help of others in a sense he can do himself. It is not presumption, therefore, for a person to want to do something beyond his own natural powers if he can get human or divine help.

Ambition   *Ambition* is the inordinate desire for honors. Such desire can be irrational, as opposed to the rational mean of magnanimity, in several ways. A man may crave honor for an excellence which is simply non-existent. He may seek honor without a thought of referring it to God, upon Whom he depends. Or he may take honor all to himself without using it to help his neighbor. In other words, seeking false honors or desiring them in a way to exclude God or the neighbor's good constitutes the vice of ambition. Men of good will and men of bad will both cherish honors. The difference lies in the approach. The good seek them in the right way. The wicked worry little how they get them, but freely use deceit and falsehood or any other means at hand.

Vainglory   It is not evil to desire praise if the motive is God's glory and the widening of one's influence for good. What is truly praiseworthy should be esteemed—provided God is acknowledged as its author and alone deserving of praise. But *vainglory*, which is the desire for empty and undeserved glory, is evil.

How vain   Glory can be vain when a man seeks something unworthy of him. It may be vain when it comes from a person of poor judgment, whose praise means little or nothing. Or glory may be vain in that a man seeks it for his own gratification without referring it to God or to the welfare of his neighbor. A magnanimous man values praise for what it is worth but is not greatly affected by it one way or the other. A vainglorious man is just the opposite. He glories in what the magnanimous man would disregard. Vainglory is more foolish than dangerous. But it can occasion disobedience, boastfulness, hypocrisy, contention, discord and obstinacy. This is its power for evil: that it prepares the way, gradually but certainly, for a man's moral ruin.

Faint-heart-edness   *Faint-heartedness* falls short of fortitude by defect. A man's opinion of himself and his abilities is too low. Whereas the presumptuous man overrates himself, his abilities, his skills and efficiency, the Milquetoast type is timid and unsure of himself. He is little in soul, and whereas his pusillanimity may masquerade as virtue it really is nothing of the sort. He shrinks from tasks well within his powers, because he has not the fortitude necessary for them. Faint-heartedness can arise from pride, because a man is afraid to face the humbling prospect of failure. He avoids it simply by not getting involved. It can arise from ignorance of one's qualifications. It can be a mask for laziness.

4. MAGNIFICENCE

Defined   *Magnificence* is the second virtue related to fortitude. Fortitude brings a man to overcome his reluctance to suffer loss of health or life. Magnificence prompts him to conquer his aversion to being separated from his wealth. The difference between physical pain and spending money shows the lower level of magnificence, which likewise is not as excellent as magnanimity. Magnanimity inspires a man to greatness in everything, while magnificence deals only with doing great things. It involves conceiving and discussing and administering lofty undertakings, with a broad and noble purpose. It may be defined as the virtue which brings a man to subdue his love for money by encouraging him to plan and execute expensive, large-scale enterprises.

Magnificence towards elf   Greatness is relative. What regards a man's own person shrinks when compared with what pertains to the Supreme Being or even to the community at large. Nevertheless a man naturally must seek his own perfection. In doing so the magnificent man realizes his position in the scheme of things. He does not intend to be lavish principally towards himself. Yet if the occasion demands that something regarding himself be done in a large way, he does not hesitate. For a wedding or a graduation or when he builds his home or plans something to last a long time, he does his best to make the occasion or building or enterprise what it should be.

Magnificence and wealth   The virtue of magnificence is not concerned merely with spending money but with spending money to produce something *significant*, something *large* and *fine* and *lasting* and *beautiful*. This actually cannot be done without wealth and is beyond the poor man. Yet he can have the habit of the virtue. For the essence of any virtue is inward will and choice. And this a man can have without riches. Even as regards the actual exercise of the virtue a poor man can have it to some extent. He can do something insignificant in itself in a relatively magnificent way.

Opposite vices   Two vices represent the excess and the privation of magnificence. *Meanness* stamps the man who loves money too much and wants to spend just as little as he can. He is not at all troubled that what it buys be worthy of him. His sole concern is to keep his money. The opposite of meanness is *wastefulness*. The mean man spends less than he ought. The wastrel spends more than he ought. He has no regard for wealth, no sense of value and may pride himself upon his carelessness about money. It is no part of magnificence to make a man mean. Just as surely it is no mark of that virtue to make a man a profligate.

5. PATIENCE AND PERSEVERANCE

Patience defined — *Patience*, the third of the virtues related to fortitude, literally means suffering or enduring. It is the virtue whereby a man calmly bears sorrow and other evils, lest a disturbed mind interfere with his leading a good life. No human being escapes his share of hardship and grief. Patience has its perfect work in helping a man to bear them, just as meekness moderates anger and charity dispels hatred and justice restrains a man from unjust injury. Patience is the root and safeguard of all the virtues, not in the sense that it causes them but in that it clears away obstacles which would be their ruin.

Patience and fortitude — *Patience and fortitude are close relations*. The act of fortitude consists both in combating fear of future dangers and in bearing with actual sorrow and pain. Patience is similar to fortitude in the latter respect, that it encourages a man to submit calmly to the evils which actually afflict him. Fortitude and patience differ, however, in that fortitude chiefly concerns fear, whereas patience functions to make a present sorrow tolerable. A man is called patient not because he refuses to escape from his burden of grief but because he suffers an actual evil without being unduly disturbed.

Perseverance — *Perseverance*, the fourth of the virtues related to fortitude, makes a man adhere firmly to good in spite of difficulties which arise from the *prolongation* of a struggle. A man of perseverance clings to his well-considered enterprises. He does not abandon an under-taking until he completes it. He stands firm regarding the things he ought, but readily gives ground in matters where he can do so properly. He does not expect to become virtu-ous suddenly, but in so far as is necessary quietly submits to the slow process. Likewise for anything difficult to get or to do he is ready to make haste slowly, without losing interest or slackening his efforts.

Opposite   *Softness*, one of the vices opposed to persever-
vices   ance, makes a man ready to give up because of the difficulties. The pleasures he has to renounce mean too much to him. He slips into the easier way of forsaking the struggle or of not even beginning it. With softness usually goes an inordinate desire to relax and play. *Perti-nacity* is the other vice opposed to perseverance. It is over-persistence. The pertinacious man goes beyond the right order of virtue by inordinately persisting in something. He is usually headstrong, self-opinionated and tenacious, be-cause he holds to his opinion or course of action more than he should. The soft man gives in too easily. It is only the persevering man who holds the virtuous course of rational moderation.

6. VICES OPPOSED TO FORTITUDE

Vices opposed   Three vices by their unreasonableness oppose
to fortitude   the moderation of fortitude. *Foolhardiness* falls short of fortitude by excess of daring; *fearlessness* by too little fear and *cowardice* by too much fear.

Cowardice—   Fear, it is worth noticing, springs from love.
the conflict   The more men love and seek something, the more they shun and fear the opposite evil. As there are different levels of excellence between the things men love and the things they fear, there arises a conflict between a wanted good and an evil they wish to avoid. A man can surrender the good to escape the evil or suffer the evil for

the sake of the good, Think of a physician facing a deadly and contagious disease. He would gladly avoid the disease he fears. Still he wants to be faithful to his professional duties. Will he risk the danger of contagion or sacrifice duty to fear? In this instance the good of duty takes precedence over the evil of the disease.

Good vs. evil This is just one example of the truth which daily experience teaches. There are certain goods to be sought more than certain evils are to be avoided. The physician is bound to fulfill his duty even at the risk of contracting the disease. When a man forfeits an obligatory good to escape injury, he is guilty of inordinate fear. Call it timidity, *cowardice* or simply fear, it amounts to the same thing. It is the privation by undue fear of the right order of fortitude. A good which ought to be chosen is abandoned to escape an evil which ought to be endured.

Cowardice and guilt *Cowardice* raises the question about the responsibility of a person who through fear abandons an obligatory good. It is reasonable to fear evil to the soul more than evils which attack the body, and to fear loss of health and life more than evils of an external sort, such as loss of money. Consequently, if a person does wrong to avoid some external evil or if he suffers bodily harm rather than lose some money, he would not be guiltless. Yet his guilt would be less. (p. 110.)

Fear lessens guilt For fear *lessens* the voluntary character of human conduct, by, as Aquinas says, imposing a certain necessity. Aristotle pointed out that things done through fear are a mixture of the voluntary and the involuntary. Fear does not modify an evil action, which remains objectively what it is. But making it less voluntary fear reduces responsibility and guilt.

Fearlessness As cowardice is opposed to fortitude by excess of fear, so *fearlessness* is opposed to fortitude by lack of due fear. A man fails to have the fear he ought to have. It is reasonable to shun evils which cannot be endured and to avoid, that is fear, evils which it would be useless to suffer. There is a fear which men properly and rightly ought to have. Its absence, far from indicating virtue, constitutes the vice of fearlessness. Whether it results from want of love or pride or vanity or simply ignorance, it is a vice.

Foolhardiness   Fearlessness falls short of fortitude by lack of proper fear; *foolhardiness* by too much daring. Daring in itself means that a man assumes the offensive against an adversary. It is perfectly reasonable to launch an offensive after proper counsel. But to rush into action without sufficient thought reveals perhaps a care-free, daring person, but certainly not a prudent man. Daring when controlled by reason and leading to speedy action is praiseworthy. But its excess, action without weighing consequences and seeking counsel, is foolhardy and wrong.

READINGS

Thomas Aquinas: *Summa Theologica*, Part II–II, qq. 123–140.
Michael Cronin: *The Science of Ethics*, i, 618–621.
Walter Farrell: *A Companion to the Summa*, iii, chapters xiv and xv.

Chapter 12

CARDINAL VIRTUES—TEMPERANCE

1. TEMPERANCE ITSELF

Definition Contrary to current usage, *temperance* does not refer only to the use of alcohol. Much less does it mean total abstinence or imply some connection with prohibition. Temperance concerns man in his enjoyment of the most agreeable and seductive pleasures. They pertain to eating and drinking, which maintain the individual, and to sexual activity, which preserves the race. In the scale of human activities they are elementary and primitive. For this reason they are in special need of the control temperance exercises by bringing them under reason and moderation. Since all these pleasures involve the sense of touch, temperance can be defined simply as the virtue which seeks to moderate the pleasures of touch.

Temperance and unessentials Everything a man wants is directed in some way to the needs of life. Such needs may refer to *necessities* or to *unnecessary but pleasant things*. Both fall under the control of temperance. Regarding basic necessities, temperance rules that man should use them as required. As for the merely agreeable things, temperance guides him to moderate their use according to circumstances of time and place and association. Man is not restricted to pleasures connected with the bare essentials of life. He may enjoy others which he finds agreeable. The temperate man wants not only the necessities of life but also pleasant, if unessential, things as long as they do not hurt him.

Temperance not the greatest virtue Aristotle says the good of the many is closer to God than the good of the individual. But the good of the many is achieved more by justice and fortitude than by temperance. Justice regulates the relations among men while fortitude meets dangers endured for the commonweal. Temperance restrains only the desires and pleasures which affect a man himself. Evidently, then, justice and fortitude are more important virtues than temperance, and prudence tops them all.

2. SAFEGUARDS OF TEMPERANCE

Safeguards of temperance For a man to be temperate, he must cultivate a healthy fear of disgrace and strive to appreciate the beauty of conduct ruled by reason, in other words, to love honesty. *Fear of disgrace* protects temperance by inspiring horror for anything shameful. A paragon of virtue would find no difficulty in avoiding shameful conduct. It would hold no attraction for him. And since he actually did nothing base there would be no grounds for fear. But with struggling, imperfectly virtuous human beings, the fear of shame and disgrace can be mighty safeguards of temperance. Disgrace consists in the censure and loss of esteem which may follow shameful conduct when it becomes known. The threat of ignominy, of being exposed, blamed and reproached, the loss of friends and reputation, in the heat of passion these can go a long way towards saving a person— if he still has a sense of shame.

Sense of shame lost For it can happen that shame is lacking. Some people become impervious to it. They no longer consider their conduct disgraceful, and boast of what ought to make them blush. Or, while fearing disgrace in theory, they have no practical dread of exposure, since they are sure their conduct will not become known. In either instance, unfortunately, the fear of disgrace ceases to function as an efficient bulwark.

Love of
honesty   Another help to temperance is *love of honesty*, which goes beyond the usual meaning of truth-telling and fair dealing. Conduct is honest when it merits honor on account of its spiritual beauty. Whatever conforms to right reason has spiritual beauty and is naturally deserving of honor and is pleasing. But not everything which is pleasing is honest, since what gratifies the senses can fall short of reason and be evil by excess.

Honesty
explained   A thing is *honest* when it accords with right reason. It is *pleasing* when it brings sensual pleasure. A thing is honest if it is desired for its own sake by the rational appetite. It is pleasant when desired for its own sake by the sensual appetite. The essence of honesty is the internal right choice of will. External conduct becomes honest when it expresses the right internal choice, the due ordering of intellect and will.

Honesty and
temperance   Honesty is especially related to temperance. For honesty is a form of spiritual beauty, which has its direct opposite in the ugly, in the disgraceful. Most disgraceful and most unbecoming to man is excess in primitive appetites, which it is the office of temperance to control. Consequently, *love of honesty and temperance are closely united*. The more a man clings to the beauty and honor of virtue, the more likely he is to escape the disfigurement of immoderate passion.

3. SOME FORMS OF TEMPERANCE

Enumerated   In practice temperance has various names according to the pleasures involved. Temperance in food is *abstinence* and in drink *sobriety*. Temperance as applied to the act of procreation is *chastity* and to the associated pleasures it is *purity*.

Abstinence   The virtue of *abstinence* concerns food in so far as eating can violate the due order of reason. It makes no difference to virtue what kind of food or how much of it a man eats, so long as he exercises due regard for his own dignity and health and for the people about him. Abstinence must be measured in all these terms. It must be exercised also when duty or necessity or charity require a man to forego food. Because food is so essential to life, considerable pleasure accompanies its use. But its very need and satisfaction make it dangerous. To say that a man should eat to live and not live to eat is not asking him to mix ashes with his food or renounce the pleasures of the table. It means he must not let the pleasures dominate reason. He must not surrender virtue to his appetite. Moderation in food can lessen sexual appetites, but more directly it saves a man from gluttony.

Gluttony   *Gluttony*, the capital vice opposed to abstinence, chiefly denotes excessive eating. But it is a mistake to think of gluttony only in terms of quantity. It has other forms. The amount of food may not be excessive, but a person may insist upon its being too costly or too fine or too rare or too extravagantly or fastidiously prepared. In the manner too of taking food a person can be gluttonous—by eating too hastily, greedily, boorishly, or too frequently.[1]

Sobriety defined   Drinking is a general term applicable to man's use of any beverage. But in connection with temperance it refers specifically to the use of alcohol. Unlike ordinary food, alcohol quickly and effectively interferes with human processes. This is why it presents a special problem and why there is the special virtue of *sobriety*. It is defined as a form of temperance especially concerned with *keeping the pleasurable use of alcohol within the bounds of moderation.*

Misuses of alcohol   No beverage in itself is evil or unlawful. It becomes so *only through abuse*. A person drinks

[1] Cf. Lewis, C. S.: *The Screwtape Letters* (New York, The Macmillan Co., 1943), pp. 86ff., for some interesting examples.

too much. Or by drinking he breaks a pledge or hurts his family or spends more money for alcohol than he should. He may have a constitution which cannot tolerate alcohol and quickly becomes the worse for it. It may be that his drinking, even in moderation, becomes a scandal for his associates and brings opprobrium upon himself and his profession. In short, alcohol can be misused in many more ways than simply by using too much of it.

Office of sobriety   Whenever naturally good things are concerned, care must be exercised to put the blame where it belongs if evil comes from them. It is no part of sobriety to indulge in the denunciations of prohibitionists and condemn a thing for its abuse. Virtue's office is to acknowledge the dangers of a good thing and to help men avoid them *by self-control.* As with similar virtues, sobriety does not aim to eliminate pleasure, but to humanize lower appetites, to safeguard men from excess and to make pleasure, as it should, contribute to the general well-being.

Drunkenness   As gluttony is opposed to abstinence, so the opposite vice of sobriety is drunkenness. It can refer to the *effect* of misusing alcohol or to the *act itself.* As the effect it is the physical and repulsive reaction, and as such is without moral character.

The act itself   It is the act itself of over-indulgence which *can* have the moral evil of drunkenness. *Can* is emphasized because, for a person to be guilty of drunkenness, he must commit the excess knowingly and willingly. If a person imbibes too much in ignorance of what he is drinking or of its potency he is not responsible. To be guilty of drunkenness a man must know what he is drinking, and its probable effects and will the excess.

Drunkenness not the greatest vice   Drunkenness, though shameful, is *not* the greatest moral fault. Evil must be measured by the good which suffers. Divine good is superior to human good and the common good to private good. Man's faults against God and his neighbor are graver than drunkenness, which directly stands opposed to the good of human reason. Nor does the high rate of people's abuse of alcohol prove it the gravest vice. If human beings often go to excess in sensual pleasures it does not follow that these excesses are the most vicious. Rather it indicates widespread human weaknesses.

Chastity and   Temperance as applied to the functions and
purity   satisfactions and allurements connected with human generation falls into two categories, which are frequently confused. *Chastity* primarily regards the sexual union itself, whereas *purity* refers rather to external acts joined to it. From the Roman goddess of love, Venus, comes the adjective venereal, which is used often to describe sexual functions and pleasures.

Venereal   Two observations need be made in regard to
pleasures   venereal pleasures. Because they are more impetuous and tyrannical than the pleasures of taste, they need *greater restraint.* Secondly, and equally important to remember, is the fact that natural acts of procreation are *not evil in themselves.* As the satisfactions of food and drink are good when enjoyed properly for the sake of health, so sexual pleasures are good when they follow moderation and the right order for preserving the human race.

Chastity   *Chastity* belongs to the soul but pertains in-
belongs to   directly to the body. For by chastity a person
the soul   brings the use of bodily members into conformity with the law of reason and right moral choice. Even so chastity remains a virtue of the soul. As long as a person holds to it in his intellect and will, not even violence can rob him of his virtue.

Purity   *Purity* refers to proper self-control in such matters as looks and touches and embraces and kisses. In themselves they are not evil. They need not be coupled with venereal pleasure. But they can be and often are. When they are joined to lust and are done for unlawful sexual satisfaction, they become evil and share in the evil to which they naturally lead.

Lust   *Lust* is opposed to chastity and purity. The more necessary something is, the more vigilantly it must be controlled. Moral evil appears when control fails. Sexual functions are as necessary to the good of society as is their rational ordering. Lust forsakes that order. It strikes not only at the good of the individual but at the very foundations of society.

Capital vice   Lust is a capital vice, which means that, because of its pleasure-giving powers, it leads to other faults. Venereal pleasures are intense and fundamentally natural to man. This is why they are especially seductive and so hard to hold in check. When they escape control of reason and give way to lust, the door is opened to many other evils. This is true of lust in all its natural and unnatural manifestations.

Forms and   Unnatural vices are those venereal acts from
effects of lust which human generation cannot follow. Fornication is the union of an unmarried man with an unmarried woman. Incest refers to sexual intercourse between persons related by blood or affinity. Adultery implies one party of an unlawful union is married. Seduction describes the violation of chastity without violence; when done with violence it is rape. But no matter the form lust takes, the lower appetites rebel and dominate the higher powers of the soul. Intelligence suffers. Counsel and judgment give way to rashness and thoughtlessness and inconstancy. Selflove and hatred of God follow, together with a fatuous love of this world and a Sybarite's disregard of the next.

4. VIRTUES ASSOCIATED WITH TEMPERANCE

Continence   Though not strictly parts of temperance, continence, clemency and meekness, modesty and humility are its close associates. *Continence* means that a person contains himself by holding to the measure of right reason. Broadly used, it refers to the passions which incite man towards something which reason would have him avoid. But since sexual pleasures are the most vehement continence generally refers to venereal allurements. While temperance *moderates* these desires, continence functions to help a man *resist* them. He is continent who stands by reason and *contains* himself from evil desires.

Clemency and meekness   *Meekness* and *clemency* agree in that they tend to restrain the assaults of anger. They differ in that clemency moderates external punishment, while meekness controls the internal anger. Meekness concerns the craving itself for revenge. Clemency regards the punishment which vengeance inflicts. Right reason should guide a man to clemency, to mitigating even deserved punishment. It should also be his guide in moderating anger. Inordinate anger, which meekness strives to control, can be a great obstacle to man's free judgment and occasion sorrow and tragedy. The fact that a man can get violently angry, and yet not be morally responsible, does not minimize the sad effects. Passion may excuse him, but it does not wipe out the injuries and miseries his anger may produce. Clemency is opposed to cruelty and hardness of heart. Cruelty inclines a man to be merciless and to enjoy the victim's suffering. It is the vice of the poltroon.

Modesty   *Modesty* differs from temperance in that temperance concerns pleasures whose restraint is especially difficult, while modesty regards those of less difficulty. According to the proper matter of modesty a word may be said about humility and its opposite pride, and about modesty in action and dress.

Humility internal virtue   *Humility* is a movement of the soul which leads a man to observe right reason in estimating his worth. It has to do essentially with restraining a man from tending inordinately to great things. But notice that it does not conflict with magnanimity. Humility restrains the appetite from aiming at great things against right reason. Magnanimity urges the mind to great things in accord with right reason. The rule of humility is true self-knowledge. A man should not esteem himself above what he is nor overlook his deficiencies. Neither should he go to the other extreme and undervalue himself. Humility, it is true, conveys the notion of praiseworthy self-abasement; but it must be of the right sort. It is not humility for a man to scorn his dignity and equate himself with irrational creatures.

Humility and externals In a secondary way humility has to do with externals. The inward disposition of humility ought to manifest itself in words and deeds and general deportment. It moderates excessive expenditures and the love of display. But if the externals are mere pretense, without interior substance of true virtue, they do not belong to humility at all. They merely perpetrate a lie. For the virtue of humility, as all virtue must be, is an inward choice of soul.

Humility and subjection Humility proper regards *man's subjection to his Creator*, for whose sake he humbles himself by being subject to other men. This subjection, however, needs analysis. Man is a complex of defects and perfections. The defects he can claim legitimately as his own. The perfections he must attribute to God. When a man contrasts his defects with the perfections his neighbor has from God, the comparison should incline him to estimate his neighbor above himself. But when the comparison involves what both he and his neighbor have received from God, then due evaluation of the gifts must be made. It is not humility to treat as inferior or even as equal things which really are not. If a man's gifts are superior, truth requires that he admit the fact and use them for his own and his neighbor's good. A man, however, may esteem his neighbor as having a good which he lacks himself, or himself as having deficiencies which his neighbor does not have, and so be led to hold his neighbor above himself.

Humility is truth   Humility must be *true;* otherwise it is not virtue. It handicaps no man in the competitive world of daily existence nor does it deprive him of the good things of life. It binds him to honest avowal of true worth and to the admission that he is not self-sufficient, that whatever good he has must be attributed to God.

Pride   Opposed to humility is *pride*, which is the inordinate craving for exaltation. By it a man wants to appear more than he really is. Right reason urges a man to want what befits him. This is the rule of humility and of true self-esteem. But the proud man is satisfied only with the unreason of over-estimating himself. This he can do in several ways. He may attribute his excellence, and it may be very real, entirely to himself, giving credit to no one—not even to his Creator. He may presume that what he has he has earned and that he owes nothing of what he is or has to any person. He may boast of what actually he neither is nor has, and thus be not only proud but a liar. Or, because of fancied excellence, he may despise others and build himself up to heroic stature.

Essence of pride   The essence of pride is man's *failing in some way to be subject to God and to His law*. When a man is guilty of other vices, it is not so much that he turns away from his last end as it is that he turns, because of ignorance or weakness or impetuous appetite, towards some attractive good. But this is not true of pride. By it a man turns away from his ultimate goal, through unwillingness to submit to God and His rule. This is what sets pride apart from the other vices and merits its being called the queen of vices. For once pride takes possession of a man, he falls an easy prey to the other capital vices.

Modesty of. A man who was a warrior and became a great
action saint remarked that he disliked voices and
gestures when they were soft and spineless or coarse and
boorish. In between is the middle ground of reason, the
domain of *modesty of action*. Restraint of external movement
falls under two virtues. In so far as externals associate men
with other human beings, their proper control belongs to
friendliness or affability. Since words and deeds and outward
deportment generally can cause others pain as well as
pleasure, men are bound to avoid hurting their fellow men
and to contribute to their happiness. This is the office of
friendliness. On the other hand, in so far as outward movements indicate inward dispositions, they belong to *truthfulness*. For by deed as well as by word a man ought to reveal himself as he truly is.

Modesty and On the subject of modesty of action Thomas
relaxation Aquinas gave remarkable attention to the need
of *relaxation*. He called it "play" and defined it as merry
and humorous words or deeds whose purpose is simply
pleasure and refreshment of spirit. With the same care
that he argued for justice and sobriety he argued for needful mental recreation. It is necessary for the person's own
and his neighbor's welfare.

For his own As a man stops working to rest his body, so
good must he pause from intellectual activity *to
refresh his soul*. It too has limits, and when a man reaches
them he gets depressed and weary. Sensible goods are his
natural domain, and to rise above them requires extra
effort. Intellectual work of all sorts demands this and takes
a heavy toll of human resources. But when a person gives
himself to the pursuit of purely spiritual realities, to contemplation and the religious life, the effort is heroic and the
need for refreshment enormously increased. As the worn-
out body needs rest, so does the weary soul. Its rest is
pleasure, which consists in loosening the tension of labor

and seeking refreshment. Otherwise the spiritual faculties will suffer and grave consequences almost surely follow. Overstrained people become hypersensitive, quarrelsome, sick and hard to live with.

For neigh-bor's good   When a man fails to relax as he should, he hurts both himself and his neighbor. It is against reason, and so is evil, for a man to be a burden to others. He can do this not only by failing to add to their happiness and pleasure but by blanketing their merriment. A mirthless man is not just devoid of playfulness. He is a positive damper upon the good spirits of others. Instead of contributing to their refreshment he obstructs it. He is vicious, boorish and rude. They are strong words. But they come, let it be remembered, from the pagan philosopher Aristotle and the Christian Thomas Aquinas.

Safeguards   *Relaxation has dangers.* Humor can be excessive and hurtful. Play can be overdone. Aquinas warned against these dangers. Relaxation must not be indecent or sought through injurious language and actions. A man should keep his balance and not become silly. As in all human affairs, men must take into account persons, time, place and other circumstances of the situation. While relaxation is necessary and lawful, it should be the reward and refreshment of duty carefully done.

Modesty in dress   The third form of modesty concerns *dress*. It applies to such items as clothing and its accessories, jewelry, make-up and the hair. These things and their proper care, it should be remembered, are not evil in themselves. Evil comes when they are used in the wrong way. This happens when a person disregards the proper standards of his class or becomes inordinately attached to dress for its own sake. Excessive attention to dress is the way small-minded people court praise and glory. Others love it for its sensual pleasure. Still others are simply unreasonably solicitous. Of this the opposite extreme is slovenliness. It is no part of virtue to be untidy or careless about clothing and personal grooming.

False modesty Worse still is the hypocrisy of showing indifference to dress to attract attention. About this St. Augustine wrote that the black of mourning weeds could be just as ostentatious as, and more dangerous than, ultra-fashionable clothes. The rule in dress must be moderation. Both too much and too little care about clothes are wrong. As in all virtue, the keynote is restraint and propriety. People should dress according to their station. Vice creeps in when dress becomes shameless, immodest or, while not being shameless or immodest, is overdone.

5. VICES OPPOSED TO TEMPERANCE

Since temperance controls the use of sensual pleasures, its opposite vices are the extremes of right use. One is the vice of *apathy;* the other, the vice of *intemperance.*

Apathy defined Apathy means insensibility, want of feeling, and in this instance it indicates an indifference to sensual pleasure. To avoid evil a man need not shun pleasure absolutely. He must indeed pursue it according to nature and right reason, but this is compatible with enjoyment. The natural functions which provide for the well-being of man and of the race are pleasant because they are so vitally necessary. Unless thrilling pleasure attracted men to them, man's welfare as well as the existence of the race would be jeopardized. By nature men must use sensual pleasures to the extent they are necessary—for man's own good and the good of the race. If anyone spurns pleasure to the detriment of his personal good or the good of the race, he is frustrating nature and guilty of apathy.

Renunciation of pleasure Yet at times, by way of exception and for just reasons, certain persons can refrain from these legitimate pleasures without being guilty of apathy or insensibility. For the sake of health a man may fast from food or go on a rigorous diet. In line of duty a military man may have to forego the gratifications of married life, and athletes sometimes treat their appetites harshly. A young man or woman may postpone marriage in order to keep a home for parents.

In the spirit-   In the spiritual order also there are valid
ual order   reasons for refraining from sensual pleasures. Persons may practice self-denial to repair spiritual ruin. Or they may renounce physical pleasures in order to cultivate the things of the soul.

Explanation   Such persons are *not* guilty of apathy or inhuman insensibility. They have a right estimate of the body and its needs and its appetites and its pleasures. But they prefer the life of the spirit. They move in a higher sphere and so sometimes are said to *despise* the pleasures of the flesh. But this phrase must be understood correctly. It is as far removed from the puritanical as it is from the lascivious. Despise means literally *to look down upon.* A man can *look down upon* his dog without condemning him or thinking him contemptible or worthless. He may love his faithful animal without raising the dog to a human level. So with persons living spiritual and detached lives. They *look down upon* sensual pleasures because they move in a higher order. But it does not follow that they regard the things they renounced as worthless, evil, contemptible, despicable or immoral.

Intemperance   *Intemperance,* the contrary of apathy, means unchecked satisfaction of the sensual appetites. It is not concerned merely with drinking too much alcohol. In general it indicates the improper pursuit of any sensual pleasure, chiefly the pleasures attached to food and drink and sex. Stubborn and headstrong, intemperance pursues the animal pleasures. In using those pleasures man cannot behave like a brute, unreasoning, unrestrained, irresponsible animal. If he does, he degrades himself. He loses his dignity, his human excellence.

Intemperance not worse crime Though the sins of intemperance are most disgraceful they are *not* the most evil. When measured against the lofty dignity a man ought to have they are indeed most shameful and unbecoming. But this is in comparison to vices of human passion more or less conforming to human nature. There are other and worse crimes: crimes against God, crimes against one's fellow man, crimes against one's own life and against nature. Without in the least lessening the evil of intemperance or its shamefulness, this fact ought not be forgotten. The most disgraceful crime need not be the most heinous.

READINGS

Thomas Aquinas: *Summa Theologica*, Part II–II, qq. 141–170.
Walter Farrell: *A Companion to the Summa*, iii, chapters xvi to xix.
James F. Kerins: *The Social Rôle of Self-Control*.

READINGS

Part II

SPECIAL ETHICS

INTRODUCTION

Special Ethics is the application of the principles and doctrine of *General Ethics* to specific problems. These may be concerned with personal ethical questions or with those which arise between one human being and another or between man and his Creator or as they concern social groups such as the family and the State. But in making these distinctions it is not intended actually to isolate the problems from one another. It is a matter of emphasis. For every ethical problem has its personal and social aspects as well as its bearing upon man's relations with his Creator. This triple bearing of ethical problems must not be lost sight of when they find separate places in the following plan.

Section I. Ethics regarding self—to give oneself his due.

Section II. Ethics regarding other persons—to give neighbor his due.

Section III. Ethics regarding God—to give the Creator his due.

Section IV. Ethics regarding the family and State—to give them their due.

I. Ethics Regarding Self

Chapter 13

PRESERVING LIFE, HEALTH AND LIMB

1. SELF-FULFILMENT

Today one hears so much about social values that *proper self-love* is forgotten or treated contemptuously. Yet man's vocation is not just to serve as a tool for social betterment. He has the obligation of self-fulfilment untainted by selfishness. Self-improvement is man's means for achieving his destiny, which cannot be divorced from his own inherent and over-all perfection. If a person strives for such an ideal, he is bound to fit cooperatively into the social pattern. For by his nature man is at once a personal and social being—not two things artificially sandwiched together, but one thing with this dual aspect. True human perfection implies development along all truly human lines. Consequently, man's duty is to provide for this growth—not in the pursuit of vicious selfishness but in steady progress towards true and complete personal moral goodness and his ultimate goal, a share in God's infinite goodness.

2. THE OBLIGATION

Body, soul and external goods What does this imply? Without losing sight of social and other obligations, it may be said that proper self-fulfilment involves duties to oneself regarding *body* and *soul* and *external goods*. Every person has a grave responsibility to give these aspects of personal perfection careful cultivation.

And the nurse   This is especially applicable to nurses, where "the possibilities of becoming warped and stunted in growth, of becoming one-sided and narrow, are present. . . ."[1] The belief that the nurse, writes Gladwin,[2] "owes her first duty to herself in order that she may make of herself the sort of person capable, willing and able to do her other duties seems inescapable." This same author in an earlier work[3] wrote that the "duty of the nurse is to make of herself the most able woman possible so that she may do good work and live a sane, wholesome, happy life." The view proposed here accepts the opinion of these experienced nurses, but goes beyond it. Men are obliged to cultivate personal perfection not merely to be happy or efficient or to escape being stunted or warped or failures in their profession. The reason is much more fundamental. If they guiltily fail to achieve due personal perfection, they sacrifice their destiny, the whole goal and purpose of living. That is why they must love themselves, do good to themselves and work for those things which can further their own perfection.

Obligation denied   Some, however, *deny* that men have grave binding ethical obligations to themselves. They argue that if a man owns a book he can do what he pleases with it. He can burn it, use it to stand on, to keep the door open, to level a table or as an ornament in the living room. He may even read it. But in any event the book is his, to do with as he wishes. In the same way a man owns himself. He is in his own keeping as the book was in his keeping. See how he controls his actions. They are his own. What meaning has ownership if a man cannot do what he wants

[1] Aikens, C. A.: *Studies in Ethics for Nurses* (Philadelphia, W. B. Saunders Co., 1943, 5th ed.), p. 207.

[2] Gladwin, M. E.: *Ethics: A Textbook for Nurses* (Philadelphia, W. B. Saunders Co., 1937, 2nd ed.), p. 307.

[3] Gladwin, M. E.: *Ethics Talks to Nurses* (Philadelphia, W. B. Saunders Co., 1930), p. 123.

with what he owns! Duties to one's fellow man are clearly
obligatory. But if a man is willing to stand the cost of hurting himself in some way, whose business is it but his own?
If he wants to burn his book, he burns it. If he wants to
destroy his life, he takes poison. If he wants to eat or drink
or smoke or indulge other appetites to the ruin of his
health, he does so. Whose health is it? Of course, he must
not hurt his neighbor. He does not own him. But his own
person he does own, to do with as he wishes.

False　　　It is true that man controls many of his actions.
analogy　　Otherwise there would be no responsibility
and no ethical problem at all. But to compare ownership
of self to ownership of a book *falls immensely short of truth.* A
human being is not a book. Neither is he an animal or a
piece of furniture or a machine or a plot of ground or a
bank account. These things a man can claim as his own—
yet not even them can he claim absolutely. But when it is a
question about his own person, the analogy breaks down
entirely. Man has *not* the same right to life and existence as
he has to possessions which he gets by purchase or work or
in some other legitimate way.

Personality　　Man did not give himself life, nor does he
and destiny　　keep himself in existence. Man is not a chattel.
He is a person, with the highest dignity of any bodily
creature and with a worth that demands respect not only
from other men but from himself. Man's destiny, as was
pointed out (p. 44), transcends this world. The impetus
towards it springs from his innermost nature. He cannot
renounce it any more than he can renounce his humanity.
He can achieve it or lose it. The choice is his. But he cannot
turn away from his destiny without revolting against his
own human nature. No such inner drive, no such obligatory
goal controls his conduct with what he owns.

Man does not　　But since he does not own himself, *he cannot*
own himself　　*treat himself as a possession.* He cannot measure

himself against a book or any other property whatsoever— no matter how valuable it might be. Man is a person, with the possession of Infinite Good and happiness as his destiny. These he must obtain or suffer irreparable loss. And to attain his goal he must have due regard not only for his neighbor but also for himself.

Basis of duty Man's duties to himself do not follow from *of self-love* justice, which involves owing something to somebody else. *They spring from love*, from man's essential obligation to desire and to reach his ultimate goal of Infinite Goodness (p. 44). Yet this does not lessen their binding force. For obligations of equal compulsion can come from different sources. Man must will his own perfection in all the departments which human nature implies. That is what self-love, self-fulfilment means. Some practical applications of this obligation will now be considered.

3. LIFE AND SUICIDE

The obliga- In the physical order man is obliged to preserve *tion* *health, life,* and *to keep his body intact*, that is, to preserve its integrity. This obliges him not to commit suicide and positively to take ordinary care to be healthy and not unreasonably to mutilate, or suffer mutilation of, his body. The source of this obligation is man's natural call to perfection. Granted the goal, it follows that he must use the means. Life, health and a whole body are such means. They are the ordinary implements to help man to self-fulfilment. And though they can be dispensed with, it can be done legitimately only when their sacrifice truly aids man's higher perfection.

Direct *Direct suicide is self-murder.* A person knowingly *suicide* and willingly chooses death. Sometimes it is spoken of as positive or negative according to the way it is done. But whether a man uses gas to stifle life or refuses food to starve himself, he snuffs out life. He aims to die.

Death is what he wants. This is *direct suicide*, and must be kept apart from *indirect suicide*.

Evil of direct self-murder *Suicide* violates the natural law, whose primary precept is that good must be done and evil avoided. That suicide is evil appears from the injury which it inflicts on the individual. *Direct suicide* stands utterly opposed to man's personal good. In all its manifestations human nature clamors for existence. Suicide cuts it off and frustrates the innate longing of the being for its destiny. The immorality of suicide appears also from the injury it inflicts upon society—even though the man himself may not admit it. Society would simply vanish if everybody suddenly decided life was just too much for him, that the fight was not worth the candle, that self-murder was preferable to existence. Yet if one man can rightly sleep his way out of the embroilment, so can everybody. Finally, the suicide assumes absolute control over what is not his. His life is not his own. He did not cause his own existence. His right to it cannot be compared with his rights to property. It is no part of self-determination to decide when one's life shall end. That rests with the Creator, whose rights suicide usurps.

Indirect suicide *Indirect suicide* is a totally different matter. It is not suicide at all. Take the instance of the four chaplains who went down with the torpedoed troopship "Dorchester." They knew that surrendering their life belts meant death. Yet they forced them upon the boys. Were the chaplains guilty of suicide? Look closely at the choice they made. They did not want to die. If they could, they would have avoided it. Death was not their purpose nor the object of their choice. They wanted others to be saved—even if it meant their own loss.

Indirect voluntary applied Here is an important application of the *indirect voluntary* (p. 99). The chaplains' action of staying aboard was not evil in itself. Their intention was of the best, to save their friends. There was a balance between the good and bad effects, and the good did not come as the direct result of the evil. All the conditions for the use of the indirect voluntary were fulfilled. The chaplains' action, far from being suicide and censurable, made them heroes.

Direct and indirect suicide compared   In both direct and indirect suicide death is foreseen. But the man who commits *direct* suicide wants death as the result of his action. The *indirect* suicide does not crave death and would avoid it if he could. He wants the good effect of an action which has also the tragic and unwanted effect of costing him his life.

4. OBLIGATION NOT ABSOLUTE

Higher good takes precedence   The chaplains' action illustrates that one's obligation to preserve life and health and bodily integrity is *not absolute*. It is open to exceptions. Under certain circumstances a man can sacrifice life itself without moral fault—indeed he may be morally bound to. Physical life and health and keeping the body entire are good things. But there are higher values. Fidelity, loyalty, patriotism, generosity, unselfishness, self-sacrifice, these are all above the physical goods of life and health. A man may give his life for his country. A physician knowingly may contract a deadly disease in line of duty. A policeman may lose an arm to save a child from being run over. In all these instances a higher good is chosen to a lower good—a good more in line with man's human perfection is preferred to a good less in line with man's higher perfection. If death results and even if it be foreseen the action is not direct suicide. The persons do not want to die. They want only the good effect of their action, yet are willing to tolerate, if necessary, the concomitant loss of life or limb or health. The ethical principle is again the indirect voluntary, and involves the reasonable choice of the higher moral good to the physical good.

Higher good in the same order   But the good need not always be of a higher order. It may be a *higher good in the same order*. The general health of the body is to be preferred to losing a diseased limb. On the principle of the indirect voluntary the surgeon proceeds to amputate a man's arm. He anticipates two effects from his action which, in itself, is not evil: the good effect of improved health and the evil effect of the man's being maimed. He wills the good effect, tolerates the evil effect. Certainly it is reasonable to sacrifice a part of the body for the sake of its entire health. Consequently, surgical operations are legitimate, even when they involve amputations and loss of the body's integrity—provided there be a lawful reason and good intention.

5. PRESERVING HEALTH

Obligation to ordinary means only   It may be asked whether a person is bound to submit to surgical operations. Does he do wrong in refusing? The answer is that a person is bound to use only the *ordinary means* of preserving life. This includes proper diet and exercise and relaxation and sleep and all the natural aids which by its constitution the body needs to keep well. A surgical operation is not such a natural aid. It may not be against nature but it certainly is not a provision of nature for man's welfare. In this sense it remains unnatural and extraordinary and a person is not obliged to undergo it. However if he is needed for the welfare of others and a cure is morally certain he should try to overcome the obstacles.

Grave inconvenience   A man is not bound to do everything absolutely and theoretically possible to maintain health. In general he is not obliged to use what are called *gravely inconvenient means*, one of which is a surgical operation. Others which might be mentioned are the cost of the treatment or operation or medicine or the journey required, the pain or fear or embarrassment to modesty involved. When prescribed medical treatment involves such difficulties, and the difficulties, it should be noted, are extremely relative, ordinarily a person is not obliged to undergo it—though he may if he wishes to.

Guilty disregard of health evil The right rational order demands that people take *ordinary* precautions to keep well. Wantonly to injure health pertains to suicide, and though few people commit direct suicide, many without a scruple inflict injury upon their bodies. They do not seem to realize that it is morally wrong. The body is an important principle of human nature. It is the medium of self-expression through which the soul operates. It ought to be as perfect as a man can make and keep it.

Practical value of good health Then again good health is essential for personal comfort, definitely to be preferred on this score to illness. More practically still, good health helps a person to get and hold desirable positions and to stay on the job. Good health makes for attractive looks, for poise, sureness and ease. It adds to a person's ability to get things done. Whereas bad health generally proves the reverse. It not only lowers physical efficiency and comfort but often has unfortunate psychological effects. A sound mind in a sound body is not universally true. Many heroic people have hurdled the obstacles of illness. But they are the exceptions.

Effects of bad health in the nurse Usually physical ailments influence for the worse a person's judgments, outlook, emotions, temper and disposition. If this is true for people generally it applies even more so to nurses. An ailing, weak, nervous and fretful nurse can be an unwholesome influence in a sickroom. A burden to herself, she can easily become a burden to the patient. By profession she is an apostle of good health; but, as with other teachings, unless she implements her doctrine with her own example of good health habits, it is not likely to prove very effective. But more seriously still, a nurse's carelessness about hygienic precautions can spread infection and become a threat to life itself. Her responsibility is not merely personal but social, involving justice; and though this will come up later, it should be noticed here in connection with the nurse's obligation to cultivate good health habits.

Cultivating good health   It belongs to other sciences to prescribe programs of hygiene and good health—not to ethics. But some negligences about health have *definite ethical aspects*. Take the matter of sleep. Night after night to curtail sleep is not just bad hygiene. It constitutes a serious threat to health and is morally wrong. Take, again, a nurse doing night duty. She ought to realize that she needs to be extra careful about keeping well. Carelessness is not merely silly; it is wrong—and if others suffer from it, it becomes worse. The human body needs a certain amount of sleep, a certain amount and the right sort of foods; it needs exercise and relaxation. To overdo them is just as wrong as failing to use them properly. Both alternatives are vices opposed to temperance (p. 181).

Time off and exercise   Too often *time off* for the nurse becomes *time on her hands*. It requires resourcefulness to use it well. A simple way of solving the problem is to let the problem dissolve in lassitude, in aimless boredom, in idle gossip or grousing, in smoking too much or in just doing nothing. It is so much easier to lie around than to stir oneself to go out for a walk or to arrange a game of golf or tennis or a bicycle ride or to go horseback riding or skating. The objection that these require too much skill or money falls flat. Enough skill to enjoy sports can be acquired by any normal human being. As for the expense, walking is still not only free but nature's own best exercise, and for the sports that take money, the amount varies considerably. A person does not have to join the best club to enjoy golf. The municipal course can do very well. Roller-skating and ice-skating are not more expensive than first-run movie houses, and a horseback ride need not cost more than a dinner. It all depends on what the person wants, and the point here is that she should want some regular and enjoyable form of exercise. It is as refreshing for the mind as it is healthful for the body.

READINGS

Charlotte A. Aikens: *Studies in Ethics for Nurses*, pp. 77–80, 231–238.

Michael Cronin: *The Science of Ethics*, ii, 52–56.

Edward F. Garesché: *Ethics and the Art of Conduct for Nurses*, Part I, ch. xvii.

Mary E. Gladwin: *Ethics*, chapters v and xiv.

Thomas V. Moore: *Principles of Ethics*, ch. v.

John J. Reardon: *Selfishness and the Social Order*, chapters i and ii.

Harold H. Titus: *Ethics for Today*, ch. xiv.

Chapter 14

AVOIDING BAD HEALTH

1. NARCOTICS IN GENERAL

Avoiding injury to health To be healthy a person must *do* the right things and *avoid* things injurious to health. The question in detail goes way beyond ethics but not in all aspects. Certainly the use and abuse of narcotics clearly pertain to good health—mental as well as physical.

Problem of narcotics The problems narcotics raise are extremely serious and difficult. Every one admits it. But too often people think of them only in terms of morphine, heroin, codeine and cocaine, opium and marihuana and other similar drugs. These the public admits are dangerous. Their pernicious effects, the need of restricting their use to medical control and of even then being severely cautious are universally conceded.

Legitimate use The use of narcotics is *not* wrong in itself. Even though they do suspend temporarily the use of reason, this is not something evil in itself. If it were then sleep would be evil. Yet for a man intentionally to interrupt the use of reason, there must be a sufficient reason. This is furnished when narcotics are used properly to relieve pain and suffering. Just as it is reasonable to lose a limb for the sake of the body's general health, so it is reasonable to profit from the beneficial effects of narcotics in the treatment of disease and illness. Aquinas himself said that it is not wrong to interfere with reason when it is done in accordance with reason.

Tobacco and alcohol Narcotics include tobacco and alcoholic beverages—a fact some people forget. And, because smoking and drinking do not seem so dangerous, they frequently get scant attention. But the great popularity of tobacco and alcohol as well as the harm which can come from them demands serious consideration. Tobacco and alcohol obviously *differ widely in their effects*—too widely for joint treatment. But in connection with both of them the fundamentals of temperance should be recalled (p. 181). Men are bound to use the things necessary for their welfare according to right reason. To live, they must eat and drink. But in addition they may, if they wish, use other things for pleasure—provided these things are reasonable and not injurious. This means that they must be in conformity with man's ultimate goal and in some way help him to its attainment. This principle must be remembered in dealing with the habits, and evils, of drinking and smoking.

2. USE OF TOBACCO

Physical effects Many old prejudices against tobacco have disappeared in recent years. Yet its *actual effects* are still questionable. They cannot be compared, of course, with what alcohol can do. "Tobacco leads," to quote Dr. Moore[1] "to no immediate impairment of reason as does alcohol. In fact the same tests that show alcohol to be a mental and muscular depressant indicate no acute effects whatever from the ordinary use of tobacco." However, "while the acute effects of smoking on mental performance are really zero or so very slight as to escape measurement, there seems good scientific evidence that smoking may have serious chronic effects on the arterial system. It seems that nicotine stimulates the adrenal glands and ultimately has a deleterious effect on the arterial system leading to local areas of degeneration." But "here again one must take into consideration the peculiar individual selective

[1] *Principles of Ethics*, pp. 65–66.

effects of drugs. One person may smoke relatively large amounts of tobacco daily with no untoward effects, another may be profoundly influenced after a few whiffs of a cigarette. The difficulty is that it is usually impossible to tell whether or not one is going to be affected until he feels the effects of an injury that has already taken place."

Smoking not   As the evidence stands today tobacco when
evil in itself   used *moderately by normal adults* seems only *slightly, if at all, harmful*. Opinions on the subject vary and individuals react to tobacco differently. But for growing boys and girls tobacco apparently has harmful effects if used in any considerable quantities. Smoking, then, while it has dangers, cannot, when done in moderation, and this must be gauged against the person concerned, be considered evil. It is not in itself morally wrong. It is not sinful.

Against   Yet, as *against* smoking, there is the fact that
smoking   many people, especially young men and women, do smoke too much and sometimes injure their health. Any athlete knows that smoking cuts down his wind. Then there is the expense, which ought not be overlooked. It is not merely having or not having "tobacco money." The question is whether the money might not be used to better advantage. It should be noticed also that tobacco is habit-forming. Even moderate smokers are often not cheerful companions when they forget their cigars or cigarettes or favorite pipes. Smoking begets a habit which can become burdensome.

For smoking   On the other hand, smoking gives much pleasure to many people and eases the burden of life. It is mildly narcotic and tranquilizing. When taken in relatively moderate quantities the harmfulness of tobacco is admittedly slight. The question, then, of smoking or not smoking for people generally and in moderation is a matter of *personal* choice. For children, however, it is a matter of obedience to their superiors.

Special problem for nurses   *For nurses*, smoking has some special problems. Granted that the moderate use of tobacco does not hurt health or lower efficiency or reduce their resistance to disease or dim their perceptions, yet it remains true that it *can* do all of these if it gets out of control—and this it can easily do. There are considerations of a more practical sort. Tobacco breath and discolored teeth and nicotined fingers and clothing strong with stale smoke are offensive to patients, and a cigarette dangling from the lips is not attractive to anybody.

Not vicious but objectionable   None of these things are vicious, but they lower the nurse's prestige and can hinder her success. A woman writer and nurse speaks out strongly about the nurse and smoking.[2] She thinks it an insidious habit, easy to acquire, hard to break, and more or less expensive. Many people find it objectionable, and few enjoy secondhand smoke. "Women," she quotes with approval, "are the worst offenders in this respect. They are not even polite about smoking on a boat or train. Men would frequently inquire if one seated near objected to them smoking but women—never." Prudence suggests that nurses remember that there are still people who dislike smoking and especially resent women doing it. When the nurse feels like having a cigarette, she must remember her standing as a professional woman—even in the face of narrow prejudices.

3. USE OF ALCOHOLIC BEVERAGES

Alcohol in itself good   A more serious problem than smoking is the *use of alcoholic beverages*. Frequently alcohol is referred to as an intoxicant, because it can produce drunkenness. But the mistake must not be made of condemning a

[2] Aikens, *Ethics for Nurses*, p. 94. And cf. Gabriel, Sister John: *Professional Problems* (Philadelphia, W. B. Saunders Co., 1937, 2nd ed.), pp. 193–194.

good thing for its abuse. Alcohol itself is not evil. Evil comes
from man's misuse of it. Centuries ago a great orator and
saint castigated the fallacy of transferring human guilt to
the innocent and good things of life. "I hear many cry when
deplorable excesses happen, 'Would there were no wine!'
Oh, folly! Oh, madness! It is the wine that causes this abuse?
No. . . . If you say, 'Would there were no wine' because of
drunkards, then you must say, going on by degrees, 'Would
there were no steel,' because of the murderers, 'Would there
were no night,' because of the thieves, 'Would there were
no light,' because of the informers and 'Would there were
no women,' because of adultery."[3]

Lawful in   As with the use of tobacco, so with alcohol as
moderation   a beverage—taken in accordance with the
virtue of sobriety (p. 184) it is a *legitimate pleasure*. As Dr.
Moore says,[4] ". . . . it is perfectly clear from reason and the
general concept of temperance that it is lawful for one to
indulge in alcoholic beverages if he does so with such moderation that he avoids all evil consequences."

Alcoholism   But the sad national fact is that multitudes do
                  not avoid all evil consequences. Today there
probably are in the United States two to three million
chronic alcoholics, that is, people who use alcohol to excess
harmful to themselves. Superintendents of penal institutions point out the great number of alcoholics among people
guilty of crime. One stated that of 12,000 commitments in
one year 8000 were alcoholics. Alcohol has proved itself
dangerous.

Sobriety   Though this fact alone does not outlaw alcohol
imperative   it does stress *the need of sobriety*. By that virtue
a man controls his appetite and uses alcohol in moderation.
But what is moderation? One man's tolerance may be much
higher than another's and even for the same person modera-

---

[3] St. John Chrysostom, quoted from *Time*, June 25, 1945.
[4] *Principles of Ethics*, p. 63.

tion does not always mean the same thing. What would be moderate for a surgeon at home with friends could be excessive when he is about to operate. To know exactly what moderation implies is often difficult, while the consequences of a mistake can be catastrophic. Sobriety is a hard hazardous road—so hard and hazardous that it may be asked whether total abstinence or something near it might be preferable to even temperate drinking.

Total abstinence for some   For the person who cannot drink without drinking too much, total abstinence is not debatable. *He must leave alcohol alone.* Excessive drinking is not merely the indulgence which makes a man beastly. It is any use which threatens his health or efficiency or causes harm in any way. Too often excessive drinking is measured in terms of obnoxious public behavior. Far different is the definition Dr. Carroll gives.[5] ". . . the hour one turns to alcohol as a necessity when facing the physically or mentally disagreeable, or uses it as an escape from any unpleasant reality, that person has become a drunkard—not a sot, but an addict. He has turned from fight to flight, from rational assimilation of the difficult to self-deception." These words should be remembered whenever the question of abstinence comes up. But leaving aside the excessive use of alcohol, a man still has a choice between drinking and not drinking. In deciding the issue he should consider what may be said *for* and *against* alcohol—not necessarily to become a total abstainer but *to know the dangers even of temperance*.

4. GOOD EFFECTS

Alcohol as food   Alcohol is not a poison but a carbohydrate, in the same family as bread or sugar. It has food value—but at a fabulously high price. Moreover, any excess of it, instead of being stored up like the starches and

[5] Carroll, R. S.: *What Price Alcohol?* (New York, The Macmillan Co., 1942), p. 155.

sugars, stays in circulation, tincturing the blood and saturating body tissue. While admitting alcohol as an occasional emergency food, Dr. Carroll shows how inadequate and dangerous it is.[6] "Only 2 per cent of the total amount of alcohol taken is eliminated by breath and kidneys; hence 98 per cent must await the slow process of oxidation, circulating meanwhile in the body fluids as a more or less toxic agent. . . . Alcohol forms no tissues, cannot be stored as energy, offers no biochemical protection, and acts only for the body's good as a very quickly oxidizing fuel . . . When compared to other foods, alcohol's place is only a ration for the starving."

Alcohol as a stimulant Although stimulating in its immediate effect, alcohol is really a *depressant*. Many of the mental and emotional reactions which people attribute to alcohol are illusory. Take for instance the sensation of increased warmth, which alcohol apparently produces. Actually far from helping a person withstand cold, alcohol lowers his resistance. It is true that at times alcohol serves usefully as a temporary stimulant, but there are other drugs equally good or better for the purpose.

Alcohol and sociability A much better defense can be made for alcohol as an *aid to sociability*. It brings people together and helps them like one another—at least temporarily. Most hosts and hostesses find alcoholic beverages make entertaining easier. Spirits rise higher and conversation flows smoothly.

Explanation These effects are probably due not so much to alcohol as to the fact that it *dispels self-consciousness*. Freed from his inhibitions the shy man rises above himself. Alcohol does not make him a better conversationalist or a better story-teller. It adds nothing to his wit or humor. It simply lowers the bars of his ordinary repressions and helps a man forget himself. He escapes from his own narrow

[6] *What Price Alcohol?*, p. 101.

self and from the monotony and sorrows of life into a brief hour of enjoyment and intenser living.

Not   While alcohol can add to life's pleasures, it is
essential   *not necessary.* Many people find pleasant re-
laxation without alcohol in conversation, music, games, reading or hobbies. Indeed alcohol can ruin these pleasures. For the same beverage which gives zest to a gathering can all too easily beget arguments, frayed tempers, ill feelings, loss of dignity and broken friendships.

Alcohol eases   Alcohol does not make a man more resource-
life's burdens   ful or more intelligent. It does not solve his
problems, but it does *help him to forget them.* William James pointed out that one reason for craving alcohol is that it is an anesthetic. It dims or obliterates a part of the field of consciousness and abolishes collateral trains of thought. This can be wholesome; it can be *just the reverse.* For men have burdens which they should *not* try to cast aside or forget. And if a man has a real problem, it should get thought and action and not just an alcoholic bath. But, as Drake says,[7] since man is a poor blundering creature and many people are caught in circumstances they cannot mend, and are beset with evils they cannot cure, "they have, in the partial anesthesia produced by alcohol, a means of comfort . . . . which is not to be despised."

As a   The medicinal value of alcohol has been dis-
medicine   puted. But today with increasingly intelligent
and fair study the verdict is certain. *Little good can be said for alcohol as a medicine.* Its worth is practically nil. Even in emergencies where it might be some help, modern phys-icians have better remedies than whiskey. But it is not merely useless; used as a medicine it has grave dangers. Dr. Carroll gives two instances of how liquor given as a medi-cine spelled ruin for two nurses. More significant still is his

[7] Drake, D.: *Problems of Conduct* (New York, Houghton Mifflin Co., 1935), p. 204.

arraignment of physicians who "think nothing of prescribing a little Scotch for the appetite, a warm toddy for indigestion, or—more dangerous—hot whiskey for the monthly cramps of a neurotic woman, and a bedtime nightcap for sleeplessness. The list of entering patients who claim that their drunkenness was a personal contribution from their home physicians is disconcertingly long and humiliating to professional pride."[8]

Alcohol produces wealth and taxes   No one disputes that every year *fortunes* are made out of alcohol. For many people the manufacture, distribution, advertising, sales promotion, and dispensing of alcoholic beverages are highly profitable. It nets, directly or indirectly, *enormous sums in taxes.* It gives employment to a large number of people and constitutes a notable market for vast quantities of farm and vineyard products.

5. BAD EFFECTS

Good and bad effects   So much, then, by way of examining some of the benefits claimed for alcohol. With regard to its *bad effects*, it must not be forgotten that numbers of people drink moderately with apparently no evil effects on health or efficiency or any appreciable shortening of days. Some can even drink freely without suffering the excesses of drunkenness. A few nations can point proudly to their devotion to alcohol and their fidelity to sobriety. These are facts, just as valid as those brought up against drinking. But the other side of the picture must be kept in view. While something can be said for moderate drinking, much can be said against it. The balance must not be struck merely on the basis of acute effects but probably even more so on the basis of chronic consequences.

A depressant   Alcohol is neither a mental nor a muscular stimulant. Though its immediate effect is

[8] *What Price Alcohol?*, p. 309. See also pp. 89–91.

stimulating, it eventually proves *depressive*. This depression depends greatly on the person and his condition. It can exist without his being conscious of it. Even 15 grams of alcohol can impair a simple skill and 35 grams of alcohol taken daily has been shown to decrease the ability to do muscular work.

Automobile The reactions of automobile drivers which
drivers ordinarily take one fifth of a second take from two to three fifths of a second for several hours after drinking a highball or a pint of beer. Two or three fifths of a second may seem insignificant, but with today's traffic and the automobile's speed the fraction of a second may spell life or death. The total number of accidents due to drinking is unknown. For alcohol can be the actual cause without the driver being or appearing intoxicated. And even when he is obviously drunk, the charge of drunken driving is sometimes not made because intoxication is difficult to prove in court.

Alcohol and While escaping blame in many automobile
health accidents, alcohol has gotten *more than its share* as the cause of disease. Fuller knowledge of the chemistry of food has freed alcohol from being held *directly* responsible for some diseases often attributed to it. A man may drink steadily and yet suffer no shortening of days as long as he eats properly and takes enough exercise. However, there is evidence that male impotence can be due to chronic alcoholism and that infants nursed by alcoholic mothers have in some instances suffered from it. Then there are other effects. Alcohol can upset the fine chemistry of life. It can reduce resistance to infection. It can open the way to diseases which might otherwise have been thrown off. It adds to invalidism and mortality. In a word alcohol adds no wealth of health or increase of vitality. On the contrary, the reports of insurance companies suggest that alcohol is a factor in bad health.

Damage to nervous system—Carroll   Injurious as alcohol can be, at least indirectly, to the body, it *most viciously attacks the nervous system*. Quickly it enters into the process of circulation and secretion and reaches the nerve cells and fibers to spread destruction. "Of all drugs," Dr. Carroll writes,[9] "influencing complex mental processes, alcohol is far and away the most versatile, with marihuana running a poor second. There is practically no abnormality possessed by any brain-affecting drug which alcohol cannot reproduce."

Alcoholism and women   Excessive drinking is always reprehensible, but is *worse in women*. More quickly than in men alcohol degrades woman and robs her of her finest qualities. Her conduct deteriorates and she not only rivals man but seems to seek even a deeper ditch in her drunken degradation. "The fineness that makes for her feminine charm is as soon blown away as ashes, by the siroccic breath of drunkenness. . . . The peculiar rapidity with which self-respect goes into solution and gross immodesty grows, and the essential helplessness of the intoxicated woman to preserve the appearance of decency, unquestionably intensifies her problem. . . . . The ease with which woman's virtue fades when she is aggressively half-drunk or defenselessly saturated is common knowledge."[10] Dignity is one thing alcohol does not preserve.

Alcohol—restraint and self-criticism   William James called alcohol the great exciter of the *Yes* function. Sobriety hesitates and says *No*. Alcohol breeds a spirit of recklessness, of expansion, of not counting the cost, of saying *Yes*. Many a social gathering which begins with dignity and alcohol gradually loses its dignity, people get careless, stories merely in poor taste become coarse, and easy familiarities degenerate into license. With wisdom an ancient author

[9] *What Price Alcohol?*, p. 107.
[10] *Ibid.*, pp. 172–173.

observed that "wine leads to folly, making even the wise to love immoderately, to dance, and to utter what had better have been kept silent." And these effects, it should be noted, do not imply drunkenness. Moderate use of alcohol can relax the moral sense and throw a sentimental or adventurous glamour over life and its basic appetites. Its further use stimulates the senses at the very moment when a man's intellectual and moral inhibitions are lessened. What too often people take for alcohol's stimulating action is really a paralysis of restraint and self-criticism. This is why so many crimes come out of drinking and why men and women flagrantly unfaithful to their duties find in themselves nothing to blame.

The cost of drinking   Finally, the *cost of drinking* must be noted. What this actually amounts to in the United States of America is incalculable. In 1945 the general public spent $7,770,000,000 for the purchase of retail alcoholic beverages. There is no reason to think that the amount has gone down since 1945. Yet this figure does not include other costs—the loss of time from work, illness, medical care, hospitalization and other services to alcoholics, such as courts and police and prison maintenance, the burden of alcoholics to friends and relatives. Even temperately used, alcohol can be a relatively heavy drain on a family's resources. Then there are other costs which cannot be measured in dollars and cents: lowered standards of living, lack of proper housing, skimping on food and clothing and recreation and education, poor home environment, separated parents and broken homes. Regular drinking begets a pathological craving for alcohol. Deprived of it the person gets restless and depressed and will sacrifice almost anything to satisfy the thirst. Honor, honesty, love, dignity, no virtue and nothing exchangeable for alcohol is safe in his keeping. The cost of drinking runs frightfully high in money, in poverty, in suffering, disgrace, broken lives and lost souls.

6. CONCLUSION

Forewarned   In this summary of drinking's good and bad
is forearmed   effects, the good effects envisaged moderate
drinking whereas the bad effects in some instances resulted
only when a person drank unwisely. It might be argued,
therefore, that these disastrous effects apply only to over-
indulgence. That is true, in a sense. But it should be remembered that when a person launches into temperate
drinking, it is the beginning, not the end, of the trail. There
is an enormous distance between the distinguished, ruddy-
faced, prosperous and genteelly drinking gentleman of
certain advertisements and the drunkard who has lost
everything. But multitudes have covered that tragic distance. No one knows how he is going to react to alcohol
until drink has had its chance with him. Some will taste and
be temperate or leave alcohol alone entirely. A minority
will drink and become drunkards. Of young people from
good homes who begin to drink daily, three out of ten will
become addicts. Thirty per cent of American youths who
drink will be guilty of conduct delinquencies within ten
years. Alcohol as a beverage is highly dangerous. Anyone
who essays to use it in moderation ought to realize what
possibly lies ahead and be forewarned.

Total absti-   Theoretically temperance is ideal. But it varies
nence safer   widely for different persons and even for the
and advis-   same person at different times. Mistakes are
able   more than possible. Then there are bad effects
which follow even moderate, controlled drinking. Even so,
there can be legitimate differences of opinion about temperance and total abstinence. Some may think the cost and
risks of using alcohol worth what they get out of it. Others
may disagree. *But no one can afford to close his mind to the
serious problems of alcohol.* They are pressing and inescapable
and tragically challenging. For many reasons total abstinence
or something close to it would be safer and advisable.

Temperance and the other cardinal virtues   *Even the moderate use of alcohol* demands that a person regard the virtue of prudence as well as of temperance. And in all likelihood he will need fortitude to face the mockery of false friends who, while defending their freedom to drink as they please, deny him the freedom of drinking little or nothing as he pleases. The virtue of justice too must be thought of. No one can rightly use for alcohol money which ought to be spent for something else. His drinking must deprive no one of his due. It is only the unthinking who overlook the threat of alcohol and fancy that as long as they do not make public spectacles of themselves they are safe. No drinking is safe in the sense that it cannot do harm. Alcohol is a complex, compelling, undeniable and crucial problem. "Drink, but drink moderately" is a half-lie. The truth is that you do not have to drink at all. But if you do, you are bound to use alcohol in such a way that *no one suffers from it.*

READINGS

Charlotte Aikens: *Studies in Ethics for Nurses,* pp. 92–95.

H. J. Anslinger and Courtney Cooper: "Marihuana Assassin of Youth," in *The American Magazine,* July, 1937.

Robert S. Carroll: *What Price Alcohol?*

Durant Drake: *Problems of Conduct,* ch. xii.

Mary E. Gladwin: *Ethics,* pp. 168–172, 192–194.

Frederick T. Merrill: *Marihuana—The New Dangerous Drug.*

Thomas V. Moore: *Principles of Ethics,* pp. 63–68.

Edward A. Strecker and Francis T. Chambers, Jr.: *Alcohol One Man's Meat.*

"Marihuana Problems," reprint from *The Journal of the American Medical Association,* April 28, 1945.

Chapter 15

PRESERVING PURITY

I. VENEREAL PLEASURES

PRESERVING THE BODY'S PURITY—CHASTITY

Venereal pleasures good in themselves Respect for the purity of the body pertains to chastity. Taken broadly, this is the virtue whereby a person *avoids all unlawful venereal pleasures* (p. 186). These spring from the organs of generation, which, becoming perceptibly active, produce pleasurable sensations. Sexual enjoyment corresponds to appetites which are all good. No natural appetite or faculty in itself is evil, dirty, unclean, wrong or impure. Though one may desire or enjoy things which circumstances make unlawful, the appetite itself is not vicious. Evil comes from man's perverted, wilful and wrong choice or use of a good thing. It has been shown that the ultimate criterion of ethical good is the natural object of a natural appetite (p. 78). But it is important to remember the hierarchy of desires and corresponding goods (p. 79). Man's complete and ultimate good must be the standard—not just the good of an isolated appetite.

Primary object of sexual appetite The appetites for food and drink regard the preservation of the individual; the sexual appetite insures the continuance of the race. This is its *primary purpose*. It brings men and women together and provides for the procreation of children. This is its natural object and shows that the object of sexual activity is not merely to give personal pleasure but to contribute to the social good by bringing new human beings into existence.

Secondary object   Yet the satisfaction of the sexual appetite does *give thrilling pleasure*. It is nature's way of inciting people to take up the burdens of a family and to compensate for a life of devotion and self-sacrifice. Moreover it fosters mutual love and affection at the same time that it is their expression. The good and happiness of the spouses is the *secondary object* of sexual activity. And when sought in the legitimate bonds of marriage it is not to be underestimated or spurned or overlooked.

Primary and secondary objects not separable   However, the secondary objectives of sexual satisfaction *cannot be separated ethically from the primary purpose*. They must be kept together. Naturally considered, the sexual function exists for the procreation of children and it is clear that children need the family if they are to mature as they should. This will be dealt with more fully in the chapter on marriage (p. 355). Here it suffices to stress the fact that sexual pleasures must be exercised in wedlock. Separated from it they are against the natural law, as being opposed to the good of the offspring as well as to the welfare of the spouses themselves.

Lawful only in marriage   As the object of sexual activity is to beget children, so must it be exercised under circumstances where children not only can be *begotten* but *where they can be properly cared for*. This means that sexual pleasures are the exclusive right of husband and wife in the permanent society of the family. Only the family adequately provides for the children's moral, religious, intellectual and social good. It alone safeguards the personal good and perfection of the spouses. It alone and normally guarantees the good of society.

The principle   From this it follows that *outside the normal use of marriage, the voluntary desiring, seeking, stim-*

ulating or enjoying of venereal pleasure is wrong. This is the fundamental principle regarding sexual morality as nature reveals it, and conduct opposed to it is morally wrong.

A matter of moral right and wrong Sexual immoralities are opposed to the *natural law* and *man's ultimate good.* They are not merely aberrations from good taste or etiquette or socially acceptable conduct, which may carry the penalty of a damaged reputation or other difficulties. Neither are they viewed simply on the basis of health. Some of these consequences may be avoided; or the person may be willing to pay for his pleasure with them. Faults against chastity are wrong because they involve the misuse of naturally good appetites. Collateral effects, which may be unpleasant or painful, are not the determining issues—though they deserve serious consideration. Notice how this view differs from those who think something is wrong only when it hurts another person. They refuse to see that moral evil always produces a privation in the guilty person, whether or not other harmful effects follow.

Venereal pleasure and responsibility It should be noted that venereal pleasures are *not evil in themselves.* Human beings naturally have sexual appetites, which normally assert themselves. Sensations may follow, pleasure itself may be experienced. Yet no one should be shocked or disconcerted or embarrassed or made to feel guilty by these physical movements of sex. They belong to human nature. As such they are acts of the *human being*—not of themselves *human acts* (p. 92). They become human and moral, and the person is responsible for them, when he makes them his own, by dallying with them, enjoying them, amplifying them with memory and imagination or by stimulating them in some other way. They become his and he becomes guilty when he yields to them outside of marriage. Sometimes these feelings and desires are called "impure." This is no condemnation of them in themselves. It means that, since they cannot be enjoyed lawfully, they are opposed to purity and can be strong inducements to evil.

Pleasure without consent   That pleasure is possible without consent is illustrated by Dr. Healy.[1] "John offers Tom some delicious-looking chocolates, and Tom avidly puts one in his mouth. While he is chewing it with much relish, John discovers that the candy is poisoned and tells Tom this. Tom immediately spits out the poisoned candy. However, since it has partially dissolved, getting rid of it takes some minutes. All during the time that Tom is trying to expel from his mouth every vestige of the poisoned candy, it is clear that he does not want it there, for he is taking every available means to put an end to it. He feels the pleasure but does not want to feel it."

Purity and the nurse   Occasionally it is said that nursing makes girls immodest. Sometimes it does and some nurses justify the fears of their parents and friends. But they are a minority. An experienced nurse puts this matter well.[2] "The nurse does many intimate disagreeable things for her patients. . . . It needs the utmost fineness and delicacy of spirit to put them at their ease, and freedom from commonness and vulgarity on the part of one who 'thinketh no evil and is not ashamed.' The nurse who is instinctively or by cultivation a lady or, to use a beautiful old-fashioned word, a gentlewoman, confronts every nursing situation without shrinking, with no prudery or false modesty, but she abstains from any mention or discussion of such tasks after they are finished. Anything necessary for the relief or comfort of a patient may be done by the right-minded nurse. It is the suggestion of coarseness, and amusement in the wrong place, too great familiarity which brings disgust and distaste."

[1] Healy, E. F.: *Moral Guidance* (Chicago, Loyola University Press, 1943), pp. 190–191.

[2] Gladwin, M. E.: *Ethics* (Philadelphia, W. B. Saunders Co., 2nd ed. 1937), pp. 231–232.

2. PURITY OF THOUGHT

Why   *Purity in deed demands purity of mind.* Human
required   conduct begins with thought, which naturally
tends to produce action. Keep the beginnings of action
pure, and external conduct will reflect the internal purity.
Another reason for stressing purity of mind is the fact that
morality springs from the will—an internal faculty. External action, of course, adds to the crime but does not constitute it. Its moral character comes from the soul. As a
result there can be faults against purity without there being
any external offense whatsoever. This means that the mind
must be kept clear of all thoughts and desires which can
become causes of evil by bringing the person to consent
to them.

Impure   These thoughts and desires, usually called
thoughts   "impure" in the sense explained, pertain to
wrong   the process of reproduction or something connected with it. *Because they can readily induce consent to unlawful venereal pleasure, they are dangerous.* Unless there be a
valid reason for thinking about them, they must be gotten
rid of at once.

Displacing   The way to do this is to *displace* them. To say
them   "I don't want to think of this," merely focuses
the attention upon the unwelcome thought-object and
tightens its grip on the mind and imagination. The simpler
way is *to think of something else*—something good and pleasant
and attractive to the imagination. The indirect attack is
much the more efficient.

Chastity and   Duty sometimes *obliges* a person to think about
duty   things ordinarily dangerous to chastity. Medical students and nurses, to have the professional knowledge
they need, must give considerable thought to matters of
sex and processes of human reproduction. To say that they
can do this without the slightest danger is being blandly
unpsychological. There is danger, but it is a lawful risk.

What they are studying is good in itself, and their reasons for dwelling upon it are the best: to give enlightened medical or nursing care. Even so, and especially in the beginning, they should guard against *morbid curiosity* and be cautious lest their studies become *causes of venereal pleasure*. If study does produce such pleasure and the students consent to it, they are guilty of unchaste thoughts, when they delight in the thought—or of unchaste desires, when their satisfaction comes from willing the action.

Day-dreaming   For young people to think about their future, project themselves into it, conjure up the life they would like to have, the companion they should like to spend it with—all this is normal. It is not to be condemned wholesalely, but it does have dangers. To plan is one thing. To live in a world of make-believe is quite another. The latter, besides being a waste of time, has other and more serious implications. Day-dreaming can have definite sexual coloring and be harmful. It then fills the mind with tantalizing images, which easily lead to sexual excitement and may eventuate in desires and even in grievously wrong acts. Such day-dreaming nourishes longings and repressions, and the more intense they become the more unhappy the person is. In general, day-dreaming is to be *condemned*, but when it becomes sexual it must be avoided not merely on psychological grounds but because it is *morally evil*.

3. PURITY IN WORD

The respect which is due the body should be observed in *language*, in the type of story told, in the way the person refers to bodily functions. They are all good, natural and essential to the welfare of the person or of the race. On either alternative they deserve respect. Any frivolous attitude towards them marks at best a shallow mind and at worst a depraved character.

Language   Being good in itself, there may be times when
and duty   language, which ordinarily would be suggestive, is *legitimate*. Nurses and physicians and students of
medicine frequently and with every justification discuss
matters touching upon sex and reproduction. Precautions
must be taken to safeguard such discussions from lascivious-
ness and to prevent their becoming sources of illicit venereal
pleasure. If a person uses language, in itself and by reason
of circumstances legitimate, to stimulate venereal pleasure
in himself or in others, that person is guilty of impurity. The
occasion may justify the language but does not rectify his
evil intention.

Language   A woman well acquainted with the nursing
and the   field writes[3] that a clean mind is "not possible
nurse   to the woman who allows herself to hear and
repeat doubtful stories; who makes or encourages suggestive
allusions, uses words with double meanings, and delights
in new vulgar phrases. Such a person grows insensitive to
delicacy and fineness in thought and feeling. As an intern
and later as a staff physician, a well-known doctor delighted
in compelling nurses to listen to doubtful stories and in-
nuendos, and the fear of being called a prude or offending
him caused many of them to laugh, to take part in and appear to enjoy his jokes, but it was noticed that when he
began to need specials for his women patients, he refused
every one of the little group who had paid a high price to
please him."

4. PURITY IN DEED

The theatre,   Here it must be recalled that offenses against
movies, art   chastity are not restricted to *external* unchaste
and reading   actions. It has been mentioned that this view
separates from the common attitude which considers only
external acts wrong. Unchaste thoughts, feelings, pleasure,

[3] Gladwin, M. E.: *Ethics* (Philadelphia, W. B. Saunders Co.,
2nd. ed., 1937), pp. 232–233.

desires are all evil when indulged in outside the due exercise of marriage. This is why the cultivation of purity meets obstacles in the world of entertainment, reading, music and the other arts. When any of these become sources of *unlawful* thoughts and desires, and there is no *adequate reason* for running the risk, they must be carefully avoided.

The human body The human body is the *creation* of God, good in all its parts and beautiful in its entirety. Of itself it is not evil nor is the sight of it wrong. But the fact is that certain sorts of exposure arouse people's passions and become occasions of unlawful venereal thoughts and desires. When the theatre or the art museum or the night club or a book or magazine is *calculated to cause such illicit venereal pleasure* it becomes evil.

Science and art On the other hand, to take a sincere esthetic or scientific interest in the human body is not wrong. *The artist as well as the medical student and the nurse can do all that art or science requires and still remain pure.* It is almost certain to involve a struggle; but a struggle in which they need not be conquered. They must realize the danger and surround themselves with all the helps they can. The spontaneous risings of passion are not evil. It is a person's consent to them that changes the physical act into a human moral act for which the agent is responsible. Hence a man must not think he has done wrong because he feels sexual stirrings. It is the attitude which determines the guilt of unchastity.

Dancing *Dancing* is an ancient and legitimate form of recreation. It is also an accepted form of artistic expression and serves the useful purpose of bringing young men and women together. As with other perfectly good things, dancing has its dangers. It can be called evil, however, only when the dancers themselves make it so. The type of dance and how the dancers conduct themselves, the music, surroundings, whether or not there has been drinking, all this must be reckoned with. But complex as the situation appears, it can be reduced to a simple principle: *all dancing which stimulates illicit venereal pleasure in the persons taking part is unlawful for them.*

Kissing—
non-sensual   No more than for the other questions so far mentioned, can the reply of a simple Yes or No be given to questions about the *morality of kissing.* Everybody recognizes that kissing can be of various sorts. There is the kiss given in games or stolen as a youthful prank. In some countries it is a formal greeting. Though it holds no such place in the United States it is a customary mark of affection among relations and close friends. Such kisses ordinarily raise no ethical problem. If they do, some abnormality must be reckoned with.

Sensual
kissing   Then there is the kiss which, while causing pleasant sensations, does not excite sexual activity or venereal pleasure. When done for the sake of these innocent pleasurable feelings it is not evil—but it is dangerous. A harmless intention can become lustful and the way be prepared for evil kissing.

Passionate
kissing   This latter manifests evident *sexual phenomena.* Because of its being prolonged or the manner in which it is done or because of the persons concerned, it activates the sex organs, rouses passion and produces venereal pleasure. In distinction to the other forms it may be called passionate. To an unbiased mind, its ethical character is certain. Since by their nature passionate kisses arouse venereal pleasure, persons who indulge in them outside of marriage are guilty of unchastity.

Petting   One of today's critical problems among young people is a practice referred to as *petting* but which has any number of names. In general, it means "a hugging, embracing, or caressing of the body that is of such a kind as ordinarily to produce venereal pleasure in the one being fondled. It does not include holding hands with a girl, stroking her hair, patting her shoulder, and the like. These latter actions do not arouse venereal pleasure in the normal person, at least ordinarily speaking."[4]

Arguments for it answered   Many young people argue that petting is all right because everybody does it. Or they say they have to do it to be somebody; a boy or girl who does not pet is simply out of the running. Or they assert that they see no harm in it, since it does not arouse their passions. These arguments probably seem unanswerable to their young champions, who are likely to consider opponents as unsympathetic, devoid of understanding and slightly antediluvian. Yet it is not to deny the conflicts and the difficulties and the sincerity of the young people to insist that their defense is inconsequential. It simply is not true that all young people pet or that they must do it to be popular. Even if everybody did it, this would not make it right. The morality of an action is not determined basically by the number or kind of people who do it. Neither is morality measured by social ostracism. Nor does the absence of normal and natural but, under the circumstances, immoral effects prove the action itself good.

Morality   The *basic principle* of sexual morality must be recalled: that the sexual appetites can be exercised lawfully only in marriage and that actions which arouse venereal pleasure cannot be indulged in outside of marriage. Since petting of itself tends to excite sexual passion and produce venereal pleasure it must be declared unlawful and immoral. This holds true even when the passions are not actually aroused. For conduct must be judged by what it naturally tends to produce—not by what it actually may or may not produce.

The automobile and parking   Associated with petting and in many instances the occasion of it is the practice of parking. Automobile riding can be an innocent and

[4] Healy, E. F., *Moral Guidance*, p. 198.

legitimate recreation. But it ought to be a ride. There is no reason for doubting the startling figures of a study made some years ago, that of the girls who went to parties in cars a great majority of them went in for petting. And that of these at least half allowed outrageously improper liberties and that of those who began by petting some 15 to 25 per cent went the limit.[5] There is also no reason to suppose that conditions have improved. The significance of these facts is that parking or the equivalent in seclusion prepares the stage for sexual liberties. If once they begin, statistics as well as a knowledge of human nature indicate where they will probably end.

Morality   As impurity must be avoided, so too must the *occasions*. If some think this a hard doctrine, let them remember, as Dr. Moore writes,[6] that "in reality one who lives up to it will be spared much bitter suffering. One who makes up his mind to enjoy the sex function only when it can be lawfully and reasonably exercised will not develop within himself a fountain of discontent by creating cravings that cannot be satisfied; nor will one have to go through the anxieties that must come from being father or mother of an illegitimate child; one will be spared the penalties of sex disease and will be able to turn one's mind to the enjoyment of the better things in life and one's efforts to the accomplishment of something worth-while."

5. ABSOLUTELY EVIL FAULTS AGAINST PURITY

Absolutely   The problems considered so far in connection
evil faults   with purity required certain circumstances
against   to make them evil. Some became evil through
chastity   evil intentions; others because of the manner
in which they were done; some could be allowed if good reason warranted them; still others were lawful within

[5] Lindsey, B. B., and Evans, W., *The Revolt of Modern Youth* (New York, 1925), pp. 56–62.

[6] *Principles of Ethics*, p. 197.

marriage but unlawful outside of it. None of them were evil absolutely. There are, however, some forms of unchastity which are *simply evil*. No intention, no circumstance of time or place or manner or person can rectify their basic privation of goodness. Nothing can justify them. Masturbation, fornication and adultery are always and everywhere wrong.

Fornication and adultery — *Fornication* and *adultery* signify sexual intercourse between a man and woman outside of marriage. They differ in two aspects: in fornication neither person is married; whereas in adultery at least one is married. Secondly, adultery besides being a crime against purity is also a violation of justice, because it trespasses upon the rights of the married person's partner.

Morality — The evil of these crimes is clear. It has been explained how the mechanism of sex focuses upon procreation and how the begetting of children implies their rearing, which can be done properly only within the permanent society of the family. It follows that the sexual functions must be exercised only within marriage, and that outside of it are unlawful. This is why both fornication and adultery are wrong—the latter being doubly evil, since it is against justice as well as purity.

Objection answered — It might be argued that if no children come of illegitimate unions there is no question of bringing them up and then the basic objection to fornication and adultery loses its force. Again it must be stressed that the morality of conduct is gauged *by its characteristic tendencies*. Conception can be frustrated, but this does not in the least alter the immorality of fornication and adultery. Of itself intercourse tends to produce new human beings. This is its normal and natural object. This is what the appetite tends to achieve. And this remains in spite of accidental circumstances or direct frustration which effectively make conception impossible. The basic morality of actions must be judged in the light of their normal and natural character.

Masturbation Although adultery and fornication are always evil they are not as unnatural as is *masturbation*, sometimes called self-abuse or the solitary vice. This is a form of self-stimulation whereby persons of either sex rouse their sexual passions and induce venereal pleasure. It is more evil than fornication or adultery, since these do not wantonly frustrate natural appetites. Self-abuse, on the contrary, attempts to satisfy the appetites in an unnatural way. For various reasons this offense against purity is frequent, especially among younger people. In addition to its utterly *evil character* two aspects need stressing.

Never lawful to advise or teach it No circumstance, no good intention, no apparent physical or psychical good coming from it *can ever justify masturbation*. Sometimes it is recommended as a means for escaping depression, for releasing tension and inducing sleep, for nervousness. Some consider it necessary occasionally for the sake of health. People in charge of young children have been known to teach them the practice in order to quiet them. All such conduct is gravely wrong. It is wrong in itself and harmful beyond calculation in the habit which it may begin. Anyone who advises it or instructs others in the practice is guilty of gravely unethical conduct and cooperates in the vice of the victim.

Physical effects All sorts of physical ills have been ascribed to masturbation—from paleness and easy blushing to insanity and suicide. That some persons guilty of self-abuse have suffered misfortunes is true. But that masturbation is the cause remains to be proved. Moderate cases may show no evident effects harmful either to body or to mind. On the other hand, masturbation replaces nervous tension with spiritual tension. Often there result shame and regret, disgust, loss of self-respect and a deep sense of guilt. Corruption of character sometimes follows. Possibly melancholia brings the person to have an unhealthy love of solitude and to be indifferent to society and conversation and art and religion and the finer things of life. Masturbation can be a grave obstacle to a happy married life. Neurasthenia, insanity, suicide can follow.

Effects are indirect These effects, when they do result, are not caused *directly* by masturbation but *indirectly*, chiefly through the unreasonable sense of guilt and self-condemnation which frequently follow. Some may think that it makes no difference whether these effects come directly or indirectly—as long as they come. Yet it does matter. The moral evil of the vice is bad enough. But in so far is it is possible, the victim should be guided and rescued from these collateral effects. This can be done by emphasizing the moral evil of masturbation, by fostering *wholesome* motives of shame and by safeguarding the person from any morbid and unreasonable sense of guilt or loss of self-respect.

Homosexuality *Homosexuality* is a tendency to find venereal pleasure in persons of the same sex. When it goes to the extent of actual perversion of sexual functions, its evil is indisputable and admitted. It is the direct frustration of a natural appetite. But it need not go to such unnatural abuses to be immoral. It is wrong even when it manifests itself in too intimate friendships between persons of the same sex, when a person looks upon his friend of the same sex as exclusively his, considers his time and attention all his own, feels jealous when the friend shows some regard for others, especially of the opposite sex. These are less unnatural, but dangerous, manifestations of homosexuality and are wrong.

Prevention Because homosexuality is difficult to overcome once it gets a foothold, *every precaution against it should be taken.* Too intimate and exclusive friendships between persons of the same sex must be avoided. Sleeping together or even sharing the same room can open the way to difficulties. Above all persons with homosexual tendencies should guard against arguing that they must give in to their weakness since it is the only way they can find satisfaction. The argument assumes the universal necessity of sexual satisfaction, whereas the truth is that, unlike food, no man or woman needs it absolutely.

READINGS

Donald Attwater (translator): *Body and Spirit*.
F. W. Foerster: *Marriage and the Sex-Problem*.
Mary E. Gladwin: *Ethics*, ch. xii.
Edwin F. Healy: *Moral Guidance*, ch. ix.
Dietrich von Hildebrand: *In Defence of Purity*.
Felix Kirsch: *Sex Education and Training in Chastity*.
C. C. Martindale: *The Difficult Commandment*.
C. C. Martindale (author of introduction): *Into Their Company*.
Thomas V. Moore: *Principles of Ethics*, pp. 190–204.

Chapter 16

INTELLECTUAL AND MORAL CULTURE

1. OBLIGATION AND EFFECTS

The obliga-
tion from
human nature
As a person is bound to use reasonable means to keep well and preserve his body so is he bound *to cultivate his mind*. The obligation springs from human nature itself. Man has intellectual faculties, but unless he exercises them they will not develop properly. Inadequate diet and exercise show up in poor health. The privation of intellectual interests tends to intellectual stagnation. Wantonly to injure the body is wrong. Likewise, to frustrate intellectual development contradicts human nature and so is as wrong as, or even worse than, physical injury.

Counteracts
lesser human
weaknesses
While the obligation of cultivating one's higher faculties springs from human nature itself, there are other reasons which make it imperative. "Cultivation of the mind," Cardinal Newman wrote,[1] "contributes much to remove from our path the temptation to many lesser forms of moral obliquity. Human nature, left to itself, is susceptible of innumerable feelings, more or less unbecoming, indecorous, petty, and miserable. It is, in no long time, clad and covered by a host of little vices and disgraceful infirmities, jealousies, slynesses, cowardices, frettings, resentments, obstinacies, crookedness in viewing things, vulgar conceit, impertinence, and selfishness. Mental cultivation, though it does not of itself touch

[1] Newman, J. H.: *Lectures on the Present Position of Catholics in England* (London, Longmans, Green and Co., 1889), pp. 391-392.

239

the greater wounds of human nature, does a good deal for these lesser defects. In proportion as our intellectual horizon recedes, and we mount up in the knowledge of men and things, so do we make progress in those qualities and that character of mind which we denote by the word 'gentleman'; "—and, it may be added, gentlewoman. Long human experience testifies that cultural pursuits lead to refined enjoyment and beget a distaste for what is vulgar and coarse.

2. AND THE NURSE

More effi-cient nursing   Newman was speaking of intellectual culture for people generally. With the nurse it finds *special application*. By profession she is dedicated to caring for the sick. But a patient is never just a sick body. It is a man or woman who is ill, a complete human being. This is the composite she must reckon with, in all its manifold complexity. Unless the nurse brings something more to the sickroom than mechanical efficiency, her work will suffer. Her training provides basic knowledge and techniques. But it does not guarantee that she will have the culture, the background, the knowledge and breadth of interest which will enable her to minister to patients' minds as well as to their bodies. For the most part such development must come by her own initiative after formal training. Then with increased opportunities she can pursue the cultural interests to complete her education.

Too much neglected   A well informed author asserts[2] that the "matter of culture and personality has been too long neglected in the life of the nurse. The curriculum . . . has been too crowded to allow time for book reviews, music interpretation, history of literature, etc. The pressure of professional duties and responsibility seems to have overshadowed the value of cultural training for the young graduate nurse. However efficient a nurse's services be,

[2] Gabriel, Sister John, *Professional Problems*, p. 139.

they will never be evaluated for all they are worth if they are not given graciously and with a certain degree of culture that will emphasize the artistic side of her personality. Effort may be necessary to acquire this culture, but someone has said, 'It is the intense effort that educates.' "

3. GROWING INTELLECTUALLY

The means   It is not enough, however, that the effort be intense. It must be *organized. Proper means must be used.* Numerous as these are, among the most accessible but too often neglected ones may be mentioned study, reading, conversation, lectures, drama, art, music and religion.

Study   A man's education is *never* completed. As long as he lives, immense unexplored fields of inquiry stretch out before him. He can close his mind and dimly enjoy a moribund life. Or he can live alertly, with an eager mind, pursuing life's most satisfying values. In any profession it is the person who keeps the spark of intellectual curiosity alive who moves forward. Some nurses are content to plod along with what they acquired in pregraduation days. Others, more wisely, realize that all that went before was a preparation and foundation. They appreciate their responsibility of building well on that foundation. They want to keep abreast of their profession. They are eager to broaden their knowledge generally or to deepen it in some specialized field. In any event they refuse to stagnate, and meet the danger with a program of planned and faithfully pursued study.

What to read   Study means *reading;* but not all reading is study. It should be evident that serious reading must have a place in the nurse's life. To read exclusively for amusement is to condition oneself for nothing else. Lighter reading, of course, often serves a useful purpose— just as sweet desserts appear in well-balanced diets. But a diet of nothing but desserts is scarcely acceptable. Good fiction, in proper doses, relaxes the mind, stimulates the imagination, broadens one's knowledge of life, deepens sympathy and promotes psychological insight.

How   Even so Robert E. Rogers deserves an attentive ear—"No summer novels! You cannot *read* by the blotting paper process. Reading is an exercise, like putting up weights. Reading should give you a good work out, with plenty of brain sweat. If you can't stand the gaff, there are always the talking movies."[3] On the extreme and ironic side, yet Rogers is more than justified in denouncing the prevalent trend to superficial reading. The nurse's reading will include fiction. But it must have a place also for professional books and periodicals and not exclude books of wider cultural scope. But whatever is read, it should not be by the *blotting paper process*.

Having books at hand   To capture leisure for reading, a person must be sure to have *the right books at hand*. Otherwise the time will most certainly be wasted. For even if it be used for reading, the reading will be what chance and not choice provides. Such haphazard reading is almost value-less and above all is unnecessary. Today books are easily accessible. They may be bought or borrowed. But to make cherished companions of a few books, they must be owned. Money thus spent is a lifetime investment which can be made on even a slim budget.

Rewards   Years in the classroom and lecture hall intro-duce the nurse to some good books and leave her with the obligation to become a lover of good reading. *Its rewards* are rich in pleasure and information. It can bring professional advancement and distinction. It widens perspective, gives encouragement, stimulates the mind. It builds up self-reliance and dispels loneliness. Yet books

[3] Rogers, R. E.: *Fine Art of Reading* (Boston, Stratford Co., 1929), p. 285.

should not be used as an escape from life's realities. They should lead readers to grapple with problems more confidently and intelligently and to live fuller and more successful lives.

Time   Too many persons screen their desertion of books behind the excuse that *they have no time.* In some instances this is true. But it is *not* true of anybody *all the time.* A man does the things he really wants to do. And not having time usually means failure to use the time he has. It is catching the odd moments that counts. Planning the day and budgeting time and making careful selection of reading matter and having it always near—this spells the difference between purposeful living and slothful, desultory existence.

Conversation   In many instances *conversation* has become a
and the   lost art. "Every conceivable beauty," writes
nurse   P. A. Goodall, speaking of nurses,[4] "is here in the world awaiting our conquering spirits, but all too often we prefer to gather in little groups and gossip of the day's events. In this way our tongues grow in agility while the depth of our minds becomes effaced." Aikens speaks of certain women who knowing nothing great to talk about, talk about small things as if they were great. "The same" she says,[5] "could truthfully be written about many groups of nurses, who . . . indulge in gossiping, endlessly, about their patients, at meals, in bedrooms, on street cars, and in public places, simply because they refuse to make the effort to direct their conversation into other channels of thought."

Better   A man talks about the things he knows and
conversation   which interest him. This is why it is important to fight *against narrow professional horizons and to cultivate broader points of view.* If a person has something to say, he

[4] Goodall, P. A.: *Ethics, The Inner Realities* (Philadelphia, F. A. Davis Co., 1942), pp. 163–164.
[5] *Ethics for Nurses,* p. 214.

probably will say it well. Yet the studied carelessness in speech which some cultivate today ought to be avoided. Slang and catch phrases indicate not only unrefined speech but slothful thinking. It scarcely aids conversation to give one's impression about almost everything with the curt, if vague, judgment, that it is divine or hysterical or out of this world or awful. Conversation also means being a good listener. It is astonishing how often people confound a good listener with a clever conversationalist.

Conversation and reading   Speech is man's way of exchanging ideas, and upon ideas the mind grows. Reading is one way of promoting this growth. Conversation is another. They are closely associated, mutually supplementary. Both, if wisely used, can contribute richly to cultural development. On the other hand, they can degenerate into real obstacles and become a morass for lazy, easily satisfied, mediocre, unambitious men and women.

Lectures, art, music, drama   *Human culture* implies acquaintance with the best products of the human spirit. *Literature* is one approach. There are others, such as *lectures*, visits to *art museums*, *music* and *drama*. For these activities school and training years leave little time. But with the coming of more leisure and freedom they should be seriously pursued. There is, of course, pleasure to be gained from them. But over and beyond that, the nurse who intelligently gives them a place in her activities will have a life all the richer for them. Their influence will reflect in her personality, in her work, above all in her association with patients. Many of them will appreciate her varied interests and cultural background, and her professional career will be all the more satisfying and successful.

Religion   *Religion* is another cultural influence which cannot be over emphasized. Man's relations to God and the expression of those relations in worship are essential to every truly human life. When they are denied

r neglected, a *warped person results*. However, since man's re-
ation to God has its own place in Special Ethics (pp. 342 ff.)
ere is no need to dwell upon the matter here.

4. MORAL CULTURE

ecessity   Culture of a dominantly intellectual sort must
be balanced with a due *cultivation of moral
abits*. It is not enough to know what virtue is and to admire
. It must find a functional place in human life.

he means   In the chapter on virtue in general some suggestions were given about cultivating virtue
nd getting rid of bad habits (p. 135). *These should be re-
alled*. For while the chief purpose of ethics is to give correct
1oral principles, the moral principles are nugatory unless
1ey find fulfilment in life. Man by his nature, by his very
onstitution and destiny must cultivate virtue. He cannot
e true to himself and wilfully disregard trying to live a
ood life.

lbsolute   Physical illness injures the body, ignorance
bligation to   blinds the mind, but unvirtuous conduct sets
irtue   the entire man in *opposition to his highest per-
ection*. For various reasons a man can sacrifice his health,
mb or life itself. For equally valid reasons a person may
enounce intellectual development. But never is he justified
1 renouncing his vocation to the good life and in following
vil conduct. His obligation to other goods is relative and
onditional. His obligation to pursue virtue is absolute.

5. THE USE OF MONEY

lace of   Of itself and directly *money* does not pertain
oney in the essentially to man's physical or moral or in-
ood life   tellectual development. But in order to make
evelopment along all these lines what it ought to be a
1an needs money and the things money can buy. Conse-

quently, men have the obligation to earn, if they are without incomes, the money they need.

Virtuous love   Such love of money is in order, is *virtuous*. No
of money   reasonable criticism can be made of the nurse
who strives to make a good income, who improves her
position, who spends carefully and saves something. There
is virtuous spending and there is virtuous saving. The nurse
should strive to make her attitude towards money reflect
both.

Saving   When money is rather plentiful, she should pro-
                  vide against the day when work may be slack.
Then there is the provision which must be made for va-
cations and against illness and perhaps against the time
when she will have to retire. Various hospitalization policies are available today as well as annuity plans. Good
insurance is probably the best means for taking care of
illness and retirement.

Investments   Unfortunately there is no such simple solution
                  to the problem of *investing one's savings*. It seems
almost futile to mention here the old warnings about investments since, though they are constantly repeated,
people go on being dupes. Yet it may do some good to urge
would-be investors to be cautious. Avoid get-rich-quick
schemes. Shy away from investments paying large rates of
interest. Seek expert advice when buying stocks and bonds.
Be suspicious of high pressure sales talk. Money is too important a means to right living to be taken lightly. To treat
it frivolously is just as wrong as to treat it miserly. Virtue
lies in the golden mean.

READINGS

Charlotte Aikens: *Studies in Ethics for Nurses*, chapters xvii an
    xxiii.
Abbé Dimnet: *The Art of Thinking*.
Mary E. Gladwin: *Ethics*, ch. xiv.

Phyllis A. Goodall: *Ethics*, ch. xiv.
Eugenia K. Spalding: *Professional Adjustments*, pp. 25–251; 431–432; 462–470.
R. H. Thouless: *How to Think Straight*.
Harold H. Titus: *Ethics for Today*, ch. xv.

II. Ethics Regarding Other Persons

Division   Ethical problems arising from people's relations with one another mostly pertain to
justice. Yet there are others which though not of justice
nevertheless impose obligations. Those that pertain to
justice involve rights originating in the natural law itself or
by reason of contractual agreements. Among those springing directly from the natural law are man's rights to *life*,
property, *truth* and to his *good name*. Contractual rights will
be considered in general and then with special application
to the nursing profession. Finally will be dealt with those
obligations which do not belong to justice.

Chapter 17

THE INNOCENT PERSON'S RIGHT TO LIFE

1. THE RIGHT

Obligation of By reason of his existence and destiny man is
perfection *bound to strive towards perfection*. This obliges him
to employ the necessary and useful means and binds his
fellow-men not to thwart his efforts without just cause. For
if he has the obligation to grow towards perfection, other
people have the obligation to respect his rights to those
means when he exercises them with due consideration. One
of those rights, indeed a primary right, is man's prerogative
to life—not in the sense that he has a right to be brought into
existence, but in the sense that once he begins to exist he
has the right to have that existence respected unless he forfeits it by criminal action.

The rights of the innocent to life evidently prohibit
murder in the strict sense of the word as well as *various
disguised forms* of the same crime. Likewise is prohibited
everything which constitutes a *threat* to an innocent person's
life or destroys his bodily integrity.

2. MURDER

Murder is an unjust voluntary act which brings about a
person's death. Its opposition to man's natural good and to
the natural law hardly need be stressed. Like suicide,
murder cuts man off from existence, from the great gift of
life, totally destroys his natural perfection, and represents
the utmost physical evil which he can suffer. But besides
being against man's personal and natural good, it infringes
upon God's sovereign right over life and death, just as

suicide does. Furthermore, it strikes deep into the social welfare. Not only does murder wantonly destroy a member of society, it attacks society's very existence. Society cannot function if men live in constant dread of violent death. Good social order demands security and peace and tranquillity and safety. Without them life stagnates and social life becomes impossible, progress stops and men degenerate. Therefore, murder is grievously wrong as infringing upon man's most essential rights, usurping God's dominion, and frustrating the social and private good.

3. LYNCHING

Definition *Lynching* is a crudely disguised form of murder. It gets its name from Charles Lynch (1736–1793) and means the summary punishment for imputed crime by a self-appointed group without due process of law. *Whether the victim be guilty or not, lynching is murder.* For the State alone has the right to execute criminals and only after due legal procedure.

In the In a nation where law is supposed to prevail
U.S.A. it is a national crime and scandal that lynchings occur. Yet lynching in the United States of America is a sad, shameful fact.

Evil *Lynching is essentially immoral.* It usurps the rights of the State. It defeats the regular process of justice. It frequently punishes the innocent. A Southern Commission on the Study of Lynching found that of 1930's 21 lynchees, two were certainly innocent of any crime and real doubt of guilt existed in at least half of the others. Many of them were defective half-wits. Lynching is a source of racial hate and bitter antagonisms. In short, it is murder. The persons involved take into their own hands without justification the right to another person's life. It is a barbarous crime and all who take part in it are guilty.

4. EUTHANASIA

Mercy-kill-
ing defined
Another version of murder is *euthanasia*, which signifies a quiet, easy death. Mercy-killing sounds brutal but is more descriptive. At the request of the person or of his relatives, a painless death is inflicted to free the sufferer from his misery or incurable malady.

Motivation
One mercy-killer gave this explanation after shooting her brother, an incurable mental patient: "I'm very glad. It was the least I could do. I didn't want to see him suffer. He had talked of suicide before he went away, but he got so bad he couldn't kill himself, so I decided to put him out of his misery." Or recall the tragic words of a father who had just killed his child: "I gave my little boy chloroform . . He's better off dead." For seventeen years he had washed and dressed and fed his imbecile son, bought the boy, who was a head taller than himself, blocks and tin soldiers to play with, and tried every means of curing him. Yet the boy never grew beyond the mental age of two, and at seventeen his father ended his misery.

Prevalence
It is a mistake to think mercy-killings are extremely rare. Although euthanasia is illegal, it is widely practiced, according to Dr. C. F. Potter, by relatives and physicians wishing to spare patients unnecessary suffering.[1] The attitude of at least some medical men towards it can be gathered from a poll taken of 4000 New York physicians in 1941. It reported 8 per cent as favoring legalized mercy-killings. Mercy-killings are said to occur in the United States at the rate of one a week; the killers are almost never convicted and the penalty may be as mild as three months in jail.

Morally
wrong
The *morality* of mercy-killing finds clear expression in its true name, *mercy murder*. If a person kills himself, it is suicide. If some one does it for him,

[1] *The Times-Herald*, Washington, D. C., February 17, 1943.

even at his request or with his consent, it is murder. For a person cannot delegate rights which he does not have, and we have seen that no one has the right to take his own life. A man cannot kill his fellow man except in self-defense, and the State can take the life only of the criminal proved guilty with due process of law. Here there is no question of self-defense and absolutely no question of capital punishment. The evil of euthanasia is perfectly clear. Yet some find arguments for it.

Argument for A typical defense occurs in Sutherland's citation of Dean Inge.[2] The Dean argued: "If I refuse to put a mangled horse or dog out of its misery, I may be fined for cruelty. If I help a human being, who is dying horribly by inches from cancer, gangrene, or locomotor ataxia . . . I may be hanged for murder." Similar reasoning is applied by Dr. C. F. Potter to war veterans returning home in a hopelessly maimed condition. "When medical science has done all it can for them," he is quoted as saying,[3] "in the way of restoring them to some semblance of physical health, there will remain a number who are admittedly incurable, who are suffering with no hope of relief from pain and anguish until death shall come after months and years of torture." Owners of horses and dogs, he explained, are required to put them to death if they are suffering hopelessly, but a human being in similar pain is denied this "kind treatment" under existing laws.

Refutation: man not merely animal This argument assumes that men can be treated like animals. The truth is *they cannot be treated like animals*, because they are not simply animals. To say, as the euthanasiasts do, that they want to control mercy-killings by having tight laws which would set up impartial committees to examine hope-

[2] Sutherland, H.: *Laws of Life* (New York, Sheed and Ward, 1936), p. 262.

[3] *The Times-Herald*, Washington, D. C., February 17, 1943.

less invalids and recommend scientific extinction, merely assumes again that such killings are moral. Euthanasia is murder, first and last, and there is no purpose which can justify it. A good end does not rectify bad means.

Destroys   It may be added that legalized euthanasia
fundamental would *destroy* the entire moral fabric of civiliza-
right   tion. That may sound extreme, but it is not; since legalized euthanasia would attack man's most primary and fundamental right to life. This denied, what rights would be safe! And unless man's natural and inalienable rights are recognized and safeguarded, society cannot endure.

5. ABORTION

Abortion and   *Abortion in general* is the expulsion from the
viability   mother's womb of a living but non-viable fetus. Non-viable does not mean dead, but that the fetus cannot live outside the womb. Father Finney lays down the following principles about viability:[4] A fetus is not viable before the end of the twenty-sixth week of gestation. In properly equipped hospitals, the fetus can be considered viable at the end of the twenty-sixth week. But outside of the hospital and under ordinary conditions, the fetus cannot be looked upon as viable until the end of the twenty-eighth week of gestation.

Accidental   The expulsion of the non-viable fetus may be
abortion   accidental, merely allowed or unintentional. Abortion is *accidental* when it happens because of some unfortunate circumstance. A young mother may fall and an abortion follow. She is not responsible for it. She did not intend it, she did not wilfully do anything which she knew would bring it about. It is not imputable to her. There is no guilt attached to it.

[4] Finney, P. A.: *Moral Problems in Hospital Practice* (St. Louis, B. Herder Book Co., 1938), p. 26.

Indirect   The *indirect*, or merely allowed, *abortion* is not
abortion   willed or intended, but happens in connection
with some legitimate medical treatment. A pregnant
woman may have a cancer that requires immediate surgery.
Even though it be foreseen that the indicated operation
certainly will cause an abortion, it may nevertheless be
done. This is allowed on the principle of the indirect
voluntary (p. 99), where from one action, the operation
for cancer, come a good and a bad effect. The good effect is
the preservation of the woman's health by the removal of
the cancer. The evil effect is the loss of the fetus. In this
instance the operation for cancer is moral because the action
itself is good, namely the excision of the cancer. The effects
follow directly from the same cause and not the good from
the evil effect. The intention of all concerned is good,
namely the preservation of the woman's health and not the
destruction of the new life. There is also a just proportion
between the good and evil effects, with justification for
permitting the evil effect.

6. DIRECT ABORTION

Finally, there is *direct abortion*. This differs from accidental
and indirect abortion in that the expulsion of the fetus is
intentional and directly willed. It does not just happen nor
is it merely allowed. It is the thing which is desired. Those
concerned want to terminate the pregnancy and they do it
by the expulsion of the living but non-viable fetus. It is
another thinly disguised form of murder.

Therapeutic   A current parody upon language refers to two
and criminal   kinds of direct abortion. *Medical or therapeutic*
abortion   describes an abortion which is directly pro-
cured to save the life of the mother. *Criminal*, however, is
used to stigmatize an abortion which is just as direct as the
therapeutic but is done for other than medical reasons.
Lack of money, fear of losing one's job or reputation or

freedom or leisure, dislike of children, these are some of the motives which bring women to have criminal or illegal abortions.

The distinc-tion widely accepted   The distinction between therapeutic and criminal abortions is accepted by many reputable physicians, who while they shy away from the criminal abortion as illegal and morally wrong nevertheless defend and perform the therapeutic type. For example Dr. Joseph B. DeLee lays down several indications as justifying a physician to induce a therapeutic abortion, yet has this to say about abortions which are generally termed criminal.[5] "Perhaps the saddest commentary on our 'modern civilization,' on our 'higher thought,' on our 'ethical movement' is the increase of the practice of criminal abortion. It is very sad to contemplate the thousands of delicate little lives destroyed every year by criminal abortionists, and, too, the maternal deaths they cause—to say nothing of the life-long invalidism that may follow in the wake of these ugly operations. Nurses are not long in training before they see how alarmingly this crime has spread, and they see, too, the lives lost and the homes wrecked by it. A nurse should never be party to such a procedure. It is always murder—in several states legally punishable as such—and often suicide." Then the authors of this much revised work of Dr. DeLee go on to speak of the therapeutic abortion. "This term," they say, "is used to distinguish the operation of ending the pregnancy before the child is viable in order to save the mother's life from the criminal operations performed by professional abortionists." They admit that the "operation . . . awakens sentiments of greatest delicacy; it involves heavy and painful responsibilities, and so no physician will perform it without

[5] Davis, M. Edward, and Carmon, Mabel C.: *DeLee's Obstetrics for Nurses* (Philadelphia, W. B. Saunders Co., 13th ed. 1944), pp. 149–150.

the counsel and moral support of at least one of his confreres."

Worth of the distinction   Therapeutic and criminal abortions differ only in motive—*not in themselves. Equally they deprive innocent human beings of life.* The operator's intention in one instance to safeguard the mother's health and in the other to safeguard something else does not change the objective fact, that a non-viable fetus is directly killed. There is *no essential moral difference* between the so-called therapeutic and criminal abortion.

Prevalence   For obvious reasons exact figures on the prevalence of direct abortions are impossible. But some suggestion of how *widespread* the practice is was given in an article by Jane Ward.[6] Twenty to 40 per cent of pregnancies terminate in abortions. Every minute of the day some woman in the United States has an abortion, and of these, 90 per cent are wives and not wayward girls. An investigator, in 1940, found evidence in Brooklyn, N. Y., that 100 abortionists had performed illegal operations at the rate of approximately 20 a week each. One testified that he had performed over 20,000 abortions, his income running into the hundred thousands, before he was convicted. An operator in Baltimore performed 4000 abortions in six years. Another, 3000 in one year. Colossal as these figures appear, they are certainly underestimates of the present situation.

The human fetus a person   The question of the morality of *direct abortion* hinges upon the nature of the human non-viable fetus. That it is a person is clear from the whole process of its development. "From the first moment of its fertilization," writes Dr. Moore,[7] "the ovum commences an orderly process of growth and development

[6] *Reader's Digest*, August 1941, "Don't Have an Abortion," pp. 17–21.

[7] *Principles of Ethics*, p. 159.

which reaches its physical limits in the early adult years of the human being. One after another functions and powers unfold themselves as the physical basis of their manifestation is laid. In all the various processes of transformation and development the organism manifests a fundamental unity, so that this embryo becomes this adult human being by the organizing activity of one and the same living principle which determines growth and development in the embryo, and manifests intelligence and the power to control conduct in the adult. An intelligent individual is a person by reason of his fundamental capability of intelligence. He does not cease to be a person because he is asleep and manifests no intelligent behavior, nor can he be denied the rights of a person when he is knocked unconscious or even when he becomes insane . . . As long as the organism that is fundamentally capable of intelligence, lives, it is a person and has the inalienable rights of a person. If the human embryo is alive, and it is alive unless it had died, it is a person." That the human embryo is a person is clear from the attitude of all reputable physicians towards criminal abortion. Their condemnation of it as illegal, immoral and simply murder postulates that the embryo is a person with the rights of a person.

Ethical character of direct abortion

Once it is seen that the human fetus is a human being, the immorality of *direct abortion* is evident. While in the womb the fetus depends for its life upon its union with the mother through the placenta and umbilical cord. Direct abortion destroys that union and so destroys the life of the fetus. Since the fetus must be treated as human, the action amounts to the direct killing of a human being, and this is evil. It is murder, intrinsically evil and no motive, however good, can justify it.

Therapeutic and criminal abortions evil

The *only* distinction between therapeutic and criminal abortions is *the motive*. To say that it can change the admittedly murderous action of the criminal abortion into the allegedly good act of a therapeutic abortion is to suppose that a good end or motive can justify an evil means. Although a bad motive or purpose makes a good action evil, a good motive or purpose cannot make an evil action good. The end or purpose does not justify the means (p. 88). In both therapeutic and criminal abortions an unborn, innocent person is intentionally killed. Intentionally and voluntarily to kill a human being who has not forfeited his right to life is murder. Consequently, since the only distinction between so-called therapeutic and criminal abortions is the motive and since there is no essential difference in the action, both must be condemned as murder and neither can ever be allowed.

The physician's "duty"   Nevertheless therapeutic abortions are allowed by civil law and there are those who would try to defend them. One of the arguments holds that the physician is bound to save life and when faced with two evils he must choose the less. Thus when the crisis occurs of either allowing mother and child to die or killing the child to save the mother, he should choose killing the child—for that is what a therapeutic abortion is.

Reply   It is, of course, the physician's duty to prefer the less of two evils—*if the evils are in the same order*. But performing an abortion or letting mother and child die are not in the same order. Death belongs to the physical order. Direct abortion belongs to the moral order and has been shown to be intrinsically evil. No physician ethically can choose the moral evil of murder over the physical evil of death, for the moral order is the higher and must be given preference over the physical. Likewise it is true that the physician is bound to save life by every means in his power—but this does not imply every means absolutely speaking. His most sacred duty is to use only those means which are *moral*, which are *ethical* and *good*. As he stands pledged by professional honor to use every *ethical* means to save life so he stands pledged to avoid every immoral and unethical means. Since direct abortion is evil, he never can be obliged professionally to perform it. Rather his professional obligation is to condemn it as murder.

The child— an "unjust aggressor" Even more specious than the argument of the physician's professional duty is the assertion that the unborn child is an *unjust aggressor* threatening the mother's life. As she would defend herself against any other assault, so, it is argued, she can defend herself against her child's threat to her life by having an abortion.

Reply No one doubts her right to kill if necessary in self-defense. Her assailant might be fully responsible for his evil intentions or he might be a maniac and not responsible. But in both instances she could defend herself appropriately. But how can her unborn child be considered an unjust aggressor in either way? Certainly not in the sense of knowing what he is doing and willing to injure her. There can be no question of any voluntary action whatsoever on the part of the fetus. Just as certainly it cannot be considered an unjust aggressor in the sense of an irresponsible assailant. The child is not a person devoid of reason threatening her with injury. In itself the unborn child is doing nothing. It is passive. And if it is its mere presence in the mother which threatens her, it is she and the father who are responsible for that presence, and not the child. In no way can it be considered an unjust aggressor and the argument fails utterly.

Mother's prior right to life Another argument in defense of therapeutic abortions insists that the mother has a prior right to life. When she is endangered by a non-viable fetus, it is urged that her right to life takes precedence over her unborn child's.

Reply On the contrary, it must be pointed out that all human beings are equal in their essential rights, whether they be adults, children or unborn babies. One of these essential rights is the right to life. No person has a greater right to life than any other person and no person's right can take precedence over another's. Consequently there can be no question of a mother's right to life being prior to her unborn child's. Their rights are equal. To concede parents a priority of life over their children would be equivalent to allowing them to dispose of their children at any time. For if they have the right of disposing of the unborn, why would they not have the same right over the born child!

The alleged   Then there is the dilemma which pictures the
dilemma   physician with the choice between letting the
mother die or killing the fetus. This dilemma, Dr. Moore insists, ". . . in practical cases is never so clear cut. An abortion is a serious matter for the mother. Some mothers have died from the abortion who might have lived and given birth to a healthy child. No physician can say with certainty: the mother will die unless I bring on a therapeutic abortion."[8]

Harmful   *Direct abortion*, whether it be therapeutic or
physical   criminal, is condemned because it is *nothing*
effects   *short of murder*. But along with its moral evil
should be mentioned the harmful physical and mental effects which often follow. Jane Ward gave vivid expression to these in her article "Don't Have an Abortion."[9] On the authority of the Surgeon General of the U. S. Public Health Service, Dr. Thomas Parran, she wrote that one fourth of all maternal deaths are caused by aborted pregnancies. For every 100 women who die in pregnancy or childbirth, twenty-four perish from abortion. Three fourths of these deaths are due to blood poisoning. Hemorrhage accounts for many more. And these appalling figures rep-

[8] *Principles of Ethics*, p. 161.
[9] *Reader's Digest*, August 1941, pp. 17–19.

resent only the *known* cases and constitute only a small fraction of the total number. Dr. Frederick J. Taussig, an outstanding authority, estimates that 9 per cent of the women who have one abortion become sterile, and the percentage doubles with those having two or more abortions. "I know of no greater tragedy," Jane Ward quotes Dr. George W. Kosmak, editor of the *American Journal of Obstetrics and Gynecology*, as saying, "than the young couple who, thinking they cannot yet afford a baby, resort to an abortion, only to find, when they are ready for a child, that the wife is sterile . . ." Infection, hemorrhage, abnormal condition of the uterus, miscarriage in later pregnancies, blindness, all these can follow on abortion. At Bellevue Hospital in New York, 22 per cent of the obstetrical patients are admitted to repair the results from abortion.

Evil mental effects Finally, but of the utmost gravity, are the mental effects of remorse, sadness, bereavement and deep melancholy. It is a fact that much marital unhappiness finds its beginning in the nervous irritability lingering after an abortion.

Harmful effects and intrinsically evil All of these results reinforce Jane Ward's advice: *Don't have an abortion.* But they have full value only when joined with the *fundamental evil of direct abortion, that it is murder*—no matter why it is done. No good intention, no civil law, no committee of physicians, no consent of mother or father or relatives can ever justify it. *Direct abortion is intrinsically evil. And evil it remains whether or not harmful effects follow.* But in a given instance these should be taken into account as powerful motives for rejecting the immoral and dangerous expediency of direct abortion.

7. ECTOPIC GESTATION

Murder, lynching, euthanasia, direct abortion are clear and simple attacks upon the right to life. But there are some other problems, involving the life of the unborn, which are not so simple. Among them may be considered as of contemporary importance *ectopic gestation*, *craniotomy*, *use of the tampon* and *pernicious vomiting*.

The problem   *Ectopic gestation* may be described briefly as a pregnancy which takes place outside of the cavity of the uterus, usually in the Fallopian tube.[10] The basic fact is that the condition menaces the mother's life and generally means death for the fetus. When the situation is discovered, the question arises about what can be done ethically to save the mother. If the fetus is *certainly* dead, though this is not always easy to know, it may and should be removed. If the fetus is living and probably viable the risk of operating may be taken when the need is urgent, providing serious and timely provision is made for the two lives at stake. The difficulty arises when the fetus is not viable and the mother's life is endangered.

Solution   The solution of the moral question involved follows a revised understanding of the pathology of tubal pregnancy. The mother's condition arises not from the increased *size* of the fetus but from the *pathological condition in the Fallopian tubes*. A sudden hemorrhage can occur at any time and result in her death. Actually, as Dr. Moore writes, ". . . after tubal pregnancy has advanced for some weeks the woman has been bleeding, is bleeding, and will bleed still more, and perhaps fatally, unless something is done to stop the hemorrhage."[11] The hemorrhage, it is pointed out, can and should be stopped, not by attacking the fetus by but blocking the cause of the hemorrhage, that is, by clamping the arteries. The fetus will die but as the *indirect result* of interrupting the blood supply to

[10] For a fuller description see DeLee and Greenhill, *Principles and Practice of Obstetrics*, 9th ed. Also Moore, *Principles of Ethics*, pp. 169–174.

[11] *Principles of Ethics*, p. 174.

stop the hemorrhage. Then the tube and the dead fetus should be removed.

8. CRANIOTOMY AND CEPHALOTRIPSY

Described   *Craniotomy* is an operation whereby the unborn child's head is opened, the brain matter destroyed so as to insure the child's death, and the child extracted by forceps or a sharp hook. *Cephalotripsy*, as generally done, is an operation in which the head of the child is compressed and crushed by means of powerful forceps, but the head is not perforated.

As usually   Dr. Finney[12] considers craniotomy and ceph-
done, direct   alotripsy to be without qualification the direct
killing   killing of the unborn child to save the mother.
They are "performed upon the living child, are directly destructive of its life, and are therefore murder. The condition of the mother, no matter how desperate, can never morally justify any operation that is directly destructive of the life of the unborn child." When these operations are, as Dr. Finney takes them to be and as they usually are described, the means of killing the child to save the mother, they stand condemned. For it is agreed that no direct killing of the child for the mother's sake is ever legitimate. It is simply murder.

As modified,   However, *need* these operations always be a
not direct   direct attack upon the child to save the
killing   mother? Dr. Moore, for example, thinks not.
He admits that craniotomy as usually described constitutes the direct killing of the child and if so performed is immoral and never legitimate. The child may not be killed to save the mother. Yet he insists that the operation today can be modified so that it is not the direct killing of the child but rather an attempt to save it. He thinks cephalotripsy likewise need not crush the skull of the unborn child but can be

[12] *Moral Problems*, pp. 82–83.

done with such care that instead of being murder it can be an operation to save its life. He gives examples of children surviving these operations to prove that they do not mean death necessarily.[13]

Dangerous operations allowed The chances of the child's surviving in perfect condition are admittedly slight. But it is *legitimate to take risks* in an operation intended to save life. It may be foreseen that a patient undergoing an operation is likely to die or perhaps almost certainly will die. Yet if there is a chance of the operation's saving him or prolonging life it may be performed.

Application Likewise for the *modified forms* of craniotomy and cephalotripsy which Dr. Moore describes. "Considering the modern advance in brain surgery," he writes, "and our knowledge of the possibility of life with a considerable brain deficit, and the actual examples cited of cases that survived the first stage of the operation for craniotomy, it would be quite possible at the present time to perform a cranial operation in certain cases that would reduce the size of the head and save the life of the child by allowing it to be born."[14] Of course the operation will be hazardous. But it is admitted that hazardous brain operations may be performed upon adults. Why then not upon the unborn child to save its life!

Practical conclusion Dr. Moore's conclusion seems *judicious and acceptable*. No one should suggest substituting conservative cranial operations for cesarean sections. Yet the mother's life must be taken into account. Where cesarean section can be performed it ought to be done. But when it is not possible, the child should not be allowed to die if a cranial operation might save it. The physician must conscientiously decide in view of all the circumstances what is to be done. The moralist can only say: No operation which

[13] *Principles of Ethics*, pp. 175–181.
[14] *Ibid.*, p. 179.

is a direct killing of the child can be performed in order to save the life of the mother, and no operation which directly kills the mother can be performed in order to save the life of the child.

9. USE OF TAMPON

Conditions for moral use There remains the problem raised by the procedure of *tamponing* the uterine cervix and vagina to check a hemorrhage of a pregnant mother. Such tamponing is clearly legitimate provided an abortion seems inevitable, the hemorrhage threatens the woman's life seriously, and the tampon is used for the express purpose of stopping the hemorrhage.[15]

Indirect voluntary This is an application of the principle of the *double effect* (p. 99). The act of tamponing is not wrong in itself; the good effect of stopping the hemorrhage and saving the mother's life balances the evil but unwilled and indirect effect of the loss of the fetus. The good effect does not result from the loss of the fetus but from stopping the hemorrhage. Yet, as has been said, the intention of all concerned must be the mother's welfare and not the killing of the fetus. It likewise should be noted that tamponing is not legitimate merely because an abortion seems inevitable. The reason is not the inevitability of the abortion but the serious threat of the hemorrhage to the mother's life.

READINGS

Michael Cronin: *The Science of Ethics*, ii, 93–109.
Patrick A. Finney: *Moral Problems in Hospital Practice.*
S. A. LaRochelle and C. T. Fink: *Handbook of Medical Ethics*, pp. 91–131; 157–170.
Charles J. McFadden: *Medical Ethics for Nurses*, chapters vi to x.
Thomas V. Moore: *Principles of Ethics*, ch. xv.
Halliday Sutherland: *Laws of Life*, ch. xvii.

[15] Cf. Finney, *Moral Problems*, pp. 110–112.

Chapter 18

PERSON'S RIGHT NOT TO BE INJURED

1. INTRODUCTION

Introduction and division   A man's right to life obliges other men to avoid not only killing him but also *injuring* him or unreasonably *threatening* him with injury. This obligation has particular importance for the nursing profession. Yet of a much wider scope, and one which will be considered first, is its application to the national tragedy of automobile accidents. The immorality of killing and maiming the innocent needs to be focused on the obligation of motorists to drive safe cars safely.

2. AUTOMOBILE ACCIDENTS

Obligation not recognized   People who would do nothing intentionally to injure their neighbor in effect jeopardize his life *with their automobiles and reckless driving.* That a moral obligation is involved seems little recognized—or if recognized is not taken seriously. The public fails to understand that the automobile is an instrument of death and destruction. A man patiently shows his son how to handle a rifle, yet jumps in his car and transforms it into a greater threat to his neighbor's life than his rifle ever was.

Reckless driving   Though his car be in perfect shape, a driver can *threaten* his neighbor by disregarding traffic regulations, by going too fast, by driving when he is not physically fit. This may arise from some handicap or because he has neglected to compensate for the handicap. Accidents have occurred when drivers legally bound to have eyeglasses failed to wear them. No one knows how

266

many accidents must be attributed to over-indulgence in alcohol. Then there is carelessness in lighting cigars or cigarettes or handling maps or thinking that the left hand alone on the wheel is as good as left and right together. Sometimes it is. In an emergency it is not. "One-armed driving" has caused accidents.

Defective car Careful driving can go a long way towards safe driving, but it cannot go the whole way *if the car itself needs repair*. A man who never would think of aiming a loaded gun at anyone drives a car with poor brakes. Some even brag about their skill in handling automobiles whose lights or tires or wheels or steering mechanism need attention. That the automobile is a dangerous weapon and that the neighbor's right to life must be respected are facts which receive scant consideration.

Not merely This obligation is not merely a question of *civil law* civil law which some states have enacted to insure safe automobiles on the road. *It is a matter of moral obligation*, binding with exactly the same force as the obligation of not killing or mutilating the innocent. The motorist, it is true, is not solely responsible for all accidents. Pedestrians too are careless, yet they likewise are bound not to be unreasonable hazards to traffic. Both motorist and pedestrian, but chiefly the motorist, since he is in possession of the dangerous weapon, have a grave moral responsibility of respecting the life of their fellow man and avoiding all unjustifiable threats upon it.

3. NURSING ACCIDENTS

Grave moral The obligation of respecting the neighbor's *duty not to* right to life establishes the foundation for the *injure* nurse's grave moral responsibility *not to injure* *patients* *patients*. The reputation of the hospital and of the nursing profession must be safeguarded and lawsuits avoided. But the basic consideration is the universal duty of respecting the neighbor's right to life and bodily integrity. Patients come to the hospital to have health restored, but sometimes instead suffer injury.

Legal aspect   The legal aspect of hospital accidents needs more attention *now* than formerly. Hospitals used to be considered purely charitable institutions and not liable to suit. That status has somewhat changed. And though verdicts against hospitals are seldom returned, the fact is they sometimes are. More and more the public is becoming critical and prosecuting claims. This is why the nurse should become acquainted with existing laws and understand her responsibilities. Ignorance of the law will not excuse her.

Hospital and nursing prestige suffer   Yet whether the hospital be found guilty or not, and though the nurse escape legal penalties, the adverse publicity is extremely unfortunate. The reputation of the hospital as well as the prestige of the nursing profession suffer. Severe disciplinary action may be taken against the nurse and the confidence of patients is weakened.

Accidents in hospitals   Aikens writes[1] that hospital accidents in the public mind suggest "an injury caused by . . . recklessness, carelessness, ignorance, or negligence." Ignorance has been dealt with (p. 103). Negligence and carelessness and recklessness are broad terms, difficult to define. Negligence signifies failure to use the care which a person of ordinary prudence would use under the same circumstances. Recklessness describes rash and thoughtless conduct. Carelessness means simply without due care and characterizes conduct which is unconcerned, heedless, thoughtless or without solicitude.

Obligation in justice when responsible   When a patient suffers injury in the course of nursing care, responsibility must be determined. Responsibility implies knowledge, free-

[1] *Ethics for Nurses*, p. 197.

dom and volition—factors very difficult to weigh in
practice. But if the nurse is certainly at fault through recklessness, carelessness, culpable ignorance or negligence, not
only is she guilty of unethical conduct but she is bound in
strict justice to repair the injury when and in so far as she
morally can (p. 164).

Restitution   If a nurse *culpably* neglects removing a heating
                 pad and the patient suffers a burn which pro-
longs his stay in the hospital, she is bound, when and to the
extent she can, to reimburse him for the extra expense which
her carelessness caused. Her obligation of restitution comes
from her relations with the patient which are not just those
of person to person but that relation plus the contractual
aspect. Patients and nurses do not sign formal contracts;
but the contractual aspect is there all the same. The patient,
it is understood, has the right to expect, and the nurse to
give, ordinary nursing care. When she guiltily falls short of
this, her unethical conduct carries the obligation of com-
pensating for the damge she has caused.

When not   Most often the responsibility is *not certain*, and
clearly   while it is important for the nurse to indemnify
responsible injuries she has caused, it is equally important
for her *to be level headed* when accidents happen for which
she is not responsible. The effects may be unfortunate, even
tragic—as in the case of the nurse putting boric acid in the
infants' formula instead of dextrose. Yet under such circumstances the nurse must keep her poise. If she was not
responsible for confusing boric acid with the dextrose, the
deaths are in no way imputable to her. Being human she
probably could not escape profound grief and regret. But
reason should control emotion and be a bulwark against
melancholy and collapse.

Practical   As far as the victim of a nurse's accident is
conclusion   concerned, *the injury remains whether or not she
was ethically guilty*. He has come to harm in the very hospital

where he came to be cured. This is the thought which should control a nurse's attitude toward accidents. By her profession she is pledged to care for the sick. Her ambition should be to avoid anything which will injure them, retard recovery, weaken their confidence or in any way interfere with their fight for health. Consequently *every precaution against accident should be taken*. Poisonous drugs should be kept separate. Bottles should be labeled and the labels protected against being rubbed off or the inscriptions smeared. Good lighting should be provided. When hurrying or tired or confused or preoccupied, the nurse should be unusually cautious. At such times experience shows that accidents are most likely to occur. Nurses should understand orders, what to do and how to do it. This implies careful reading and concentrated attention. If any doubt exists, if a mistake seems to have been made, if the order is not clear, the nurse must lay the problem before her superior. She cannot act in an uncertain frame of mind. In such instances probabilism has no place, since the patient's welfare is an end which must be attained (p. 125).

READINGS

Charlotte A. Aikens: *Studies in Ethics for Nurses*, ch. xvi.
Thomas V. Moore: *Principles of Ethics*, ch. xii.
Modern Hospital, "When Is a Private Hospital Liable for Negligence of Its Nurses?," November, 1933.

Chapter 19

MUTILATING OPERATIONS

1. DEFINITION AND DIVISION

Mutilating operations deprive the body of some member or suppress the due functioning of some organ. In this broad sense every operation is a mutilation, for it does not mean simply excising an organ but any procedure which deprives the body of its completeness or proper activity. Such operations may be for the sake of health, when they are called therapeutic, or by the State for crime, when they are termed punitive. Both of these are lawful. On the contrary, mutilation of healthy organs without just cause or of the innocent by the State are unlawful. Finally, *therapeutic operation* must not be confused with *therapeutic abortion* (p. 254). The latter is an operation to protect the mother, but is performed upon her non-viable fetus with the express intention not of saving it but of killing it.

2. LAWFUL MUTILATION—THERAPEUTIC OPERATIONS

Diseased organs　*Operations for the sake of health are evidently legitimate.* A person has a right to health and an obligation of preserving it. He is bound to use all the means ordinarily necessary or helpful. Extraordinary means he *may* use if he wishes; mutilating operations are among these. Whenever such an operation is deemed necessary to restore a person's health or to remove a threatened danger to it, the operation is lawful. Centuries before operations were as commonplace as they are today Thomas Aquinas pointed out their reasonableness. Since the members of the body exist for its over-all welfare, they can be sacrificed for the benefit of man's general health. He insisted, however, that consent had to be given either by the man himself or by someone with authority over him.

Organs not diseased but dangerous — Even though an organ be not diseased, it may *under certain circumstances* be removed. For example, a surgeon while operating for hernia may remove a healthy appendix, provided that he foresees that it may form adhesions and make another abdominal operation necessary. Likewise, men and women going to live where competent medical service in emergencies cannot be had may have the appendix removed. For even though it is healthy at the time, it can become a serious threat to life. Such operations are legitimate in view of the fact that, as far as is known, the removal of the appendix inflicts no notable injury upon the body. Whereas, on the contrary, its presence under certain circumstances constitutes a real threat to life. On the basis, then, of Aquinas' argument, that the parts of the body exist for the general welfare of the whole, it seems reasonable and prudent, if the person wishes to do so, to take the precaution of having his appendix out before putting himself beyond the reach of medical care.

3. PUNITIVE MUTILATIONS BY THE STATE

Right and expediency — The *right* of the State to mutilate criminals needs to be distinguished from the *expediency* of such punishment. The State can be shown to have the right. But under given circumstances whether it should exercise the right is another question entirely.

Punishment must be reasonable — For punishment to be reasonable and just it must not only be a rightful exercise of the State's authority. *It must also be judged in terms of its value for achieving the hoped-for good*. It can very well happen that the State exercise its prerogative of punishing criminals with mutilation yet inflict an unreasonable punishment. For it might fall far short of deterring criminals from further crime. To punish sex crimes by sterilization can be an incentive, rather than a detriment, to criminal conduct. Hence, the *right* of punishing by mutilation must not be confused with its *expediency;* nor, because the State has the right, should such punishment automatically be thought just and reasonable. *Here the question concerns solely the State's right.*

State's right   *That the State has the right is clear.* For if the State can take the life of criminals for heinous crime (p. 286) it can inflict mutilations upon them for lesser crimes. Such punishment obviously conflicts with the nature of the condemned person. But it conforms with natural reason in relation to the common good. This is why it can be inflicted only by the authority whose concern it is to safeguard the common good, that is, by competent civil authority. Private persons have no right to take the law into their hands.

4. UNLAWFUL MUTILATION

The State and the innocent   Though the State can justly mutilate criminals, *it has no right whatsoever to maim innocent men and women* or interfere in any way with the body's proper functioning. The State has definite rights in relation to its citizens. For just reasons it can take their money and goods as well as their lives. But it does not have supreme dominion over them. It cannot directly take life, unless that life be forfeited by criminal action. For life is not of its giving nor under its absolute control—no more than a man's life falls under his own decision to keep or destroy. Man does not (p. 204) have supreme dominion over his own life. It belongs to God alone. Likewise for the State. It does not have supreme dominion over a man's life, unless he loses his right and the State is obliged to separate him from society by death or by imprisonment.

Unnecessary Neither can any person mutilate himself nor
mutilation have himself mutilated nor mutilate another
person, unless there is a question of removing a diseased
organ or removing a threat to the body's general health.
For man has supreme control over the life and body neither
of himself nor of his fellow-man. And since he himself has
not the right, he cannot commission a surgeon to do what
he has no right to do himself. The surgeon, on the other
hand, obviously has no right over other persons' lives and
bodies.

5. STERILIZATION

Definition A prevalent sort of mutilating operation which
and division needs special attention is *sterilization*. In general this is any process of rendering sterile. More specifically
it indicates medical or physical treatment which frustrates
the power of procreation in men and women. It may be
done by the excision of certain organs, by incision or by
some treatment which destroys temporarily or permanently
the functioning of organs necessary for procreation. Two
kinds are distinguished: *indirect*, to remove diseased organs,
and *direct*, to prevent conception.

Indirect Sterilization is *indirect* when the operation, or
lawful whatever takes its place, is needed and intended, to remove diseased organs or to restore the person's
general health. Such sterilization, as any other operation
required for the sake of health, is legitimate.

Explanation The sterilizing effect is not intended as the end
of the operation any more than the loss of a
leg is the desired end of an amputation. The sterilizing
effects are subordinate, secondary, indirectly willed, tolerated. The person's health is threatened and the operation
is performed to save it.

Ethical The ethical principle involved is the indirect
principle voluntary or the principle of the *double effect*
(p. 99). The action itself is good. The beneficial effects of

restored health favorably balance the evil result of sterilization. The good does not follow from the evil but is correlative with it. The intention of all concerned is good. They want the person's health restored, and they lament or merely tolerate the unavoidable suppression of the procreative powers.

6. DIRECT, OR PREVENTATIVE, STERILIZATION IN GENERAL

Defined   *Direct, or preventative*, describes sterilization when the intention and specific purpose of the process is to remove or render inactive healthy organs in order to make procreation impossible. There is here no question of treating diseased organs or removing a present threat to the person's health. The intention is of quite another sort. It may be to secure the person's own alleged good or to promote the social good, in which case it is called *eugenic*. In either instance the act of sterilization is direct in the sense that it is sterilization which is intended and wanted.

Never lawful   Preventative sterilization, in behalf either of the private or of the social good, which is intended as an end or as a means to an end, *is never lawful*. The intention of those concerned, no matter how lofty it may be, cannot rectify a process which is fundamentally and universally evil (p. 88).

Evil mutilation   On several scores its *evil character* appears. First, it is the unjustifiable mutilation or destruction of the natural faculty of generation. There is no question of excising or treating a diseased organ or remedying a defective function. It is solely a question of depriving the body of its natural powers of generation to effect the supposed good of preventing the danger of pregnancy or of avoiding undesirable offspring. It is an unjustifiable interference in a natural and important function. For if there are valid reasons against parents' having children, there are ethical ways of preventing conception (p. 378).

Unwarranted frustration   Again, direct sterilization is an *unwarranted frustration* of nature by rendering futile the normal relations of the sexes, since the natural purpose of sexual intercourse is the procreation and birth of children. Consequently, such sterilization is opposed to the fundamental nature of marriage (p. 354). Finally, direct sterilization opens the door to serious abuses and excesses, facilitates licentious living, undisciplined habits, and venereal diseases.

7. DIRECT STERILIZATION FOR PRIVATE GOOD IMMORAL

Described   Before direct sterilization for the social good is considered, something more should be said about *sterilization for private good*. This is an operation, or its equivalent, performed upon either sex in order to forestall pregnancy.

Reasons   The reasons given are manifold. A woman has a heart or lung condition or too narrow a pelvis. Perhaps no children are wanted because of finances or comfort or freedom or because there is grave fear that they might be deformed or diseased. So she is sterilized to preclude the possibility of conception. The good intended is the good of the mother or of the child, but it is attained through the means of an unethical operation.

Policy in some hospitals   Some hospitals have a policy of suggesting sterilization to all mothers who (1) are to have a third cesarean section; (2) have had sufficient children in the opinion of the attending physician; (3) or have a condition deemed serious enough to cause trouble during pregnancy. If the woman is too ill to give her consent, the husband is asked to sign for her.

Never lawful   Further to the arguments given against direct sterilization in general, Pius XI's treatise on

Christian Marriage may be quoted. Here, let it be noted, the Holy Father argues against it on the ground both of Revelation and of reason. ". . . . Christian doctrine establishes, and the light of human reason makes it most clear, that private individuals have no other power over the members of their bodies than that which pertains to their natural ends; and they are not free to destroy or mutilate their members, or in any other way render themselves unfit for their natural functions, except when no other provision can be made for the good of the whole body."

No matter how simple   No matter how painless or simple the process which produces sterilization may be *it is always a grave mutilation*. For it effectively frustrates a most important human function. From such an operation come directly two effects. Both of them are evil: the mutilation and the sterility. The remote good effect intended, of safeguarding the mother from pregnancy or a future child from disease or deformity, results from an evil means. Nor is the evil effect of sterilization merely tolerated as unavoidable. It is what is most specifically intended. Consequently, all such operations, or their equivalents, intended to sterilize men and women *are unlawful*.

8. EUGENIC STERILIZATION IMMORAL

Its legal status   *Eugenic*, or direct, sterilization for the social good is championed as an efficient means for improving the human stock by preventing undesirable persons from having inferior children. By 1936 twenty-seven states of the Union had voluntary or compulsory sterilization laws, though in some states they were dead letters. These laws regard abnormal and degenerate persons who are deemed unfit to breed. In general, they provide that cases in which sterilization is indicated be brought before a medical and administrative board, where parents or guardians will be heard with the right of appeal.

A fact and a   The rational disproof of *eugenic sterilization* as a
moral issue   measure of social welfare faces an indisputable
fact. There are persons who should not have children. To
accomplish this, sterilization is an infallible means. This is
the attraction which sterilization has for some earnest
social-minded people. But they overlook the *fundamental
moral issue* in the expectation of the good they hope from it.
Yet, before the question is asked whether or not sterilization
is an apt eugenic measure, its essential morality must be
decided.

Against   The *evil character of direct sterilization has been
nature*   shown* (p. 276). It unjustifiably frustrates a
natural appetite and function, is opposed to marriage, and
paves the way for grave moral delinquencies. This is the
fundamental immorality of eugenic sterilization. Even
though it were proved beyond the shadow of a doubt that
it would achieve all that is claimed for it, it would still
remain evil and unlawful. But there are other and forcible
arguments against it.

Invasion of   Pius XI wrote that "Public magistrates have
personal   no direct power over the bodies of their sub-
rights   jects. Therefore, where no crime has taken
place and there is no cause present for grave punishment,
they can never directly harm, or tamper with the integrity
of the body, either for the reasons of eugenics or for any
other reason. St. Thomas teaches (*Sum. Theol.*, II–II, Q.
108, a. 4, ad 2) this when, inquiring whether human judges
for the sake of preventing future evils can inflict punishment, he admits that the power indeed exists as regards
certain other forms of evil, but justly and properly denies
it as regards the maiming of the body. 'No one who is
guiltless may be punished by a human tribunal either by
flogging to death, or mutilation, or by beating.'"

Sterilization   Eugenic sterilization as a method of improving
and feeble-   the race *supposes* that feeble-mindedness is in-
mindedness   herited as a Mendelian unit recessive and that

it can, therefore, be stamped out by sterilizing everybody who shows the symptoms. *This supposition is unscientific.* Dr. Moore insists[1] that "low grade mentality is no more a unit character than low stature, and we could no more eliminate it, by sterilizing a few thousand morons, than we could make all those of the next generation tall by locking up or sterilizing a few thousand short men."

Sterilization and eugenics Dr. E. D. Plass, head of the Department of Obstetrics and Gynecology, University of Iowa, likewise opposes eugenic sterilization *as unscientific.* "Our knowledge of human genetics has not yet reached the point where it can be proved definitely that so-called eugenic sterilization will materially decrease the proportion of inferior individuals in the population . . . Those sterilization laws which are compulsory have generally been little invoked and have proved practically useless."[2]

A mistake In a more ironic vein Dr. J. B. S. Haldane, eminent professor of biology at the University of London, adds his testimony. "I personally regard compulsory sterilization as a piece of crude Americanism like the complete prohibition of alcoholic beverages. But I look to the common sense of the American people to realize that here, as with prohibition, a mistake has been made."[2]

Expediency no absolute guide It may be conceded that in some instances eugenic sterilization might produce some good results. But this does *not* prove it legitimate. *Expediency alone is not a valid criterion of right and wrong.* Eugenic sterilization is fundamentally wrong; so no argument of expediency can justify it. Furthermore, an over-emphasis upon expediency easily can blind people to the justice and love which should characterize their relations with their fellow-man. Dr. Moore states[3] that "the sterilization move-

[1] *Principles of Ethics*, p. 251.
[2] Quoted from *America*, January 16, 1943, "Eugenists in Virginia Betray Science and Democracy," by J. E. Coogan, S.J.
[3] *Principles of Ethics*, p. 251.

ment . . . has been responsible for the neglect of the just and kindly treatment of the mental defective in which alone can be found the true solution of the problem."

Two false basic principles   Ultimately arguments to justify eugenic sterilization rest upon *two principles, pernicious in the extreme and flatly contradictory of personal human rights*. The first false principle is that man has a right to physical love divorced from reproduction in so far as the latter is a natural consequence of intercourse. The second one is that the child is nothing but a citizen and must look to the State as the reason of its existence. Consequently, the State has an absolute right over births.

Intercourse not divorce- able from reproduction   Among human beings, sexual union and the happiness of the partners are intimately bound up with the reproductive and educative functions. For people to enjoy the one while frustrating the other sharply *opposes them to the natural law*, which balances the burdens of begetting and raising children with the satisfactions of physical love. Furthermore, to divorce sex satisfaction from the possibility of fertilization probably will multiply illicit unions, increase immorality and spread venereal disease.

"Free love"   Finally, the separation of sexual gratification from its normal consequences is but one instance of the doctrine of "free love," which denies man's spiritual nature and rests on a thorough-going materialistic basis. As such, "free love" stands utterly opposed to an ethics founded upon the facts that man cannot be identified with brute animals and that his morals cannot be established by appealing to brutish instincts and behavior.

State absolutism   The second false principle underlying the doctrine of eugenic sterilization involves an entire philosophy of the State's autonomy. Followed out to its logical conclusion, it leads to State absolutism of the worst sort. For it supposes that the State has rights over the child prior and superior to the family's.

No mutila-tion of the innocent

The State does have certain rights over its citizens. But they do not include, and most certainly exclude, any rights which would imply that it could mutilate innocent citizens. The citizen does *not* exist because of, or solely for the sake of, the State. On the contrary, the State exists *for the citizen*, to help him in so far as it can to achieve his due perfection. Among his due and proper and rightful perfections are bodily integrity and the faculty of generation. These are his prior to, and independently of, the State. It did not confer them upon him. And as long as he is not proved a criminal by due process of law, the State cannot lawfully deprive him of them.

Burden of defectives worth the price

To refuse the State the right to mutilate innocent citizens may result in a number of defective children being born. But this disadvantage is more than compensated for *in the good it accomplishes of preserving personal and familial rights*. The burden of these unfortunates upon society, if it truly be a burden, is not too high a price to pay for preserving natural and sacred human rights and prerogatives.

Legalized sterilization multiplies abuses

Legalized eugenic sterilization can pave the way for *grave abuses*. An example of this appeared in *Time*.[4] It reported that the Girls' Industrial School of Beloit, Kansas, the students of which were girls under nineteen convicted of minor crimes, had spent $4000 in two years for some 62 sterilizations. Almost one half of the inmates were surgically rendered incapable of having children. In 1917 Kansas legalized sterilization. The law specifically lists idiocy and social disease as the *only* legal causes, requires a thirty-day notice of hearings to interested parties. Since Beloit's entrance requirements are an I.Q. of better than 50 and the absence of venereal disease, and since inadequate notice was some-

[4] Nov. 8, 1937.

times given, all these sterilizations appear illegal. It was charged that the school records showed one girl was sterilized because she had a bad temper, others because they were "incorrigible," "obstreperous," or partial to "fights." A Kansas City *Star* reporter found an eighteen-year-old Beloit student who said, "All of us girls had been threatened before with sterilization unless we behaved ourselves. I knew it wouldn't do any good to kick although I didn't want it done . . . Mother heard . . . after it was over and protested. . . ." The former superintendent during whose tenure of office the sterilizations occurred thought the sterilizations "the finest service to society the Girls' Industrial School has ever contributed."

Sterilization unnecessary If marriages and reproduction by defectives should ever seriously menace society with grave disorders, the State can adequately protect itself by segregating the unfit. In doing this the State indirectly prevents marriages of innocent persons. But this is justifiable on the same grounds as the segregation of idiots and insane and other persons who are a perpetual danger to their fellow-men.

READINGS

B. Cunningham: *The Morality of Organic Transplantation.*
Patrick A. Finney: *Moral Problems in Hospital Practice*, section v. pp. 145-166.
S. A. LaRochelle and C. T. Fink: *Handbook of Medical Ethics*, pp. 131-157.
Charles J. McFadden: *Medical Ethics for Nurses*, chapters xii and xiii.
Thomas V. Moore: *Principles of Ethics*, pp. 250-253.
Halliday Sutherland: *Laws of Life*, ch. viii.

Chapter 20

CRIMINAL'S RIGHT TO LIFE

1. SELF-DEFENSE

Principle stated When a person's rights suffer *unjust* attack, he may defend them—with force, if necessary, even to the extent of wounding or killing the assailant. The assailant is not, it is true, a legally proved criminal. But it is also true that his wanton attack automatically puts him outside the respect ordinarily due him. By his unjust action he forfeits his rights, and the person suffering the attack may use appropriate means to preserve them. However, he is not *obliged* to use force, since force is an extraordinary means and a man is obliged to use only ordinary means. If a man wants to resist unjust attack with violence, he may do so. But, unless there be exceptional circumstances, he is not morally bound to.

Principle defended The morality of self-defense, that is, of the right of a private citizen to wound or take the life of another man in defense of his own rights, is brought out clearly by Thomas Aquinas.[1] Nothing prevents an act from having two effects, of which one is intended while the other is beside the intention. It is the intended act which specifies the morality of the action, not the effect which is beside the intention. Self-defense has the two effects of saving one's own life and wounding or slaying the aggressor. Since the intention is *to save one's own life*, self-defense is lawful, for it is natural for everything to strive to keep itself in existence.

[1] *Summa Theologica*, II–II, V. 64, a. 7.

283

Right inten-   In self-defense a man must have the *right in-*
tion   *tention*. No private citizen can intend the death
of another in self-defense. Only the public authority
acting for the commonwealth can wilfully take human
life. Even the sheriff who executes a condemned criminal
must have in mind the public good. Likewise the soldier
in battle must not be moved by animosity. He must
intend not the satisfaction of a personal grudge or of hate
but the preservation of the common good. Similarly in self-
defense, a man must will not the wounding or slaying of
his assailant but his own safety.

Due order   In exercising the prerogative of self-defense,
        due order must be kept. A private person may not
assume the rights and duties of the State. Under attack his
first thought should be an appeal to the proper authorities.
This is demanded by the common good. And it is only when
such appeal fails or cannot be made that the private citizen
may take the law into his own hands and use force.

Actual unjust   Secondly, for self-defense to be ethical the
attack   *attack must be unjust*. An escaping convict when
fired upon by the police cannot justly kill them to save his
life or to escape. Then again, the attack must be actual—not
just threatened or past. For if past or merely threatened,
it would not be a case of self-defense.

No undue   Finally, *the force used must be in reasonable balance*
violence   *with the threatened damage*. If calling for help
takes care of the situation, that should be done—not killing
or wounding the assailant. If disarming is enough, he should
not be wounded or killed. Wounding and killing are a last
resort. Private persons may kill only if there is no other way
of stopping an attack and the injury threatened is grave
enough to merit such defense.

Irresponsible   A man's right to stop an unjust aggressor holds
aggressor   *whether or not the assailant is responsible* for his
actions. The reason is that natural rights are not the product

of another's voluntary activity. A man has them in virtue of what he is. When they are attacked, he can defend them no matter what the condition of the assailant is. He may be a maniac, a sleepwalker, a man made irrational by alcohol, anger or lust. Even so, he may be stopped by means appropriate to the need.

Just cause for killing unjust aggressor   There must be, of course, a *just proportion* between the threatened injury and the method used to prevent it. For the extreme measure of killing the assailant, there must be a proportionately grave cause. Life itself or some severe injury must be threatened or the possession involved must be very valuable. However, it need not always be money or property. A woman, for example, may wound or even kill an assailant in order to preserve her chastity.

Right of defending others   A question may be raised about a person's obligation to help another defend himself. There is no doubt about his *right* to do so. For if a person can justly defend himself, so can another do it for him or help him do it.

The obligation   But as regards the *obligation* of going to the assistance of another, a distinction appears between duty as based on justice or on love of neighbor. *In justice* a man is bound to do his duty. Thus a policeman must defend the innocent against unjust attack, even at grave danger to his own life. He stands committed to this by his oath of office. In other instances, there may not be an obligation of justice, yet the duty of assistance remains in virtue of *the love* men owe one another. For not only must they respect one another's right to life; they are bound also to help one another keep that life. And so upon their neighbor being attacked unjustly, they are morally bound to lend him assistance—although not to the extent of endangering their own life or suffering some other extreme injury.

2. CAPITAL PUNISHMENT

Definition   *Capital punishment* means the penalty of death, pronounced by a competent tribunal after due process of law and executed by proper authority. Of late years opposition to it has grown strong and bitter. Statistical proof is urged to show that it does not remedy the evils it seeks to cure. In most of these discussions, unfortunately, two aspects of the problem are not kept distinct.

Right and   The first regards the *right* of the State to impose
expediency   the death penalty. The other bears on its *expediency*. In practice, right and expediency should be united. For enlightened legislation implies that it is within the jurisdiction of the law-making body and that it will accomplish its end. Whether or not capital punishment is an efficacious measure of controlling crime and safeguarding the common good is a question which must be answered *in the light of factual evidence*. This must be gathered circumstantially and with due regard for variations of time and place and economic, social, cultural, religious and educational development. The problem here is not to defend or condemn the prudence or expediency of capital punishment in any given instance, but merely to settle the question of the *State's right* to impose it when necessary.

Capital pun-   The State exists to maintain order and to make
ishment is   it possible for citizens to achieve their due
State's right   perfection. As men are bound to preserve health and life, so the State is bound to guarantee security, life, property and peace. But such an obligation implies use of the means necessary to fulfill it. Under certain circumstances one of these means is capital punishment.

Argument   The argument for this severest of all penalties
                  rests on an analogy between *the State and the human body*. Parts are related to the whole as the imperfect to the perfect. They exist naturally for the good of the entire body. Thus if an amputation is indicated because an

organ is diseased or infectious, it is useful and advisable to sacrifice the part for the good of the whole body. Likewise the individual is related to the community as part to the whole. If a man prove dangerous and infectious to the community on account of crime, it is advisable and advantageous to execute him in order to preserve the common good.

An objection   It may be objected that this argument looks upon human beings merely as pawns of the State, that the State may use them or execute them for its own sake. Is it not killing persons to preserve itself? In other words, is not the State using people merely as means to its own end?

Its truth   The objection straddles a truth and a misconception. The *truth* is that no State can use an innocent human being merely as a means to its perfection. Human persons are not just parts or members of society. They do not exist for the sake of society or of the State. Rather society and the State exist for them. A human being is a person, existing for himself, in the sense that he is not just a means to anything else in nature. That is the truth of the objection.

Its misconception   Its *misconception*, however, arises from failing to understand that by crime a man forfeits some of his rights and dignity. He departs from the order of reason. He falls away from the dignity of his manhood, in so far as he is naturally free and exists for himself. Hence, it is evil in itself to kill a man while he preserves his dignity. But it may be good to execute a man who has done evil, even as it is to kill a beast. For a bad man is worse than a beast and is more harmful. This is why the civil authority can withhold natural rights from such a person and treat him as a mere part of society. And *if it proves necessary*, it can execute him, with due process of law, for the sake of the common good.

Imposing Legitimate authority may impose the supreme
capital pun- penalty when it is necessary to preserve the
ishment common good. *When is this necessary?* No general rule seems possible. It will vary with the temperament
and the traditions of the peoples and the needs of different
social units. However, this much is clear. Since capital
punishment is so severe and irreversible, since mistakes are
so easy and treachery possible, capital punishment should
be inflicted only when there is no question of the accused
man's guilt. Secondly, it should be invoked only when it is
clear that no other mode of punishment will serve and when
the supreme penalty can be expected to achieve what less
severe means could not be expected to accomplish in behalf
of the common good.

Right of *Only the State* can inflict death for crime. For
execution the killing of a criminal is lawful only inasmuch as it is directed to the welfare of the whole community. No private citizen or group of citizens can take the
law into their own hands either to try, condemn or execute
a man accused of crime or to execute a criminal after he
has been tried and condemned to death by legitimate
authority (p. 250). The imposition of the death penalty
belongs exclusively to legitimate authority. So does the actual
execution. Some particular person will have to do it. But
he does it in the name and by the authority of the State and
the entire community.

3. MUTILATING CRIMINALS

The right As the State has the right to execute criminals,
so may it inflict mutilation for lesser crimes
(p. 272). In former days this was an ordinary mode of punishment in some countries. But as society becomes more
refined it tends to abrogate cruder forms of punishment.
Today, for the most part, the penalty of mutilation is not
imposed—though the State has the right to invoke it.

Sterilization   Theoretical as mutilation of criminals is, it has a pertinent aspect in the suggestion that *certain sex crimes* be punished with sterilization. Such a proposal has grave implications. They are not answered by merely repeating that, since the State has the right to mutilate criminals, it can sterilize persons of either sex who are found guilty. For such punishment to be lawful it must fulfill the requirement of deterring from crime.

Not lawful   In many instances the penalty of sterilization would be *no deterrent at all*. Not only would it give the criminal his liberty and leave him free to harass society, but it might easily be an added incentive to crime and facilitate the spread of disease. Dr. McFadden is quite right in concluding[2] that "in practice, sterilization is immoral when imposed by the State as a punishment for sex crime. It serves no purpose, whereas there are countless real punishments which the state can inflict. . . ."

READINGS

Thomas Aquinas: *Summa Theologica*, Part II–II, q. 64, aa. 2, 3 and 7.
Michael Cronin: *The Science of Ethics*, ii, 93–103.
Edwin F. Healy: *Moral Guidance*, pp. 156–162; 167–170.
Charles J. McFadden: *Medical Ethics for Nurses*, pp. 248–251 and ch. xiii.
Charles C. Miltner: *The Elements of Ethics*, ch. xviii.

[2] McFadden, Charles J.: *Medical Ethics for Nurses* (Philadelphia, F. A. Davis Co., 1946), pp. 248–250.

Chapter 21

THE RIGHT TO TRUTH

1. TRUTH AND LYING

Language   Man is a social animal, and society is a product of human nature characterized by language. The purpose of language is *communication*. But that language may serve its purpose men must have confidence in one another.

Right to truth   Though not precisely the same as man's right to property, the right to truth is similar in that it is *a natural right*. This follows from the fact that men owe one another whatever is necessary for the welfare of society. Society implies language, and language implies mutual trustworthiness. Without this confidence in one another economic life would stop. All legal procedure would cease. Treaties, contracts and agreements, as well as the simplest statements which go to make up human life, would be valueless and society would disintegrate. Since truthfulness is so essential to society, men have the right and the obligation of preserving it. Both the right and its complementary obligation flow naturally from man's social nature and the necessity of safeguarding whatever society needs for its welfare.

Moral truth and lying   As evil in general is the privation of a due good, lying, which is a form of evil, consists in the *privation of the truth* man's speech should have. The truth here referred to is not the truth of the intellect reflecting reality (logical truth). The truth that lying opposes is the conformity which should exist between a man's speech and what he holds to be true. This is *moral* truth. Thus a man may be quite in error, yet, if his speech reflect his true state of mind, he is not guilty of lying.

Lie defined   A *lie* is a violation of moral truth. It is an *intentional falsification* through speech, writing, gesture or action of any sort, whereby a man expresses himself contrary to his real state of mind. Lies usually deceive or at least are intended to do so. But whether or not the falsification succeeds does not change the character of the lie. Deception in intent or outcome is not the essence of lying.

Lying intrin-   The question whether it is ever lawful to tell
sically evil   a lie must be answered in the *negative. Lying is evil in itself and always evil.* The primary moral criterion is the correspondence of an object with a natural appetite. Any act in which a faculty is used for an end or object which is opposed to its natural end is unnatural and so morally bad. This criterion applied to lying exposes lying as being against the nature of language. For the essence of language is to reveal the mind of the speaker. When men speak falsely they frustrate the natural faculty of speech. They use it not to reflect their thought but, quite oppositely, to falsify it. Such conduct is clearly a deprivation of due truth and is evil.

Contrary to   Another argument to prove the evil of lying
social good   follows from the *need of truthfulness to society,* which exists for man's welfare. Unless language rests firmly in mutual trustworthiness, it will become valueless. All social institutions imply men's ability to communicate with one another. Charge their communications with distrust and suspicion, and these institutions will fail. Law courts will close. All reporting will become a mockery. Business and economic life will sicken. Social intercourse will become hollow pretense. No professional advice will carry weight. No agreement of any sort will have worth, because

it will have no certain meaning. In short, society with its institutions will be paralyzed and nothing but confusion will reign.

Contrary to neighbor's good   Lying is also *against the neighbor's good*. It is true that men do not have a right to every truth. There are secrets which must be kept. Yet the proper object of the human intelligence is truth. This it naturally seeks and to this it has a natural right. Therefore, intentionally to lead it into error by lying is clearly against the due good of the intellect and so is clearly wrong and immoral. Lying is an evil. And to inflict evil upon one's fellow man without justification is wrong.

Contrary to human dignity and the speaker's own good   Under pressure a man may think a lie will help him out of a difficulty. But no matter what benefits lying may produce in the physical or material order, it remains something evil in itself and *opposed to man's true dignity and good*. It often springs from lack of courage, from selfishness, vanity, greed or some other unworthy character weakness. For a man voluntarily to consent to evil is wrong. He exchanges his highest good for something inferior. He wilfully breaks down his integrity. Should he come to be known as a liar, the unenviable reputation will prove a serious handicap. Lies are danger signals which people are quick to read, and the results can gravely interfere with his business or professional success.

2. TRUTH AND THE NURSE

False charting   An important application of truth-telling and its opposite vice of lying to the nursing profession is in the matter of *keeping charts and records*. It is not uncommon to have medicines and other treatments recorded before they actually have been given. One author describes what an examination of the records at midnight disclosed. All the patients slept soundly to seven o'clock in the morning. Six ounces of milk were taken by several at 2:30 and 6:30 A.M. Digitalis was given at 3 A.M. and whiskey to another patient at 5 A.M. Temperature, pulse and respiration were all charted as of 6 A.M.[1]

The obliga-tion   To nurses who falsify records there is no use talking about charts and reports being neat, precise, comprehensive and terse. They must first realize that all reports must be truthful and not the products of imagination. *Intentionally false charting and recording are simply lying and immoral.* Their gravity depends upon the injury which may follow—and for which the nurse will be responsible. It has been said that good-looking charts are commoner than good charts. But no chart can be good unless it is truthful, and no nurse is worthy of her profession who lies in her charting.

false charting

The double standard   Another difficulty about truthfulness which nurses face arises in their *relations with patients*. "There is," writes Charlotte Aikens,[2] "probably no ethical question which seems to a serious-minded nurse more puzzling than the matter of telling the truth. From the beginning of her career she is impressed with the idea that in the eyes of many members of the medical profession, it is an unpardonable sin to lie to a doctor about a patient, but perfectly pardonable, and frequently very desirable, to lie to a patient about his own condition. Thus this 'double standard' as to truth in medical affairs confronts a nurse and adds to the confusion of her own ideas of duty, all along the way."

No double standard   From what has been said about the evil of lying, it should be clear that *no double standard is possible*. If a statement is a lie, it is evil and never permissible whether the person concerned be patient or doctor. This is not to say that under all circumstances patients

[1] Aikens, Charlotte: *Ethics for Nurses*, page 117. And Cf. Gabriel, Sr. John: *Professional Problems*, pp. 92–93.

[2] *Ethics for Nurses*, p. 100.

must be told the truth. It means that they may never be told lies. To say that from time immemorial this sort of lie (for the patient's benefit) has been cited as excusable when dealing with the sick is simply to dismiss the question without settling or even facing it.

Lying never permissible   The notion that patients must not be told the truth seems born of fear that it will set them back. This presumption, however, is *secondary* to the morality itself of lying. The good of the patient must be considered, but it is not the ultimate ethical norm. Lying has been proved evil in itself. It can never be moral, just as murder can never be moral, no matter what good may come of it. Even if a lie could certainly save a life, it would not be permissible.

Not necessary for patient   But is lying so necessary for the patient's welfare? At best it must be admitted that only *in very extraordinary and rare cases* could a life be saved by a lie. There is evidence that the nervous systems of patients and friends on whom the experiment has been tried of telling the truth about their condition when a lie would have been easier have shown an amazing immunity from the depressing effects. Patients critically ill have greater resources than is credited to them. Their condition with its diminished reflexes seems to cushion the shock.

Truth helpful   To know the truth sometimes has a calming influence on patients. The uncertainty, hope, despair, fears of the worst coupled with the desperation of clinging to the last slim possibility, suspicion of attendants and that something is being kept secret, all this generates an unwholesome state of mind. Then again, if a patient should come to know that the nurse or physician lied to him, he will lose confidence in them. On the other hand, correct information may clear the atmosphere. The patient's trust in physician and nurse is bolstered, and he may become more cooperative.

3. SECRECY

Secrecy and the nurse   Men have a right to truth, and all lying is evil. Yet everybody agrees that there are *secrets which must be kept*. Lawyers, clergymen, counselors, doctors and nurses acquire knowledge which they are solemnly bound not to reveal. In line of duty the nurse shares the history of many lives. She must realize that promiscuous truth-telling can lead to *disastrous consequences* for herself as well as for others. Yet it is said that one of the most frequent complaints about the trained nurse is that she does not keep sacred her patient's affairs.

The obliga-tion   Most nurses realize that they should treat information coming to them in a professional way *as an inviolable secret*. The obligation binds in virtue of the nurse's office, even though no explicit promise is asked for or given. It is an implicit agreement between the nurse and her patient, pertaining to justice. Consequently, any *unjust* revelation of a secret is immoral. Its malice will depend on the injury which it may do. For such injury as comes from her willful indiscretion, the nurse is responsible; and she is bound to repair it as far as she can.

Absolute obligation   Of obligations to keep knowledge confidential, there is one that admits of no exception what-soever. It is *absolute* and restricted to the obligation of the priest *to keep the seal of Sacramental Confession*. Without the person's explicit and formally expressed permission no priest can reveal anything told him in confession. No con-sideration of personal safety or profit or the person's own good or the good of society can ever justify his breaking this seal.

Nurse's obli-gation relative to social good   The nurse's obligation of secrecy is not abso-lute, but *relative*. It *admits of exceptions*. In some instances she not only may, but is bound to, reveal confidential information. She must, for example, report births and deaths. Quarantinable diseases have to be made known to the authorities. A criminal fleeing justice has no right to be protected by a physician or a nurse. In such instances the good of society is clearly at stake, and it must be preferred to the private good.

Relative to good of a third party   The nurse's obligation to secrecy is relative also to the *good of a third party*. Dr. Moore[3] gives the example of a nurse who knows her patient has syphilis. She is asked by the father of the man's fiancée whether this is so. "The proper course," advises Dr. Moore, "would be to refer him to the young man's physician; but if for some reason this were impossible she would be justified in bringing about the postponement of the marriage by communicating her knowledge to the father. In fact circumstances may arise where charity to a third party demands that information be proffered in order to spare the third party a greater injury than would arise by the revelation of a secret to the parties so intimately concerned."

Relative to the patient's good   The good of the State and the good of the third party can oblige the nurse to reveal confidential information. The *patient's own good* may force her to do it. If a patient discloses something bearing on his illness in such a way as to influence the diagnosis or treatment, the nurse should inform the physician.

Relative to the nurse's own good   Furthermore, the *nurse's own good* can allow her to reveal professional secrets. The normal nurse-patient relationship does not imply that she must suffer grave injury for the sake of secrecy. On the contrary, she can reveal confidential information to save her reputation or honor or to avoid any other grave damage.

Relative to unconscious patient   The nurse should be loyal especially to the *unconscious or delirious patient*. Suppose he confesses to stealing some money. Is the nurse

[3] *Principles of Ethics*, pp. 99-100.

bound to report this to the police? Certainly not. As Sister Gabriel[4] writes: "A patient who is unconscious is not responsible for what he may say; therefore, the fact that the patient acknowledged that he had stolen money is no certainty that he did so. No trained nurse should think twice about what a patient mutters while in an unconscious state. It should never be discussed; no further reference to what was said should be allowed after it has crossed the patient's lips." She must learn the art of forgetting.

4. EVASION, EQUIVOCATION AND MENTAL RESERVATION

Clash between truth and secrecy   Professional confidences and other secrets must be kept. Lying is never permissible. What is the nurse to do when these obligations *apparently clash?* There may be patients who would certainly be injured by knowing the truth and they should not be told it. Even so, the escape cannot be a lie. It is wrong and unnecessary. For there are *legitimate ways* of avoiding the truth and of preserving secrecy without telling a lie.

Refer to authority; silence   When possible, the simplest procedure is for the nurse to say at once and decisively that she has *no right to make any statement*. She can protect herself behind the rule of many hospitals that nurses are not allowed to give out information about patients. Often enough, however, this is not sufficient to protect the secret. And the same may be said for *silence*. Only rarely will it be helpful.

Evasion   A more practical escape is *evasion*. For example, a patient may ask whether he has cancer. His nurse, who knows he has but who was not present at the operation and has not seen the laboratory report, may truthfully say, "I was not present at the operation. I have not seen the laboratory report. You will have to ask Dr. Smith." She uses some harmless but true state-

[4] *Professional Problems*, p. 81.

ment to turn the question aside. For her to say that she is not permitted to tell is probably worse than blurting out the truth. Even though the patient has nothing seriously wrong, such a reply may suggest the worst.

Equivocation   *Equivocation* is another and ingenious way of avoiding a direct lie. It is a reply with two meanings. The wrong one, it is hoped, will be taken, though the right meaning is possible. The responsibility of choosing is not the speaker's but the hearer's. Thus, to the question, "How is your patient doing?" the nurse may reply, "He is doing as well as can be expected." The person, who had no right to the information, leaves feeling that the patient is in good shape, whereas he actually may be critically ill— though in view of his malady he is no worse than might be expected. A similar example is the comment of a man who was invited to admire the latest painting his friend had done. He looked at the picture and remarked, "How could you do it?"

Mental   *Mental reservation* sometimes can be used to
reservation   save a secret which must be kept. It is a mode
explained   of speaking which leaves something unsaid, some condition or qualification unspecified, but *which, under the circumstances, the hearer can supply*. Whether he actually does so is immaterial. It may be foreseen that he will not be able to make the necessary adjustment. Even so, if the required conditions are fulfilled, the use of mental reservation is lawful.

Examples   Some reporters asked an important foreign diplomat, as he emerged from the White House, what he had discussed with the President. "Oh," he said, "nothing much." Everybody knew the meeting was highly important. His reply simply meant that he had nothing to say for publication. Similarly, a nurse knows her patient has syphilis. Yet to the question of an inquisitive visitor she replies, "I do not know"—meaning that she has no knowledge she has a right to give. Again, a priest on the witness stand may know very well from the accused man's confession that he is guilty. Yet he states that he does not know—meaning he has no knowledge which he is free to use.

Criticism   Some critics condemn the use of mental reservation as being no better than lying and equally destructive of the mutual confidence which language must have if it is to be a valid coin of communication. This criticism *holds* if mental reservation is used in such a way that neither *words* nor *circumstances give a hint to the truth*. The criticism is equally well taken, if mental reservation of any kind is used indiscriminately and without justification.

Conditions   It can be used *lawfully* only when (1) it gives some hint by words or circumstances of the true meaning; (2) there is a grave reason for concealment; and (3) the intention of the speaker is honest—not to deceive but to preserve the secret which he is bound to keep concealed.

Word of   These ways of dodging the truth are *not sub-*
warning   *stitutes* for the truth. It is only when a person is not free to tell the truth, when it is important and right and necessary that the knowledge be kept confidential, that some way must be found for protecting the secret other than the evil expedient of lying. Except when one is *bound by justice or charity* not to speak the truth, there should be no thought of juggling words, of equivocation or mental reservation. The student nurse cannot begin too early to cultivate the habit of telling patients in reply to questions about their condition that she is not permitted to answer such questions, but that she will be glad to refer them to the physician or to the supervisor. If a nurse builds up this attitude, her problems about truthfulness and lying in nursing are not likely to be numerous or grave.

READINGS

Charlotte Aikens: *Studies in Ethics for Nurses,* chapters viii and ix.

Michael Cronin: *The Science of Ethics,* ii, pp. 67–79.

Durant Drake: *Problems of Conduct,* ch. xix.

Edward F. Garesché: *Ethics and the Art of Conduct for Nurses,* pp. 108–111.

Mary E. Gladwin: *Ethics,* pp. 196–200 and ch. x.

Edwin F. Healy: *Moral Guidance,* pp. 242–249.

S. A. LaRochelle and C. T. Fink: *Handbook of Medical Ethics,* pp. 274–295.

Charles J. McFadden: *Medical Ethics for Nurses,* ch. xiv.

Thomas V. Moore: *Principles of Ethics,* chapters vii and ix.

Harold H. Titus: *Ethics for Today,* ch. xvi.

Chapter 22

THE RIGHT TO PROPERTY AND A GOOD NAME

1. NATURAL RIGHT TO PROPERTY AND OPPONENTS

Natural right The right to own property is *a natural right*. It concerns external material goods and belongs to persons as ordinarily understood or to moral or juridical persons, such as corporations.

Opponents It is opposed to Communism and to Socialism, both of which deny it. It is opposed also to any view which attributes the right to own property to be dependent upon some concession of the State. "Who gives the individual or some group within society the right to the exclusive ownership of certain things? Obviously," replies H. H. Titus,[1] "the right is granted by society and may be changed from time to time through changes in custom or in law." Against such doctrines the *natural right* of private ownership must be vindicated.

2. RIGHT TO OWN PROPERTY NATURAL

Incentive to be industrious The right to own property is natural because men need it as an incentive to be as industrious as they should be. In order to have the necessities of life and, above all, to have what is required to *live up to human perfections*, men have to work hard and over long periods of time. Such industry generally will not be displayed unless men can own what they make, use it, save it or invest it— in short, call it their own. Ordinarily, men will not under-

[1] Titus, H. H.: *Ethics for Today* (New York, American Book Co., 1936), p. 355.

take difficult and tiring work unless they can foresee owning the fruit of their labor. Such expectation will not exist unless the right to private property is acknowledged and safeguarded.

Order and peace   The right of private ownership can be shown to be natural also from the fact that man has a natural right *to use external goods for his own welfare*. But in order that this right be exercised orderly and peacefully, everybody must have the right to become a permanent owner of property. Unless this condition prevails disorder and turmoil will envelop society and make man's use of the things he needs extremely difficult or impossible. His needs, it should be noted, are not merely of the present. A man must look into the future, to provide for himself and his family. Those needs, furthermore, are not just of a material sort. Development along educational and cultural lines must be provided for.

Incentive to efficiency   Another reason for holding to the private ownership of property is the fact that men need the prospect of profit and of keeping what they make in order to work out *more efficient ways* of manufacture, of labor and of organization. Private enterprise has brought about most of the inventions which have created the modern world. Yet the spirit of enterprise flourishes only if men have reasonable hopes of profiting from the products of their ingenuity and from the risks and sacrifices they must face. In the natural order human beings are not going to exert themselves unless there is fair promise of reward and they can anticipate having and controlling it.

No substitute found   On a *purely empirical* basis, it can be argued in behalf of the right of private ownership that in the *natural order* no adequate substitute for it has been found. As Dr. J. A. Ryan[2] wrote, "Property in those kinds

[2] Ryan, J. A., and Millar, M. F. X.: *The State and the Church* (New York, The Macmillan Co., 1930), p. 278.

of goods which meet man's immediate wants, such as food, clothing, and shelter, is directly necessary for individual welfare; therefore, the individual has a natural right to acquire them as his own. Property and goods which have a more remote relation to individual needs, such as land, machinery, and the instruments of production generally, is not directly and immediately necessary for the individual; but the *institution* of private property in such goods is essential to human welfare, inasmuch as no other arrangement is adequate."

Human faculties and products Finally the right of private ownership can be shown to be natural on the basis of man's *personal control* of his faculties and powers. They are his to use or abuse. If he chooses to use them, then he should have control of what they produce and what he earns by them. For these reasons, then, private property is man's right by nature. It does not come to him from society or from the State. It is his in virtue of his humanity, as an individual and as a social being, and, as with his right to life, it must be respected.

Objection It may be objected that private ownership of property has caused suffering and tragedy, created violent extremes of wealth and poverty, fomented bitter unrest and turmoil. It has reduced free men to the level of economic slaves. It has changed children into weary old men before they were even youths. It has taken old men and cast them pitilessly upon a gigantic heap of used human labor.

Reply The evils attributed to private ownership of wealth are heralded by the champions of Communism. Multitudes are quick to believe, slow to think, little aware of the consequences of their belief. That these evils have existed is past doubting. But *that they were caused by the private ownership of wealth* is quite another matter, and this is precisely the question at issue. They can be shown to have been due not to private ownership but to man's selfish, unloving, unjust and wicked *misuse* of that ownership. To attribute them to the right itself is like blaming the vice of gluttony upon man's right to eat.

3. RIGHT NOT ABSOLUTE

Right not   Natural and inviolable as the right of private
absolute   ownership is, *it is not absolute*. Even though a
man by nature can acquire and use and bequeath property, yet his possession and use are conditioned by the same natural law which guarantees him the right. Negatively, no man can use his property to hurt his fellow man. On the positive side, he is bound by *love and friendship* to be open-handed, neighborly, generous and ready to lend or give in reason according to need. Both Aquinas and Aristotle insist that though property may be owned and administered by private persons, *the use of it ought to be common.* This does not imply that other people share equal rights with the owner, but that he should be liberal and considerate in using his property to help others in their need.

In justice   By *justice* a man with property is bound to
                     assist others who are in absolute distress. To a
starving man he is bound to give food. And if a major portion of the community is in dire need, even a major portion of his property must be surrendered to lighten the distress.

Private own-   It should be clear from these restrictions that
ership not   the right of private ownership does *not isolate*
antisocial   a man and his wealth from society or from the
common good nor give him absolute control over it. By justice and love men have obligations to use their property for the benefit of society. This aspect of the right of private property should not be overlooked—although it frequently has been.

4. PUBLIC OWNERSHIP

The right of private ownership, it may be noted briefly, does not *exclude public ownership*. The State can own and administer certain properties, real estate of various sorts, transportation and communication facilities, power plants and mines. Nothing said in behalf of private property conflicts in theory with the ownership rights of the State. In practice, the extremely pertinent question arises as to just where private ownership should end and public begin. This is a complex problem which need not be treated here, where the issue is simply the right of individual citizens to acquire and enjoy their own property in peace.

5. VIOLATIONS OF THE RIGHT

Obligation to respect other's property The right of ownership generates a corresponding obligation in others to respect it, to avoid transgressions which would deprive a man of his property or of its use. Some of the more flagrant violations may be considered, with special application to the nursing profession.

Theft The most obvious fault against the neighbor's property is *theft*, whereby a person takes outright the property of another. Actually this sort of immorality is relatively uncommon in the nursing profession— although some authorities report that practically all schools have trouble with students who steal. When a person is guilty of theft he is bound in so far as he can to restore to its full value what has been taken (p. 164).

Borrowing People who would shrink from "stealing" a penny will nevertheless *make loans which they have no intention of repaying*. Borrowing money is not wrong. When appropriate need arises there are dignified and businesslike ways of doing it. First, the need should be serious, and a loan should be the best way of handling it. Then, repayment should be foreseen and planned. To borrow without a plan or intention of repaying or to see clearly that the loan cannot be repaid is stealing, no matter by what name it may be called.

Extravagance   Still other persons who would blush at the suspicion of theft will *live beyond their incomes*, and on the inevitable day of reckoning inform the creditors that they are sorry. There just is no money. Very close to this fault is the practice of installment buying *without any prospects of how the payments are to be met*. As a matter of fact, there may be no intention of meeting them. The article is used as long as its owners can be stalled off. Only then is it surrendered and the process is started all over again with another merchant.

Not paying bills   A legitimately contracted bill binds one to pay. Needlessly to postpone payment, to make no positive effort to solve the problem, eventually to wear out the creditor and sigh with relief when he gives up the fight, is gravely unjust. *Valid debts must be met*. If a person cannot pay, he should inform the creditor and plan to satisfy the debt, no matter how small the amounts by the week or month may be.

Misusing other people's property   Another violation of property rights is to *misuse other people's things*. "Many nurses," Aikens[3] writes, "have the mistaken idea that because the property belongs to the city or to a corporation it makes little or no difference to anyone whether they are careless or extravagant or not in the way they handle supplies in their department. 'Use all you want to, the city pays for it,' or 'we don't have to pay for it' are remarks frequently heard that are indicative of the attitude of some nurses, especially in larger institutions."

In particular   In the hospital, as well as in the patients' homes, care of supplies requires that worn linen and defective appliances should be exchanged for new

[3] *Ethics for Nurses*, p. 141.

articles, not cast aside or destroyed or appropriated. Linen, towels, pillow covers, sheets, should be used as intended and not for dust cloths or ironing board covers. Ice-caps and hot-water bottles should not be put in coverings where pins may damage them. To these abuses of property may be added others: taking ward supplies for one's private use; reading other peoples' letters; using hospital charts and other stationery for personal correspondence; eating things belonging to patients or sampling delicacies furnished by the hospital especially for them.

Gravity None of these faults is likely to be serious in itself. But they evidence lack of high ideals and want of understanding in the nurse. Her own personal shortcomings may not be grave; but when they are multiplied by a large personnel and estimated on an annual basis, the financial loss to the institution can easily run into astonishing figures and perhaps force some curtailment of charity. But serious as these infractions of property rights are, the main objection is that they are unjust, immoral, equivalent to stealing, and make the offender liable to restitution.

Alienating affection and adultery Husbands and wives do not own each other in the sense that they may own a piece of land or a bankbook or an automobile or a house. But in virtue of their marriage vows they have pledged their affection exclusively to each other. Anyone, therefore, who comes between them and wins the affection of husband or wife is stealing his neighbor's property. The action, besides being utterly opposed to the love and neighborliness which should unite men, flatly contradicts the justice which guarantees to each person what is his own. In a real sense, a man and his wife belong to each other in accordance with the rights of marital intercourse. When these are violated, the crime is opposed both to the virtue of purity and to the virtue of justice. It is not merely fornication but adultery. And the guilty are bound to make such satisfaction as circumstances allow.

6. RIGHT TO A GOOD NAME

Value of a good name　　Just as a person has a natural right to life and property and truth, he has a natural right to his *good name*, to his *reputation*. A man's reputation is the good opinion which people have of him. It is a valued and necessary possession, whether it be considered from the man's own point of view or from the more social aspect of his family or the commonweal. A man's right to his reputation demands reasonable respect. Any unjust infringement upon it constitutes moral evil and, since it is in the order of justice, obliges the person to such reparation as can be made.

Absolute right　　When a man's good name rests upon fact, it *can never be assailed justly*. For any attack upon it would be a lie and lying is in itself evil. No good intention, then, nor apparent good coming from such an attack can make it right. In this sense a man's right to his good name is absolute.

Conditioned right　　But a man can have a *good but to some extent undeserved reputation*. He may be guilty of conduct which, if it became known, would discredit his good name. To such a reputation a man's right is not absolute. Rather it is conditioned—by his own higher good, by the good of another person or by the good of the society in which he lives.

Injury to reputation　　Under certain circumstances not only would revelations imperiling his good name be right but even *might be obligatory*. Thus an intern takes advantage of a situation to make improper advances to a nurse. The good reputation he has enjoyed will suffer if she reports his misconduct. Yet she *can and should inform* the proper authorities.

Detraction and calumny   Unjustly taking away another's good name constitutes detraction, which usually is distinguished from calumny. When the injurious and unjust revelation is true, it is *detraction*. When false, it is more exactly *calumny*. To the injustice of detraction calumny adds the malice of lying.

The nurse and detraction   Any *unjust* revelation injurious to another's good name is *detraction*—whether it be the plain detraction of telling the truth or calumny in stating what is false. As Dr. Moore[4] writes, "The nurse, no more than any other person, may make any false statements, but she must be particularly careful how she circulates true statements that may be to the detriment of another. She has no duty to illuminate the public on the relative merits and demerits of physicians." "Physicians, too," Dr. Moore adds, "must also remember that a nurse has a reputation to make and sustain, and they should take as much care of the nurse's reputation as they expect a nurse to take of the physician's good name."

Ethics

Evil consequences   The harmful effects of detraction and calumny cannot be excused on the grounds that the detrimental revelations were not intended, were just a slip of the tongue, that no harm was meant, that what was said was true anyway. Such considerations may diminish culpability but they generally do not lessen the evil consequences. A *thoughtless criticism of a person can be just as damaging as a deliberate calumny*. This is why nurses should cultivate great discreetness of speech.

Need of reticence   "A large part of the training," writes Charlotte Aikens,[5] "for which a nurse must be responsible in herself is the training of her tongue, the cultivation in herself of habits of reticence, habits of refraining from discussing the affairs of patients with people who have no

[4] *Principles of Ethics*, pp. 94–95.
[5] *Ethics for Nurses*, p. 114.

right to be told anything about them, of refraining from discussing with patients matters with which they have no concern and which she often does not fully understand. Endless trouble, untold hours of agony have been caused by the thoughtless habit of some nurse talking with patients about things of which she herself has little real knowledge."

Rash judg-   Detraction and calumny lower the victim's
ment   reputation in the mind of others. *Rash judg-*
ment is a person's own quick, unreasoned assent in his own mind to the faults of another. Thus a nurse misses her watch and at once judges the maid to be the thief. Later she finds it where she herself had put it for safe keeping. Such conduct, even though it never finds expression in words, is morally wrong. It violates the right which persons have for other people to think well of them.

The nurse and   Because of her position of trust with physicians
rash judgment   and surgeons and patients, the nurse must be *extremely cautious* in her judgments, expressed or not expressed. If she is to safeguard the good name of her associates in speech she must first guard her mind in forming opinions about them. This is why she must avoid all rash judgments. It does not imply that she must be blind to reality or refuse to appraise the character and work of those about her. It means that such appraisals must be based on evidence and be approached with justice and charity.

Thoughtless   There is usually among nurses a high regard
speech   for honesty and a wholesome eagerness to avoid major faults. Yet among them as well as among people generally there is all too little consideration given to the harm and bitterness and sorrow and ill-will which thoughtless speech can and does cause.

READINGS

Charlotte Aikens: *Studies in Ethics for Nurses*, ch. xi.
Michael Cronin: *The Science of Ethics*, ii, chapters iv to viii.

Mary E. Gladwin: *Ethics*, p. 190.
Edwin F. Healy: *Moral Guidance*, pp. 215–230; 249–256.
William J. McDonald: *The Social Value of Property According to St. Thomas Aquinas*.
Thomas V. Moore: *Principles of Ethics*, ch. xi.
Harold H. Titus: *Ethics for Today*, ch. xxii.

Chapter 23

CONTRACTUAL RIGHTS BETWEEN NURSE AND PATIENT

1. CONTRACTS IN GENERAL

Introductory　Many of the problems which occur in the nursing profession involve natural rights and obligations, such as the right to life and property and truth and reputation. Other problems pertain to obligations which have a *contractual character* and arise between the nurse on the one hand and the patient or physician or hospital on the other.

Contract defined　A *contract* in general is an agreement between two or more persons, binding one or all in justice to some specific obligation. For a contract to be valid the agreement must be *mutual* and entered into with *knowledge* and *freedom* and be *willed* by the contracting parties. They must have the *intention* of binding themselves and *show* it in some way.

Kinds of contracts　Of the many kinds of contracts, three deserve mention here. On the basis of their *effects*, contracts are bilateral or unilateral. The bilateral contract obligates both parties in justice, whereas the unilateral obligates only one side.

Explicit or implicit　If the *manner of consent* is considered, contracts are express, or explicit, and tacit, or implicit. A contract is *explicit* when the parties give their consent formally by written or spoken word. It is *tacit*, or implicit, when the contractual obligation is assumed in virtue of accepting an office which carries the obligation with it.

Finally, a contract may be called conditioned or absolute according as it *does or does not carry certain qualifications*.

Justice and charity   Not every aspect of the problems arising between the nurse and the patient or between her and the physician or the hospital bears *solely* upon justice measured in contractual terms. Most of the problems to be considered are too complex for that. They involve, many of them, natural obligations of justice which the contractual aspect merely accentuates. But over and above justice is charity. The obligations of justice must not be considered so exclusively that the duty of loving one's neighbor and doing good to him is forgotten or neglected.

2. CONTRACT WITH THE PATIENT

The nurse's contract   When a nurse undertakes the care of a patient ordinarily she is not asked to sign a formal agreement. By the fact she is a nurse and freely accepts a case she assumes the obligations of an *implicit, bilateral* and *conditioned contract*. Her agrement is *implicit*, since the obligations result not from an oral or written consent but in virtue of the act itself of accepting the office. For this reason the contract is sometimes referred to as a quasi-contract. It is *bilateral* since the nurse on the one hand and the patient, or those acting for him, on the other confer upon each other certain rights and duties: the nurse to fulfill her office with reasonable competence and the other parties to give her just compensation. And it is *conditioned* in the sense that the nurse's obligation regards the skill and diligence which can be expected in the light of what the known mental and physical conditions of the patient reasonably require.

Legal decisions   Doctor Moore cites several legal decisions defining the nature of the nurse's contract with the patient. The Supreme Court of Illinois stated that:[1]

[1] *Principles of Ethics*, p. 121, Dr. Moore's source is Oswald v. Nehls et al. 84 N.E. 622.

"The agreement 'to nurse' an adult person necessarily conveys the idea that the object of the care is sick or is an invalid. It means more than mere watchfulness. It means such care of the person and attention to the surroundings as will conduce to the comfort and hasten the recovery of the patient. The practice of medicine, . . . necessarily requires a knowledge of all those things a professional nurse is supposed to know. It embraces much more. It includes the application of knowledge of medicine, of disease, and the loss of health."

The District Court of Appeals, Second District California, spoke in a similar vein of the nurse's duty—

"The duty of a nurse, and assuming that a nurse must only exercise the ordinary care which a trained and skilled nurse would be required to use, is a continuous duty . . . . The powers of resistance, the condition of the patient, must of necessity have much to do with the application of remedies, either by a physician or a nurse, and all this duty could only be observed by a constant and unremitting care and attention, which is just as obligatory upon the nurse as is the duty of applying the remedy directed by the physician in charge."[2]

Patient's importance   The decision of a civil court is not necessary to bring home the fact that the nurse's *first allegiance is to the patient*. The nurse has duties to the hospital and to the physician; but of the three, the patient comes first. He is the reason for the hospital's existence as well as for the physician's profession. The patient, Charlotte Aikens[3] writes, is the most important person in the entire hospital. "He is the reason for its existence. His welfare and his comfort are and should always be given first consideration . . . throughout a nurse's whole career, the patient's welfare while she is in charge should never be placed in the background of her thought or plans." This obligation flows from the tacit contract which the nurse makes in accepting a case. She agrees to render such service

[2] *Principles of Ethics*, p. 122. The source is Williams v. Pomona Valley Hospital Ass'n. 131 Pac. 888–890.

[3] *Ethics for Nurses*, p. 43.

as reasonably can be expected. This includes giving the patient all the attention and skill which he has a right to expect of the professional nurse.

Patient's feelings   For a nurse to appreciate the feelings of a patient, occasionally she should be a patient herself. But even then she might miss the shock, which many patients suffer, from being transplanted from their normal world into the abnormal sphere of hospital or sick room. For many persons it is intensely painful. The very prospect of hospitalization is upsetting. Their imagination is fired with the thought that the hospital is the place of last resource. They may be tortured with anxiety about their family or children or home conditions. The drain upon savings, the prospects of debt, loss of position or time or wages or property are additional worries. The nurse must have the *imagination and sympathy to share this burden with the patient, if she is to give the care which her contract implies.* She must think of the patient not as a case but as a human being—not isolated but in a tangled array of human relations.

Patient's safety— ordinary circumstances   Ordinary nursing care obliges the nurse on duty to exercise *unremitting and enlightened attention.* It means safeguarding the patient from accidents: from hot water bottles, heating pads, light bulbs, falls or any other injury which reasonably can be foreseen and provided against. Failure on this score constitutes negligence and may make the nurse or the hospital or even the physician liable to suit. If the patient suffers injury from the nurse's gross negligence or culpable ignorance, she is responsible and bound to repair the injury in so far as she can.

Patient's safety— unusual circumstances   Granted that the contract demands ordinary nursing care, the question may be asked what obligation has the nurse under *unusual circumstances.* Fire breaks out in a hospital. *Must* the nurse sacrifice her life for the patient? Or consider the situation of a nurse whose patient, unknown to her, is a gangster. *Must* she defend him against his enemies at grave personal risk? The question is not whether she *may* do so. For she may if she wants to. But is she *obliged* under the circumstances and in justice to endanger her life for the patient?

Ordinary   The answer is no. Unless there be some special
nursing care   and explicit agreement to the contrary, *the nurse is bound only to give ordinary nursing care*. This does not involve the obligation of heroic self-sacrifice. On the other hand, if a nurse should discover after accepting a case that the patient has a dangerous disease, she must stay. Such a threat to her life is a strictly professional hazard. In becoming a nurse she accepted it and when it occurs she justly cannot refuse to face it.

Leaving a   The same must be said about the obligation
patient   of a nurse to stay on a disagreeable case—at least until she can go without injury to the patient. Among the reasons which might make her want to leave may be noted objections on the score of morality, extra work and incompatibility. The nurse may object to being in a family where the people are leading evil lives. Or she may find her patient has undergone an illegal operation. Even so, she *cannot leave as long as her departure might hurt the patient*. Extra work becomes a cause of difficulty, for instance, when the patient's servant leaves. If another cannot be found, the nurse must manage as best she can.

Incompati-   Incompatibility may develop between the
bility   nurse and the patient or between her and the patient's family or relatives. The situation is trying as well as challenging. For the nurse must be able to cope not only with the ideal patient and family but with unreasonable and interfering people as well. Indeed the crotchety type will prove her mettle more fully than congenial people. To

admit she cannot get along with disagreeable persons is to confess failure in an important attribute of successful nursing. No matter how painful the situation, a nurse cannot leave until a substitution is made with all due regard for the patient. The principle is simply that *the good of the patient comes first*, which principle the nurse accepts in virtue of her profession and tacit contract.

Respect for patient's property   Justice demands that personal property be treated with due respect (p. 305). This applies especially to the nurse's *handling of the patient's belongings*. Carelessness and waste and damage may not be out and out theft, but they are violations of property rights. Women patients complain of the nurse's free use of their expensive soaps and powders and perfumes and handkerchiefs. They resent the assumed joint ownership of their flowers and fruits and candies and other delicacies. Their objections spring validly from the virtue of justice, which is likewise the basis of the nurse's obligation to avoid these faults.

Respect for patient's affairs   By her special relations with the patient the nurse is bound *to respect his private affairs* (p. 295). They should not be discussed with other patients or nurses, with one's friends or family, not with anybody except in so far as duty makes it necessary. Likewise, and in virtue of justice, the nurse should refrain from reading the charts of other patients. She has no right whatsoever to them. The same must be said regarding patients' letters. They should be read only at the patient's explicit request and treated with the utmost propriety.

Patient's religion in general   The nurse's obligation to her patient as regards *his religion* is as delicate as it is solemn. Her office is specifically to lead the patient back to health. Yet religion often plays, and indeed should play, an important rôle in the patient's life, in his recovery, and, if this is hopeless, in his attitude towards death. On this score and in virtue of her office, the nurse must be prepared to help her patient.

Tolerance   She need not accept or admire or respect or be tolerant of the patient's religious *views*. But she is bound to respect and show tolerance for the *patient*— for his honesty and integrity. No one who admits that truth exists can accept the current attitude that any religion is as true as another. If one man says that Christ is God and another says that Christ is not God, they both cannot be right. But granting diversity of religious belief and the Catholic position which holds the Catholic Church to be the one and only true Church established by Christ, Catholic nurses, as well as non-Catholic nurses, can do all that justice and charity require for their patients—no matter what their religion may be.

Catholic   If the patient is a Catholic and dangerously
patient in   ill, the nurse should see that a priest is sum-
particular   moned. The patient's hair should be combed, face washed, mouth rinsed out. Bed and room should be tidied. If the sacrament of the Last Anointing is to be given, the nurse should sponge the patient's eyes, ears, nostrils, mouth, hands and feet. For the patient's confession, a chair should be placed beside the bed and the patient raised to a comfortable position. The nurse should withdraw and prevent any intrusion while the priest hears the patient's confession and gives spiritual consolation. When the priest brings Holy Communion a table should be prepared, covered with a clean white cloth and provided with a candlestick and wax candles, crucifix, two small glasses, one with holy water in it and the other with plain water, and a tablespoon. During the ceremony all should kneel and keep a respectful silence.

Non-Catholic If the patient is a non-Catholic, the nurse,
patient   Catholic or non-Catholic, should be courteous and respectful and ready to bring the clergyman anything

he might need. The only limitation upon the Catholic nurse is that she should not actually and formally participate in a non-Catholic religious service. On this score difficulties are not likely to arise.

Calling a non-Catholic clergyman A problem sometimes does confront the Catholic nurse with a non-Catholic patient when she is asked to summon a non-Catholic clergyman. By the laws of her Church she cannot call a minister or a rabbi for the *explicit purpose* of having him attend the members of his Church. This does not mean, however, that the non-Catholic patient must be deprived of the consolations of his own religion. On the contrary, the problem is easily solved. The Catholic nurse, although she herself cannot call in the non-Catholic clergyman, can have the patient request some relative or friend or another nurse to do it.

Assisting the dying In practice there is no need for any bitterness or ill-will. Rather here is an opportunity for the exercise of truly Christian charity. A most effective means for accomplishing this is an admirable movement founded by Monsignor Markham. It is called *The Apostolate to Assist Dying Non-Catholics*.[4] Every nurse should be acquainted with *The Apostolate* and the publications it provides to help her in preparing souls to meet God.

Baptizing As the nurse should know what to do in the conferring of the last rites, so she should be prepared when the need of emergency baptism arises. It often happens that unless the nurse does the baptizing the person is likely to die unbaptized. In view of this situation the nurse should be aware of her duty, should know how to administer emergency baptism and, finally, should be able to judge whether or not under the circumstances she

[4] Information about the Apostolate may be secured from Msgr. Raphael Markham, Compton Road, Hartwell, Cincinnati 15, Ohio.

should. Good intentions do not justify indiscriminate baptizing. There are generally many aspects to consider and they must all be weighed with prudence and intelligence. This applies to all nurses, no matter what their own religious beliefs. For in view of their office, they rightly can be expected to have the necessary knowledge about baptism and know how to use it.[5]

Patient's gratitude and gifts The contract between patient and nurse calls for ordinary nursing service in consideration for a stipulated salary. This the nurse has a right to expect. But she should expect nothing beyond it. Most patients upon recovery feel they have paid the debt in full when they meet the bill. Occasionally they may show their appreciation by some extra gift. A nurse's acceptance is no crime against justice or charity. Yet it can be very imprudent, undignified and injurious to the nursing profession.

Gifts of money There is no problem about inexpensive little gifts. Difficulties arise when the gift is money given in recognition of service or of what perhaps was considered extra service. To accept money under these circumstances is *rightly forbidden by all reputable schools*. It can easily lead to lowered standards of nursing. For what constitutes "extra service"? Every patient, no matter what his financial standing, is entitled to the best service the nurse can give while she is on duty. There is no place for a sliding scale between service rendered and expected extra pay. Money gifts come close to conventional "tipping," which hardly can be harmonized with the dignity of a professional woman. No nurse will call attention to her devotedness or seek recognition in the hope of reward. When it is offered,

[5] For more detailed information on this problem see the author's booklet, *Emergency Baptism* (Milwaukee, Bruce Publishing Company, 1945) and McFadden, C. J.: *Medical Ethics for Nurses* (Philadelphia, F. A. Davis Co., 1946), pp. 195–213.

she must not wound the person's feelings. Yet she must with all courtesy and firmness explain that her salary covers all obligations.

Nurse and male patients Ordinarily men patients do not offer any special problem of nursing technique. There may occasionally arise some embarrassment, but it will quickly pass if the nurse is the right type. Everything necessary for the relief and comfort of a male patient can be done by the clean-minded nurse. It is the suggestion of vulgarity, of misplaced humor, of coarse familiarity which is disgusting. If a male patient proves objectionable, the nurse can easily and with no show of temper give warning that she will not tolerate such conduct. The man will know how serious she is. Success under such circumstances depends upon the nurse's own virtue and ideals.

Catheterizing male patient The situation of a nurse's having to catheterize a male patient is almost too exceptional to deserve mention. The extreme exception occurs when the patient is in severe distress and no physician or male nurse or intern can be had. Under such circumstances the dignity of the nurse does not suffer. It is her duty to relieve pain. However, for her own sake and if the patient does not object, another woman should be present.

Emotional problems The actual problems which arise between the nurse and the male patient are rather *emotional than technical*. In many ways a sick man is at the mercy of the nurse. Physically he is weak or perhaps even helpless. He is likely to be confused, unstable and slightly afraid, with deep capacities for being comforted and mothered. There is the nurse in spotless uniform and cap, poised, confident, well groomed and attractive. It is not astonishing that some patients come to depend upon their nurse and begin to think themselves in love with her.

Nurse-patient romance The entire situation encourages intimacies and makes it easy for the nurse to be too friendly.

The close association of the sickroom, from which the women nearest and dearest to the patient are excluded, has on more than one occasion broken up families. With good reason wives and sweethearts fear the influence of the nurse. But for exactly the same good reasons the nurse *should be aware of the dangers and be faithful to her office in justice and charity.*

Married man If the patient is married or betrothed, the nurse's position and responsibility are perfectly clear. *In strictest justice*, she is bound to respect the rights of the man's wife or fiancée. The husband who thinks his wife does not understand and appreciate him is not uncommon. Without perhaps being aware of it he may give the nurse an affection which he is not free to give and which she cannot accept without being guilty of grave injustice. She would blush at the thought of stealing another woman's purse or jewelry. To steal a married or affianced man's love is infinitely worse.

Practical conclusion Consequently *the nurse should be on her guard*. It is easy to forestall difficulty by checking advances which lead to familiarity. The grave violations of justice and charity and purity which they may entail should dissuade the nurse from allowing herself to become emotionally involved. Moreover she should realize the situation has other dangers. Most often the man's affection is superficial, springing from the peculiar circumstances of the sickroom. The husband, writes Charlotte Aikens,[6] "who hints about marriage and asks the nurse to wait until he secures a divorce, is a problem far too common in this modern world. The nurse who is tempted to become a 'home-breaker' by encouraging these suggestions should hesitate a long time. The whole situation spells danger for her and is a severe test of character. It is a time when she

[6] *Ethics for Nurses*, pp. 127–128.

should seek wise advice from some experienced disinterested person."

Patient's
husband
A similar situation arises occasionally from the attentions of a patient's husband. The nurse's obligation to avoid the man's advances springs from strict justice. Sister John Gabriel speaks with great practical wisdom when she writes[7] that: "A nurse placed in such a position should be on constant guard in order to give no encouragement to such a man's attentions; her dignity and her reticence in his presence will convey her message to him. If it is absolutely necessary that she dine with him, no time should be wasted in frivolous conversation. The nurse should give out the impression that her mind is entirely occupied with her patient, and that it is imperative for her to hasten with her meal and return to the bedside as soon as possible. Should an opportunity present itself, without interfering with the regular order of the house, for the nurse to take her meal before the husband comes in, she should take advantage of it and do so. Every possible means should be used to avoid any advances on the part of this man and to make him feel that a nurse is not the type of woman he evidently thinks her to be."

Unmarried
male patient
Even if the man is free to bestow his affections and the nurse can honorably return them, yet *the patient-nurse romance should be considered warily*. First of all the man may be a philanderer out for conquest, and at his pleasure will leave his victim to suffer and be sorry. Again, the attachment may not be love at all. It easily can be due to the unnatural environment of the sick room. Perhaps he is utterly sincere, but simply does not understand what is happening to him. It is the nurse's duty to grasp the situation and prevent a hasty engagement.

Caution
If the attachment is real, the engagement can tolerate postponement. Let both parties wait. Give the man a chance to leave the sick room and return

[7] *Professional Problems*, pp. 91–92.

to his normal life and to his usual activities and friends. A romance proved in this way has some chance of enduring. On the other hand taking advantage of a sick man holds little promise of happiness. A patient who finds his nurse attractive may recover more quickly. But for the student nurse a serious love affair is for the most part unfortunate. It obtrudes into her thinking, interferes with her work, narrows her interests, gives an emotional outlook to all her reactions—in short creates an obstacle to her nursing career. For graduate as well as for student nurses, a hasty engagement harbors little except misery. If the nurse has her heart set on marital unhappiness, a thoughtless nurse-patient romance is one of the best ways to achieve it.

Male patient in hotel Finally there is the problem of the nurse attending a male patient in a hotel. Unless the man's wife or some other woman member of the family can be present, the nurse should do all she can to have the patient removed to a hospital. *This failing and if the patient is very ill, she should stay until her professional services can be dispensed with.* The situation is dangerous. It can attract severe criticism upon the nurse and the nursing profession. In the instance of a critically ill man, she has the right and obligation to risk this criticism in virtue of her professional loyalty to the sick. The great need of the patient warrants her acceptance of such a case and justifies the risk. But when the need passes, her obligation also ceases and she is bound to leave as soon as she can.

READINGS

Charlotte Aikens: *Studies in Ethics for Nurses*, pp. 40–46, ch. xvi, pp. 307–310.

Michael Cronin: *The Science of Ethics*, ii, 298–353.

Joseph B. McAllister: *Emergency Baptism*.

Charles J. McFadden: *Medical Ethics for Nurses*, chapters xi and xv.

Thomas V. Moore: *Principles of Ethics*, pp. 120–125.

Chapter 24

CONTRACTUAL RIGHTS—NURSE, PHYSICIAN AND HOSPITAL

1. CONTRACT BETWEEN NURSE AND PHYSICIAN

Whether the hospital or the patient or the physician employs the nurse, she works *under the instructions of the physician*. If the physician himself engages her, the situation is clear. He expects her, and she agrees, to render the nursing care he prescribes. If the hospital or the patient or someone acting in his name employs her, the understanding is the same. She is there to collaborate with, and be subordinate to, the physician in charge. In accepting the position, the nurse makes at least an implicit contract to carry out the orders of the physician in charge.

2. EFFECTS

Loyalty *The nurse's first duty is loyalty.* There may be some physicians who do not deserve it and who dishonor their profession. But they are exceptions. The vast majority are devoted and able men. This should be the presumption until the opposite in a given instance is proved. In virtue of her profession as well as of her implicit contract, she owes him not only efficient care of the patient but also such evidences of loyalty as will strengthen the patient's confidence in him. For the patient's welfare is directly concerned. The ". . . confidence of the patient in his physician," writes Charlotte Aikens,[1] "is one of the important elements in the management of his illness, and

[1] *Ethics for Nurses*, p. 47.

nothing should be said or done that would weaken this faith or create doubts as to the character or ability or methods of the physician on whom he is depending." *Ordinarily* the nurse should carry out the physician's orders without dispute or argument. And she should avoid adverse criticism. Its basis may be her own inexperience and not the physician's ineptitude.

No diag-
nosing
The nurse's office is *to assist* the physician. It is his responsibility to diagnose disease and prescribe drugs and treatments. Yet too often nurses encourage patients in interpreting symptoms. Sometimes this is done innocently, the nurse merely agreeing or disagreeing with the patient's guesses. But this is just the situation which the nurse should avoid. By agreeing with the patient she makes his diagnosis her own. Aside from the harm which this may do the patient and the discord it may occasion between him and his physician, it is simply outside the rights of the nurse.

No prescrib-
ing medicine
Likewise the nurse *should not prescribe* for her patient. Legally this right belongs exclusively to the physician. For the nurse to dispense medicine without explicit orders from the physician is entirely outside her duties. The same may be said for any general or blanket orders or a physician's telling a nurse to use her own judgment. She has no legal right, no moral justification and on the contrary every duty of refusing cooperation in any such procedure. However, a physician may have "standing orders" written in a book kept for that purpose and the nurse, of course, may follow such instructions.

No changing
of physician's
order
A slightly different question concerns the nurse's changing the physician's order. For instance, instead of the sodium amytal ordered, the supervisor decides that one-half grain of codeine would be better. She tells the nurse to make the substitution and chart the sodium amytal as given. Such a procedure is not

only disloyalty to the physician; it amounts to the nurse's prescribing medicine for the patient, which is illegal and renders the nurse liable. It involves the lie of false charting. It reveals gross lack of judgment in the supervisor and a mistaken sense of obedience in the nurse who makes the substitution. If the nurse thought that the amytal was inappropriate, she should have brought it to the physician's notice. If he insisted upon it, she should have carried out his orders.

No discontinuing treatment   A similar problem concerns the nurse discontinuing a prescribed treatment. She thinks the patient is dying and that it is useless or perhaps even cruel to inflict him with further discomfort. Under certain conditions this might seem sensible. But, unless the nurse consults the physician and receives his approval, to discontinue it on her own initiative is equivalent to usurping his office. She has neither the duty nor the right to diagnosis. For that the physician is responsible by civil as well as moral law. Consequently it is the nurse's duty to continue the treatment according to instructions. If she is doubtful about it, let her appeal to the physician. Any other procedure violates the relations which in virtue of her contract the nurse has with the physician.

3. NURSE AND MALPRACTICING PHYSICIAN

A more delicate problem arises when the physician in charge is clearly guilty of malpractice. Even though the nurse's first duty is to the patient, she must consider several aspects of the situation. Her first impulse may be to leave the case. But before obeying it she should reflect that a patient in the hands of a dishonest or inept practitioner needs her services even more than the patient under competent medical care. When she is sure of her ground, that her judgment of the physician is certainly correct, she can suggest discreetly to the family the advisability of bringing in a consultant. With care she can do this without making definite charges against the attending physician. If she is young and inexperienced, her first thought should be to seek the advice of a capable and experienced nurse.

4. NURSE AND PHYSICIAN'S MISTAKE

The general rule for the nurse regarding physician's orders is that she should obey them unless she fears they may be injurious. Her first duty is to the patient, who expects her to know whether the physician has made a serious mistake. Consequently, there arises the nurse's responsibility when she thinks a grave error has been made. The principle involved is that *it is wrong to endanger another person's life unjustly.* In this instance the patient's welfare depends upon the nurse's choice, so she cannot act in doubt or follow merely a probably safe course. She must refrain from administering the drug or medicine until she has solved her doubt. She may refer the question to the supervisor, or, if this cannot be done, she should mention it to the physician. In the event he holds to an order which she thinks will cost the patient's life, she is bound by civil as well as the moral law to refuse her cooperation.

5. THE NURSE AND THE HOSPITAL

The contract When the student enters a nursing school or a nurse joins a hospital staff she assumes obligations with the institution arising from a contract which is at least implicit. In some instances it may be explicit and formal. Usually it is not. Still the contractual element is there, just as it is between the nurse and the patient and between her and the physician.

Loyalty One of the most elementary obligations of the nurse's contractual relations with the hospital is *loyalty.* For a hospital to function well, it must have the confidence of the medical staff as well as of the patients. This confidence is built up by the nurses.

In particular More specifically loyalty means that nurses will be careful in criticizing one another and the institution. This does not imply that they must close their eyes to personal and institutional deficiencies. But it does obligate them *to voice their criticism only where it will do good*. Loyalty means that the nurse will defend her institution, keep inviolate information she may have about it or people associated with it or its patients or its affairs. She will safeguard its good name by her conduct both on and off duty. In many ways she cannot divorce herself from it. Criticism of her easily turns into condemnation of her hospital.

Keeping rules Persons join a hospital staff of their own free will. If they are unwilling to assume the obligations which the institution lays upon them, they should not seek admission. Their presence gives evidence to their tacit acceptance of the regulations. If they find the rules unreasonable or for some reason prefer not to obey them, they should leave. The institution rightly expects obedience from members of its staff. It existed before they came; it will continue to exist when they leave. If the rules are obsolete or ineffective or useless or needlessly annoying, *the problem should be taken up with the authorities*. It is indefensible for a person wantonly to disregard regulations which by entering, and being part of, an institution she agrees to accept and to obey.

Respecting property The virtue of justice requires due respect for other people's property. This obligation is emphasized by the nurse's contract with the hospital. It has every right to expect the nurse *to be considerate of its property*. This implies that she will not appropriate or waste or destroy or use it extravagantly. If an accident occurs resulting in damage, she should report it at once, so that the loss may be minimized. Sometimes this will require courage, but the nurse's fortitude and convictions about justice should hold her to duty. By the very nature of her work she is entrusted with equipment and other valuables. She must be aware of her trust and live up to it. It is a matter of strict justice. Wilful violations impose the obligation of restitution.

A special   Inasmuch as radium is so precious the nurse's
problem   responsibility for it deserves a special word. A material so valuable deserves extraordinary care. Her agreement with the hospital implies ordinary rights and duties. Consequently the nurse should not be made responsible for radium. There should be explicit rules governing its use and providing for its safe-keeping. When radium is lost it is often because responsibility for its safety was not definitely fixed.

Leaving a   The duration of a nurse's employment is de-
position   termined by her contract. But even when there is no formal agreement, there may be an implicit understanding. In either instance this must be lived up to as a contractual obligation binding in justice. At the expiration of the time tacitly or explicitly agreed upon the nurse may accept another position. But until then, she is not free.

No agree-   If there is no agreement, tacit or otherwise,
ment   and if the nurse wishes to change her position, she must give due notice. Thirty days is considered adequate. Should she consent to stay beyond that time she should adhere to her agreement.

Agreements   Fidelity to such arrangements is extremely
must be ful-   important from the point of view of moral
filled   integrity. Failure to fulfil one's agreements is both unjust and immoral. There is also a practical consideration. For the new position the nurse will need a reference from her last employer. It is not likely to be one she can be proud of if she unreasonably embarrasses the institution from which she will have to obtain the required recommendation.

READINGS

Charlotte Aikens: *Studies in Ethics for Nurses*, pp. 46–47, 114, 166–167, 303–306.

Sr. John Gabriel: *Professional Problems*, pp. 81–82, 88, 141, 154, 172, 178–179, 189.

Edward F. Garesché: *Ethics and the Art of Conduct for Nurses*, pp. 285–286; ch. xxii, Part II.

Thomas V. Moore: *Principles of Ethics*, pp. 125–133.

Chapter 25

LOVE OF NEIGHBOR

1. IN GENERAL

Men need   In addition to obligations of justice men must
one another   recognize other duties. By nature they are
social beings, set to seek their perfections not merely as
individual persons but as persons living in society (p. 33).
This begets *the need and duty* of people to help one another to
attain that perfection and happiness to which they are
destined as individuals and as social beings.

Obligations   The obligations of charity sometimes are not
of charity   as clearly defined as those of justice. Yet they
are none the less *real and important and binding*. Everyone is
obligated by the law of fraternal love to will everything
that is for his neighbor's true welfare. This duty flows from
the very nature of man and of society and of men's responsibilities towards one another. Love of neighbor, thinking of
him kindly, speaking and conducting oneself towards him
kindly are not obligations limited to the nursing profession.
But the nursing profession offers unique opportunities for
their practice.[1]

[1] The importance of brotherly love in the Christian view of
life is exemplified in St. John's insistence upon it: "Dearly beloved, let us love one another: for charity is of God. And every one
that loveth is born of God and knoweth God. He that loveth not,
knoweth not God: for God is charity. . . . If we love one another,
God abideth in us: and His charity is perfected in us . . . God is
charity: and he that abideth in charity, abideth in God, and God
in him . . . If any man say: I love God, and hateth his brother: he
is a liar. For he that loveth not his brother, whom he seeth, how
can he love God, whom he seeth not? And this commandment we
have from God, that he, who loveth God, love also his brother."
First Epistle, iv, 7, 8, 12, 16, 20–21.

Charity to-wards all   By profession the nurse is associated in life's most dramatic moments, in its beginnings and its endings. She shares in the tragedies, joys and sorrows, hopes and despairs which like a chain join birth to death. Such association should widen and deepen her view of life and *incline her to be kindly disposed towards her patients and associates*. For the most part she has to take them as they come. This means that she must rise above all prejudice—whether it be racial or national or social or religious. She must see all human beings as members of the human family, with the same destiny as herself and perhaps even greater need for kindness and love. Her attitude cannot be negative. She positively must strive, because of the challenges of her work and environment, to play no favorites and to harbor no antipathies.

Causes of narrowness   In spite of what would appear ideal conditions for the nurse to cultivate a kindly heart, a broad and tolerant disposition towards human beings, *the reverse all too frequently occurs*. Close association with people over a period of time can distort one's point of view. Judgments and attitudes become unbalanced and acrimonious. Concentration upon the job of the moment may shut out its human side. Lack of intellectual development and experience with life can produce narrowness as also can an improper balance between professional duties and legitimate outside interests.

Cultivating fraternal charity   To cultivate charity and human sympathy the nurse must cherish kindly thoughts and feelings. In many instances to know people is to like them. Acquaintance with human beings helps to avoid an insular mind and insulated feelings.

Human un-derstanding   People are born, live, think and act differently. Sometimes one need not and should not agree with them. Yet at all times one should strive to interpret and make allowances in the light of their temperament and environment, of their culture and education, of their social or national or racial or religious background. This demands a generous range of knowledge and experience, which daily life furnishes to a large extent. But its contributions need to be supplemented by a rich interest in friends outside one's profession and in those humanizing activities which make recreation hours valuable lessons in human solidarity and friendliness.

2. VICES OPPOSED TO LOVE OF NEIGHBOR

Impatient language — The more particular duties of charity relative to the nurse can be considered from the aspect of what is *to be avoided* and then of what she *positively should do* to show her kindly thoughtfulness of others. No one can deny that the nurse has many excuses for being impatient. Patients are not always reasonable in their demands nor tolerant of delays and other inconveniences. A nurse has not several sets of hands. But what good comes of her pointing this out to a patient who asks for a glass of water while she is busy elsewhere! There are few days when she is not provoked to impatience. Yet the nurse who cultivates kindness will restrain the impetuous word and turn aside wrath with a gentle answer.

Impatient actions — Actions as well as language can express impatience. Quick staccato footsteps, slamming doors, snatching a thermometer, almost throwing an article at a patient or grabbing a spoon from him when he fumbles, manifest impatience as clearly and even more bitingly than language. It takes no more time and considerably less energy to be calm and kind than to flare up in a tempest of impatience. As with all virtue charity pays rich dividends in personal satisfaction and happiness. While these are legitimate motives, they are not basic. Men must be kind to one another in virtue of the obligations of fraternal love.

Hatred   Hatred is too rare a vice to deserve more than passing mention. Seldom do persons harbor such mutual dislike that they want to injure each other and desire only evil for their enemy. When such hate exists it is gravely immoral. It is so utterly opposed to the love which should bind people together.

Animosities   *Personal animosities*, though not as grievous as hatred, are more frequent. They spread untold unhappiness and destroy the goodwill which should inspire associates. Instead of being united they find themselves separated by various antagonisms, sometimes so vague that they balk explanation. The best way to overcome animosity is for the persons to come to know each other better. This is a necessary and in most instances an effective step towards cordial relations. But when people refuse even to speak to each other they are not likely to know each other better. One of them must make the first move and, swallowing pride, show his desire for reconciliation by some friendly word or favor.

Revenge   Too often people think of *revenge rather than of reconciliation*. Revenge means returning injury for injury. It must not be confused with restitution, which is an obligation in justice to repair damage or give to another what is owed him. Revenge is quite different. When a man gives back a loan or pays damages for an injury, he is fulfilling an obligation of justice. But when he "pays back" slander with slander, resentment with resentment, insult with insult, and injury with injury, he is guilty of revenge.

Evil of revenge   Not only is revenge opposed to the virtue of neighborly love, which demands that a man will what is for his neighbor's welfare. In addition it attacks a man's own moral good and happiness. To harbor thoughts of revenge begets a gloomy interior. By meeting evil with evil a man forfeits opportunities for spiritual growth, for personal nobility and self-development and self-control. No external hurt or insult can really injure a man unless he allows it to sink into his soul and fester there.

3. HELPING OTHERS

Helping others   Love of neighbor implies *positive efforts* to help him. The obligation rests on no expectation of what the person himself may get out of it, but flows from the nature of man and his position in society. Men are bound to help one another. Otherwise the welfare of the social group as well as of the individual suffers. When a person needs help which another person reasonably can give he is bound to give that help. His voluntary refusal makes him responsible for the injury which follows. The evil of his selfishness must be weighed against the gravity of the harm done.

Charitable speech   Probably more ill-will and unhappiness are caused by unloving speech than by anything else. The individual instances may not be significant, but the collectivity is enormous. Charitable speech does not consist merely in avoiding lies and keeping secrets and confidences. These are the obligations of justice. Nor does it specifically regard purity of language, of shunning what is obscene or lascivious or risqué or suggestive. This belongs to the virtue of purity. Charity in speech imposes the duty of governing one's language in such a way that besides being inoffensive *it will do positive good*.

Motive   It is true that a nurse's saucy or flippant or discourteous language may cost a hospital a gift or donation. But such a motive for charity seems hardly admirable. The real motive must be the obligation of neighborly love, the duty which human beings owe one another to be kind and helpful. The motive of expediency is not fundamental or ultimately worthy of human dignity. Consideration, however, for the patient is not an appeal to

expediency. The nurse must remember that she is caring
for a human being, body and soul, not just a body. Her
conversation has a great deal to do with the influence she
is going to exercise upon the patient.

Against   To make sure her speech is as it should be the
gossip   nurse must carefully *avoid gossip*. It can easily
become the unjust revelation of other people's business or
ruin their good names or cause unhappiness in another
way. Gossip can do all of this and is opposed to justice. But
even when gossip does not violate justice it often trespasses
upon the love people owe one another. Feelings are hurt,
friendships weakened. M. E. Gladwin summarizes its evil:
gossip causes one "to form a wrong estimate of her work;
narrows her outlook on life; stunts her growth morally and
spiritually; is a treasonable injustice to the sick people
whom she serves; and causes a nurse to forget the greatest
rule ever laid down for human conduct, 'Whatsoever ye
would that men should do to you, do ye even so to them.' "[2]
It is a safe prediction that no single factor would bring
more happiness into the world than the elimination of
criticism, tale-bearing and unkindly speech.

Materially   Too often the obligation of helping one's
               neighbor is thought of solely in terms of ma-
terial assistance. This is a duty, of course. And in a world
where public agencies have taken over many works of
charity people are prone to lose sight of their personal
obligation. This obligation endures. If the person himself
does not assist directly, then he is bound according to his
means to contribute to the public funds, such as the Community Chest.

Spiritually   But beyond the obligation of helping one's
               neighbor *materially* is the duty of coming to his
aid *spiritually*. It has been pointed out how the nurse is
bound to look after the patient's spiritual welfare. Charity

[2] *Ethics*, pp. 221–222.

enforces that obligation. When the spiritual need is extreme, the nurse is bound to do all she can to bring the needed assistance. Nothing should stand in the way of her calling in the priest for a dying person. No matter his past, no matter what he has done or left undone, she should obtain a priest for the dying man. And the same must be said regarding baptism—only here she may herself have the duty of administering the sacrament (p. 319).

Fraternal   A delicate yet clear duty of charity obliges one
correction to warn an associate in danger of doing wrong.
Admittedly the situation demands prudence. Immoderate zeal creates the busybody, who is a pest in any institution. Culpable failure to give due warning makes one responsible for the harm which follows. As usual virtue strikes a balance between the duty of giving advice and of avoiding undue meddling in other people's affairs.

The rule   The rule is simple and clear. The obligation
              of warning another is binding when the danger
is evident and grave, when there is time to prevent the evil from happening and it is likely that the advice will be heeded. If one is sure it will be spurned, the obligation ceases of offering it. At best it would be useless and might create only bad feelings.

Example   Thus if an experienced nurse knows a student
              is endangering her career by foolish conduct
and if she thinks her advice will be accepted, she is bound to offer it. If she knows it will be rejected, she need not bother. However, if she holds a position of authority, her obligation rests upon justice as well as charity. Then, even though she foresees only rejection of her warning, she is obliged to give it and to use appropriate means for securing obedience.

Cheerfulness Thomas Aquinas insisted upon people's obli-
                gation to make life happier and more cheer-
ful (p. 192). As with other duties of charity this springs from

the need men have of one another to attain due human
perfection. The duty of cheerfulness relative to the nurse
takes on special importance in view of the difficulties of her
environment. Much that goes into her daily existence will
not be conducive to a sparkling smile. Yet hardly anything
can be more welcome in the sick room than a cheerful
disposition, cheerful words, a cheerful attitude and a
cheerful demeanor.

4. DRESS AND ETIQUETTE

Modest and Love of neighbor implies consideration in
pleasing matters of dress. Clothes should not merely
not offend; they should be positively pleasing. Downright
immodesty or lubricity are excluded as opposed to the
virtue of purity. But charity goes beyond this to calculate
the effect a dress may have upon others. If a woman fears
it may occasion evil thoughts and desires she should not
wear it. This attitude is far from universal today, when
clothes are sometimes designed, worn and advertised for
their sex appeal. Such catering to the lower passions is
utterly opposed to modesty and charity.

The uniform While on duty the nurse wears the uniform.
Yet there are many types of uniforms and
many more ways of wearing them. The uniform should be
neat, immaculate and fresh—but not too starched. Even
the most carefully worn uniform, however, can be spoiled
by ill-chosen accessories. Rings, bracelets, elaborate hair-
dos, overdone lipstick and make-up, incarnadined finger-
nails, frivolous shoes, are some of the items which can
detract from a nurse's appearance. Not only may they be
annoying to the patient but they can be obstacles to the
nurse's success.

Dress off- Dress is much more of a problem when the
duty nurse is off duty. In many ways clothes manifest the wearer's tastes and character. This is why they

should be chosen and worn carefully. Conservatism is admirable, yet there is no virtue in dowdiness or slovenliness. If a person's attire shows good taste and quality, is comfortable, hygienic and suited to the occasion, it is bound to do credit to the wearer and be pleasing. "Take great care," advised Lord Chesterfield, "to be always dressed like the reasonable people of your age, in the place where you are; whose dress is never spoken of, as either too negligent or too much studied."

Manners and etiquette   Good manners and etiquette do not *in themselves stand for virtue*. A man may be perfect in both and be a knave. Yet good manners and etiquette can be evidences of a kindly heart, indicative of a person who thinks of the comfort and pleasure of others. Too much stress upon formal standards of etiquette can be silly. But the opposite extreme is as bad or worse. Manners and etiquette can be helpful props to social intercourse. They make people socially dependable.

And kindliness   Punctilious obedience to social customs is no substitute for a kindly heart. The ideal is to keep them together: friendly and thoughtful care for others coupled *with a knowledge of the socially acceptable ways of showing it*. Because of her profession the nurse should strive to acquire not only the interior virtue of charity which urges her to be considerate of others, but also the technical details of good manners and etiquette.[3] Ignorance of them reflects unfavorably upon her and her profession and can be a cause of annoyance to patient and friends alike.

[3] Two useful books on this subject: Emily Post's *Etiquette, The Blue Book of Social Usage* (New York, Funk and Wagnalls, 1945) and Eleanor Boykin's *This Way Please* (New York, The Macmillan Co., 1940).

READINGS

Charlotte Aikens: *Studies in Ethics for Nurses*, pp. 80–83, ch. xviii, pp. 253–256.

Michael Cronin: *The Science of Ethics*, ii, 66–68.

Edwin F. Healy: *Moral Guidance*, pp. 41–43.

Charles C. Miltner: *The Elements of Ethics*, ch. ix.

Thomas V. Moore: *Principles of Ethics*, ch. viii.

III. Ethics Regarding God

Chapter 26

DUTIES TO GOD

1. GOD'S EXISTENCE

Philosophical Ethics is a *segment* of the philosophical syn-
postulate thesis. In the system itself the segments are
mutually interdependent, with the result that any separation of ethics from the entirety of philosophy is bound to
be unfortunate. Ethics must be conceived in terms of the
integrated system, making its contribution to the perfection
of the whole and in turn drawing from it. The truths or
principles which in this way one branch of philosophy
borrows from another are termed postulates.

Postulates As used here *postulate does not mean hypothesis.*
not hypotheses An hypothesis is an assumption from which,
whether it be true or not, certain conclusions follow. A
postulate, on the other hand, is a truth which one science
borrows from another. The truth belongs to its proper
science where it is validated. Once this is done, other
sciences can use it in their own investigations.

God exists Natural theology, one of the divisions of
philosophy, deals with the existence and the
nature of the Supreme Being. Unaided by divine revelation
human reason can show that such a being exists, the
Creator and Ruler of the universe and of all things in it.
Ethics lifts this truth from natural theology and makes it a
postulate for an examination of man's duties to God. For
upon God's existence being known, man must recognize

obligations towards Him no less than towards himself and
his fellow man.

2. DUTIES TO GOD

In general   *In a sense all man's duties refer to God.* Directly or
indirectly God lays them upon men and in
various ways they guide man back to God, his ultimate goal.
Human beings cannot wilfully disregard any duty without
failing in their duty to God. But among man's duties there
are some which pertain to God *directly.* These are the duties
which, in the light of human reason alone, are to be considered now. They can be summarized under the virtues
of hope, love and religion.

Hope   *Hope* is the virtue by which man confidently
expects from God what he needs to attain his
goal. No one can view the demands and dangers of life, its
trials and hardships and manifold opportunities for moral
failure without realizing his inadequacies. To know that
God exists as the Creator and Governor of the world obligates man to trust that God will provide all he must have
to achieve his destiny—if he does his part.

Love   *Love* is of two kinds. One sort regards the usefulness of the person loved. This is the love of
concupiscence. The other kind regards the good of the beloved.
This is the love of *benevolence.* Man's relations with God
must include both the love of concupiscence and the love
of benevolence. It is clear, from the virtue of hope, that
man must look to the Supreme Being to help him achieve
his due perfection. In this sense, then, man must love God
for what He can do for him, and thus love is included in
hope. Man is bound also to love God for His own sake,
because of His preeminent dignity and worth. God is
infinitely good and the source and destiny of all created
beings. But, since God is above all creatures, right order
requires that man love the Supreme Being above all things
and subordinate love of creatures to love of God.

Religion   *Religion* signifies the honor and worship which creatures owe the Supreme Being because of His excellency and absolute dominion. The duty of worshipping God does not oblige man because of some pious feeling or because religion comforts him and corresponds to some indefinable longing for something outside and beyond himself or because he has done wrong or because it will make his existence more meaningful or more useful to society.

Essence of   Whatever worth these motives have they are
religion   not the quintessential basis of religion. This lies precisely in the fact of *man's subordination to his Creator* or, to put it reversely, in God's transcendence to the world. Wherefore the creature must turn to the Supreme Being with the highest honor and tribute of which he is capable.

3. WORSHIP

God deserves   Man's highest activity is the activity of his
man's best   *intellect and will*. Anything short of this is not man's best. Yet the Supreme Being deserves man's best. This follows from the ultimate rule of morality that man's conduct must conform to right reason. This demands that honor and reverence be proportionate to the dignity and excellence of the person to whom they are owed. Since acts of religion concern the Supreme Being, man's honor and reverence of Him must be the best—must be, therefore, of the soul, internal acts of will and intellect.

Gratitude   Moreover man's *gratitude* to God must be considered. To Him man owes his existence and his preservation in existence. From Him he hopes to receive what he needs to live well. All this obliges man to be grateful. But man's gratitude must be of the highest order, manifestive of his intellectual and volitional life. Otherwise, again, man's response to God's goodness and dominion would not be the best and to that extent would be unworthy of Him.

Knowledge   This implies that man must strive *to know and love God*. Knowledge is neither innate nor automatic. It requires effort. It means that a man must widen and deepen his knowledge of God. While men and women as they grow older advance in the understanding of the world and its interests, all too frequently they live as adults with a child's conception of God. As there is growth in other intellectual fields, so there should be growth in man's knowledge of God and in his understanding of his relations with Him.

Love and action   Still knowledge alone is not enough. *It must flow into action*. Men must strive to offer God acts of adoration and love and gratitude and sorrow for failures and to ask His help in his needs and anxieties. These acts are the essential attributes of religion. They do not exclude, but on the contrary include, doing good to the neighbor. Yet religion must have God as its *primary* objective —nothing else. External action of any sort, unless it have a background of these most truly religious activities of mind and will, falls short of being completely authentic. Religion is of the soul, of man's most truly human self.

Penitence   Remembering God's transcendence and goodness and his obligations, man must view his moral failures with sorrow and regret and desire earnestly to make amends. Penitence leads him to no idle or numbing remorse. Rather it guides him back to God, more than ever aware of his weakness and God's omnipotence and love. With fuller understanding, he resolves anew to live up to his ideals and to expiate for his lapses.

Petition   Man's conviction that God rules the universe in its minutest detail as well as in its most magnificent development obliges him to go to God for help and guidance. His lapses only reaffirm his weaknesses. He realizes how high his destiny is, how difficult and hazardous the way, how flagging his zeal. Even with the best of intentions and efforts he cannot look upon himself as self-sufficient. Like everything else in creation, he depends upon God. But unlike creatures beneath him, man can know God and love God. With the highest faculties of his soul, then, man must acknowledge God's dominion and his own subjection and inadequacy and seek from God what he needs to reach his ultimate goal.

The question of external worship   Anyone who admits the existence of God must admit the duty of internal worship. But why is man obliged to supplement *internal worship with external actions*: with words and song, with signs and symbols and gestures and ceremonies? Religion must be of the soul; why then bring in these externals?

Answer   *External worship* is doubly justified. First, the body as God's creation is bound as all other creatures are to pay God such honor as it can. Being physical it uses such means of worship as fall within its nature. Secondly, man is a composite of body and soul, which constitute not two things but one thing, a human being. A characteristic of this union is the interaction between soul and body. The activity of either is intensified by the activity of the other. External action arouses mental and voluntary activity. And when thought and resolution eventuate in physical action, the intellectual and voluntary activities are enlivened. The action becomes the action of the entire person. This general truth must be considered with regard to man's obligation of religion. His worship must be essentially of his intellect and will. But such interior worship is completed and intensified by the cooperation of the body and its faculties. Since man is bound to internal worship, he is obliged also to use the means for doing it well. Since these externals can help him, he should not neglect to use them.

Social wor- For the same reasons men must offer God
ship *social worship*. Society as such is His creation.
It must as such offer Him its worship. Just as external
worship is a practically necessary means to the essentials
of internal worship, so is social worship an important help
which should be used. When united, men can do difficult
things more easily. There is a spirit, something contagious,
about team work, about doing things together. Men generally recognize this fact in their ordinary affairs. It would
be unreasonable, therefore, to exclude social worship from
man's duties of religion when it can do so much to help
him honor God properly.

Practical Under *ordinary circumstances* it is not enough for
consequence man to draw away from his fellow human
beings and in the solitude of his own mind adore and
worship God. That only partially fulfills the virtue of religion. To be complete it must include vocal prayer, by
oneself and with other people. Attitudes of body, such as
kneeling or standing, can focus the attention. A building
set apart for worship and appropriately adorned also makes
man's worship more worthy of its sublime object. These
adjuncts to worship are not *absolutely* necessary but they are
important enough to make their use morally obligatory. Those who
spurn the proper externals of religion, such as buildings,
rites, ceremonials, gestures, congregational prayer and
singing, manifest their ignorance either of human psychology or of the creature's obligation to worship God as
fully and completely as he can.

4. FAILURE IN DUTIES TO GOD

False religious From the relation of man to his Creator, it
notions follows that natural religion must be basically
the same for all men, since they are equally the creatures
of God. Historically, men all over the globe and in all
degrees of civilization have recognized a Supreme Being

SPECIAL ETHICS

and acknowledged the obligations of worshipping Him. But this worship has sometimes taken repulsive forms, which cannot be defended even on the plane of natural religion. Such practices as human sacrifice and various forms of unchastity can be termed nothing but perversions. Well intentioned as the votaries may have been, such actions prove a degenerate religious outlook. They fall lamentably short of the natural and rational dignity and excellence which divine worship ought to have.

Against the virtue of religion   Man can fail in his worship of God either negatively by refusing to give God due honor or positively by honoring Him in a wrong way or by paying divine honor to something unworthy of it. The first vice is termed irreligion. The latter carries the general title of superstition.

Irreligion   *Irreligion* is the lack or privation of due worship of God. It is downright irreverence or the performance of acts contrary to God's excellence. Here belong such evils as challenging God's wisdom or power or goodness or existence, speaking impiously of God or sacred things, cursing God or tempting Him as a famous atheist did. Watch in hand he cried out to his audience that if God existed he dared him to strike him dead in three minutes! Three minutes passed. "You see," he exclaimed, "there is no God."

Superstition   *Superstition* in general is any wrong or perverted form of worship. Usually, if not always, it has something of divine worship about it. But what might be worthy is used either in the wrong way or directed to wrong ends. This distinction indicates two kinds of superstition: giving God a worship unworthy of Him or honoring creatures with a worship due to God.

Unworthy worship   Worship of God is *unworthy* when it is false, absurd, superfluous or rendered in some unbecoming way. A recent example of this was the use of poisonous snakes in so-called religious gatherings. Instances likewise occur of unworthy worship when people through a false sense of devotion confidently proclaim dubious miracles, visions, revelations and other miraculous events. The result is to cheapen religion and draw upon it bitter criticism.

Substitutes for God   The sort of superstition in which creatures are in various ways substituted for God takes the forms of idolatry, divination and magic.

Idolatry   *Idolatry* is superstition at its worst. By it men give creatures the honor due God. What the creature happens to be matters little. Whether it be a mountain or an ocean, a totem pole or a statue, a king or an emperor, the essential evil of idolatry is that it arrogates to creatures the worship due God alone.

Divination defined   *Divination* is the art of learning hidden events, of unlocking the future, or knowing what man cannot naturally know and what he cannot expect to know without a special revelation from God. This leaves only an appeal to some hidden, mysterious force. To it the votary turns, perhaps not explicitly, but at least implicitly—since the knowledge is expected and cannot be looked for from God or natural causes. Some current forms of divination are fortune-telling and its variants of palmistry, phrenology and crystal gazing, astrology, interpretation of dreams, the use of the ouija board.

Licit for fun   When all concerned indulge in these practices for the sake of amusement and without any faith in their preternatural power they are not guilty of superstition.

A danger   Yet there exists an *element of danger* even in such apparently harmless fortune-telling as "reading" tea leaves or cutting cards. The person may be encouraged to wonder whether there is not something in it after all. Likewise the use of the ouija board for fun can

cause embarrassment and occasion suspicion and mistrust
among friends. In general these practices smacking of
divination are best left alone. They begin as entertainment
but can end by being physically and emotionally and
psychologically upsetting and leading a person to be
seriously and morbidly fascinated by them.

Evil of   The evil of divination lies *in attributing divine*
divination   *attributes to creatures.* This does not happen
when things are used according to their natural powers.
But the power of things is not always clear. Without a doubt
divination in all its forms is largely hocus-pocus. Whether
or not there is some connection between a person's palm
and his character or whether the stars influence life need
not be settled here.

The principle   It is enough to lay down the general principle.
                  Whenever unusual effects occur, the question
is whether the means used has the natural power of producing them. If it has, then it is right to use it. For causes
can be employed lawfully to produce their natural effects.
But if it is certain that the means cannot produce the
effect, then the effect must be attributed to some other
power, which is working through the agent as the visible
sign of its operation. To employ the counterfeit causes of
divination is implicitly to invoke the power of the hidden
agent, and this is not allowable.

The malice of   For in appealing seriously to such devices
divination   people are attributing to them *powers belonging*
only to God. It is one of His attributes to know the past,
present and future. He knows not only what must happen
but even such events as fall under man's free will. To suppose that human beings or any medium which they might
use could reveal these free human acts is to ascribe divine
power to something beneath God.

Magic   *Magic* is the form of superstition which, with-
                  out God's help, seeks to accomplish something

completely beyond man's power or the power of the means employed. Here belong such practices as "chain prayers," wearing amulets or charms, saying prayers a certain number of times or in a certain place or in a certain way and attributing the prayer's efficacy to the circumstances of time, place, manner or number. Likewise under magic fall the various concoctions and practices which without therapeutic power are employed to cure illness.

Summary   All forms of irreligion and superstition must be carefully avoided as derogatory of God's honor and glory. On the positive side creatures must give God as complete a worship as they can, and as worthy as possible of man's high dignity and God's transcendent excellence.

READINGS

Michael Cronin: *The Science of Ethics*, ii, ch. i.

Edward F. Garesché: *Ethics and the Art of Conduct for Nurses*, Part I, chapters xv and xvi.

Paul J. Glenn: *Ethics*, pp. 151–170.

Edwin F. Healy: *Moral Guidance*, ch. iv.

Charles C. Miltner: *The Elements of Ethics*, ch. iv.

Thomas V. Moore: *Principles of Ethics*, chapters xxiii to xxvii.

IV. Ethics Regarding the Family and the State

Chapter 27

THE FAMILY AND MARRIAGE

1. INTRODUCTION

The family and the State Birth normally makes a child a member of two social groups, *the family and the State*. Both make essential and profound and manifold contributions to his development. Both lay upon him their special obligations. As a man is bound to live up to his duties towards himself, his fellow human beings and towards God, so man's nature and destiny obligate him to fulfil his duties to the family and the State.

Orgin of societies Societies exist because man needs other human beings *not only that he may be born but that he may live*. He himself cannot supply the necessaries of a completely human life, much less those that are required to live well—as distinguished from merely living. Contrary to the view of Thomas Hobbes (1588–1679) society is not the product of man's need to protect himself against enemies. It springs from innermost and vital human requirements. Aristotle's (384–322 B. C.) statement was reaffirmed by Thomas Aquinas (1225–1274), that a man who was not fitted for society or who was so independent that he did not need it was either a beast or a god.

Society— definition and kinds *Society* in general is any group of human beings associated for some particular purpose. The formation may follow from inner drives of human nature, and then it is *natural*. Or it may follow from the free decision of people to organize for some special end. Then it is *artificial*.

Perfect and imperfect   By reason of self-sufficiency, a society is perfect or imperfect. It is *perfect* when it has everything it needs for fulfilling its purpose and to that extent is independent of other societies. It is *imperfect* when its resources fail to meet its own requirements. In their respective orders the State and the Church are perfect societies: the family, imperfect. Although the family provides the needs of daily life, it cannot supply all that is required for its own complete functioning. For example, it needs police and military protection.

2. MARRIAGE

Family defined   The *family* is a group of persons, established by nature, for mutual support, sharing in the daily needs of life, partaking of the same table and sharing the same hearth.

Family life accepted freely   Although springing from natural inclinations, family life is *not forced upon men and women*. They accept it freely and bind themselves to its obligations. One of them is the due respect for authority and subordination in the family: the conjugal society of husband and wife, the parental-filial society between parents and children, and the servile society of master and servants. The family is the primal unit of the State, but because it does not suffice for its own perfect functioning the family is called imperfect in contrast to the State.

The family and marriage   The conjugal society between husband and wife, or *marriage*, is the basic group within the family. It is the marital contract which determines the family, binds husband and wife to their familial obligations and joins their fortunes together in the lives of their children. Marriage is the originating as well as the central fact

of the family and becomes pivotal in any discussion about
it.

Marriage   *Marriage* may be summarized in a definition,
defined   which can then be explained. By nature marriage is the permanent union of one man and one woman,
legitimately constituted by contract with a view to the
personal good of the partners and to the procreation and
education of children.

3. NATURALNESS OF MARRIAGE

Rooted in   *By nature* means that marriage and its purposes
human nature are rooted in the physical structure of men
and women and in their spiritual and bodily cravings. This
is so true that marriage may be said to be forced upon
human beings with all the urgency of their innermost being.
But the necessity does not destroy the power of choice. It
is a *moral* necessity conformable with free will. Men and
women may or may not follow nature's promptings. Yet
whether they marry or not, nature's appetites endure. Even
when denied satisfaction, they remain as deep and strong
inclinations and furnish ample reason for calling marriage
natural.

Mutual needs   Marriage's naturalness appears also from the
          mutual assistance married people give each
other. Among the activities of life some are appropriate
to men and others to women. In matrimony the sexes
complement each other and each makes its proper contribution according to nature's plan.

4. MARRIAGE CONTRACT

The contract   This natural foundation of marriage, lodged
         in human nature, whereby marriage and fam-
ily life appear attractive furnishes one of the *background
causes* of marriage. But the *proximate efficient cause is the
contract*, which is made by the free and expressed consent

of the man and woman. By it they transfer mutual rights over each other's bodies for the procreation of children and establish a common life for their mutual advantage. The free consent of the man and woman constitutes the contract. And the contract makes the marriage.

Conditions not arbitrary Yet the contract is not a collection of arbitrary conditions which the spouses accept. Marriage corresponds to natural yearnings. It rests upon the moral law and must conform to it. People may marry or not marry. *But if they marry they must accept marriage as nature determines it and the contract must embrace these determinations.*

5. THE ENDS OF MARRIAGE

The ends of marriage The purposes, or ends, of marriage are *twofold*. The *primary end* is the procreation and education of children. The *secondary end* is the mutual assistance and allaying of passion which result from married life. Unfortunately at times the primary ends have been exaggerated at the expense of the secondary purposes of marriage. This was due in no small measure to Saint Augustine (354–430), who held that marital intercourse had to be justified by the intention of begetting children. His influence was far-reaching and enduring, but met a wholesome corrective in Thomas Aquinas. He too insisted upon the primary end of marriage as being the procreation and education of children, yet broke with the tradition of minimizing the secondary ends. Balanced and reasonable and complete as Aquinas' view was, it took a century to gain wide acceptance.

Primary end Biologically considered marriage clearly reveals its *primary end*. Every aspect of the sexual mechanism evidences nature's provision for human reproduction. But children unlike animals need great care over a long period of time. Their dependency is not merely *physical* but *intellectual* and *spiritual*. If the baby is to grow into a well-developed person, its progress along all lines must be provided for with patience and intelligence. Since nature's aim is the continuation of the race, it is clear that the primary end must include not merely the procreation of children but also their proper upbringing.

Secondary The *secondary or accessory ends* of marriage are
end defined those benefits which come to husband and wife from marriage apart from its primary purpose.

Explained Physically men and women *need each other* as a help and support in life. Together they make an efficient team. In the mental and moral spheres they also need each other. For men and women differ widely in perfection and virtue, in refinement and affection and sympathies and interests.

In particular Marriage furnishes a *legitimate and regulated way of satisfying sexual appetites*. In it men and women honorably and reasonably fulfil nature's fundamental purpose. Under secondary ends also may be mentioned such benefits as the safeguarding of woman's dignity and guaranteeing her justice and equity. Marriage establishes and helps to preserve friendship among families. It fosters mutual respect between the spouses as partners in the familial enterprise, protects public morality and widens the scope of social friendships.

Marriage, the Marriage should be the *most perfect of all human*
union of per- *friendships*. But what distinguishes married love
sons is that the blending of lives exists between persons of opposite sex, to complement each other physically and spiritually. Although the union is physical, it must be remembered that human beings are not animals. They are composites of body and soul. Consequently if this union is to represent the union of the complete persons it must be *not merely of the body but also of the mind and will*. Whenever sex is treated as something complete in itself and as isolated from conjugal love, its significance is falsified.

Marital act between human beings   That a man's activity be specifically human it must be lifted out of the physical and made to reflect the attributes of personality. Consequently the purpose of the marital act in relation to man as a human being cannot be purely biological and utilitarian in the sense that its sole purpose is to produce children. This would amount to predicating it of man simply as an animal and divorcing it from his higher excellence. The conjugal act is biological and procreative. But it has the deeper significance of a unique expression of human love, which is achieved when intercourse is regarded as *involving the entire human being* and not just the body.

Children   The child brings to the parents as persons and to their married love and union *a new perfection*. From their status as man and woman, marriage lifts them into the perfection of husband and wife. And to this children add the perfection of fatherhood and motherhood. While the procreation and education of children is the primary end of marriage, the contribution which children can make to the development and happiness of their parents must not be overlooked nor minimized.

Social ends of marriage   Of all man's natural acts, only procreation by its nature is ordained to the common good. Marriage looks to the private good, but its primary purpose centers in the continuance of the race. The secondary ends contribute also to the social good. In marriage human personality is perfected, and so indirectly the social good is benefited. For whoever seeks his own proper good seeks the good of the community.

More specifically   More specifically it may be pointed out that marriage is a *training ground for citizenship*. It affords the development and expansion of the personalities of husband and wife and children and by the necessary domestic adjustments prepares them to be better social units. Strong family life insures the nation's welfare.

Aquinas and   The traditional emphasis upon marriage's
the social   social character is exemplified by the way
aspect   Thomas Aquinas used it to condemn sexual
vices. While gluttony injures the individual, inordinate
sexual indulgence harms the race. Promiscuity is evil because it is opposed to the procreation and education of
children and antagonistic to the common good. Likewise
on the basis of the common good he argues against marriage between close relatives. Such unions might hinder the
procreation of children and certainly would obstruct the
control of the sex appetite. Moreover marriage between
close relations would interfere with the formation and
preservation of new friendships among the members of
society. Marriage is definitely not a private affair. To
isolate it from the social good is a tragic but all too prevalent contemporary error.

Complex   Since marriage and the generation of children
character of   bear upon the continuance of the race, the
marriage   welfare of the State and the perpetuation of
the Church these institutions have an interest in it. Yet
there need not be conflict. Each has its own domain. In so
far as marriage is for the good of the race, it falls under
natural law. In so far as it is a political good, it is subject
to the State. In so far as it is for the spiritual welfare of the
spouses, it is governed by the Church law.

6. MONOGAMY

Types of   *Monogamous* marriage, signifying the union of
marital states   one man with one woman, differs from domestic societies which exist in conditions of promiscuity,
polygyny or polyandry. *Sexual promiscuity* designates the
theory that originally all women of a group or tribe belonged indifferently to all the men. Polygamy means the
condition of having more than one husband or wife at
once. It occurs either as *polygyny*, the union of one man
with several women, or *polyandry*, the marriage of one

woman with several men. Promiscuity, polygyny and polyandry are opposed to monogamy, which alone secures the perfection of marriage.

Promiscuity immoral   *Promiscuity* never formed a general stage in man's social history. But independently of its actual occurrence, it is immoral. Though sexual communism would provide to some extent for new life, it would fail to assure children of the "good life" they should have. The care that a child needs would be impossible, not to mention its wider education. Furthermore, sexual communism is opposed to the good of the race, which demands that members of society be safeguarded properly. But how is this possible where neither children would know their parents nor parents know their children? As regards the good of the parents, sexual promiscuity might quiet passion, but it would fail to satisfy the other secondary purposes of marriage. Finally sexual promiscuity apparently leads to sterility and most certainly would breed selfishness, suspicion, enmities, dissensions, jealousies and hatred—all of which would undermine social tranquillity if not make it actually impossible.

Polyandry rare   *Polyandry* is a domestic union of one woman simultaneously with several men. Compared with polygyny its occurrence is exceptional. On the basis of evidence, polyandry never belonged to any of the great types of social organization. And even where it has occurred, it may have been a corruption of the one-husband marriage. In any event there is no proof that polyandry was ever more widespread than it is today, when it exists within narrow limits among a few uncivilized peoples.

Immoral   The *opposition of polyandry to the natural law* appears from its effects upon the good of the offspring and of the parents. Unlike polygyny it cannot accelerate the multiplication of the race. A woman can bear no more children by having several husbands than by having one. And although polyandry does not absolutely prevent conception, it seems to encourage sterility. But even if polyandry raised no obstacles to procreation, it would still fail to provide for the proper education of the offspring. With the fatherhood of the child uncertain, its proper upbringing would be impossible. Finally, the human ends of marriage—perfection of conjugal love, mutual help, development of personality—all those things which make for a happy family life are impossible in the polyandric union. In many ways it is more debasing for the woman than promiscuity.

Polygyny tends to monogamy   In various cultures and religious sects *polygyny* appears rather frequently. Yet where it does occur, it tends in practice to monogamy both from the social and sexual points of view. The woman first married often holds a higher place than the others or is the principal wife. There is also evidence that where the husband is supposed to cohabit in turn with his wives there may be a favorite and the union, at least temporarily, is practically monogamous.

Polygyny and primary purpose of marriage   *Polygyny* far from hindering procreation rather multiplies it, since each wife can have as many children as if her union were monogamous. The rearing of offspring, too, as far as *essentials* go, is possible under the polygynous system. Simply on the basis of the natural law and apart from Christian law, polygynous unions may be true and valid marriages. Even so, polygyny must be rejected. Its evil is evident from the fact that, at best, it satisfies only the most elementary demands of the natural law. Children can be born, but their education will be realized only in essentials, and other ends of marriage scarcely can be attained at all.

Degrades woman   *Polygyny precludes the good of the spouses*, their personal development and happiness. There is no equality between husband and wife, where the husband claims her entire attention and service but she shares the husband with other wives. By nature she is his equal, endowed with the same faculties, tending to the same goal and destiny. But in polygyny she cannot take her place in the family as her husband's equal. Her dignity as mother suffers. She is degraded.

Perfect love impossible Such inequality obstructs true human love. One of its characteristics is to claim the person loved wholly for oneself, to honor the loved one and to desire a return of love equal to what one gives. In the polygynous union a wife cannot be loved as an equal. Her husband is not exclusively her own, so that return of love is impossible.

Breeds dissension *Polygyny* furnishes a fertile field for jealousy. The wives will vie with one another for their husband's affection. There will be rivalry for various household functions. When older women find themselves replaced by younger and newer wives, they inevitably will feel bitter and be victims of envy and hate. Under such circumstances little peace and harmony will pervade the household.

Socially detrimental The inadequacies of polygyny to secure the primary and secondary ends of marriage manifest *its opposition to the social good*. If children's education falls short of what it ought to be, if the family is divided against itself, wanting in mutual love and dignity and enthusiasm for the higher and more truly human ideals and values, the tone of society will deteriorate. Since these are the results which can be expected from a polygynous system, its immorality is clear.

Immoral Since polygyny provides for the continuance of the race, it is *not utterly incompatible* with the elementary dictates of the natural moral law. But it does make the proper education of progeny difficult and practically makes impossible the secondary and social objectives of marriage. Consequently polygyny is opposed to the obligations of the natural law taken in their completeness, and is to be condemned.[1]

[1] On the problem of polygyny being allowed by the Law of Moses, see Ostheimer, A. L.: *The Family* (Washington, Catholic University Press, 1939), pp. 118–119.

Positive argument for monogamy The inadequacies of promiscuity, polyandry and polygyny argue *negatively* for monogamy.
Positively its natural necessity is shown from the fact that male and female birth rates are almost equal, with the difference slightly in favor of the males. From this Dr. Moore concludes[2] that "neither polygamy nor polyandry can be a normal condition of the human race. Biologically there is no ground for the contention of some extremists that the stronger sex drives of the male should allow him two or more wives. Monogamy is founded, not only on reason, but also on biological conditions over which we have no control." Another argument, already touched upon, for monogamy comes from psychological considerations. The nature of married life presupposes a friendship which mutually centers in the spouses. Each gives the other a sort of love which if it is to be the perfecting agent of personality and human living must be exclusive.

READINGS

Michael Cronin: *The Science of Ethics*, ii, chapters xiii and xiv.
F. W. Foerster: *Marriage and the Sex-Problem.*
Edward F. Garesché: *Ethics and the Art of Conduct for Nurses*, ch. xxiii, Part I.
Mary E. Gladwin: *Ethics*, pp. 268–271.
Paul J. Glenn: *Ethics*, pp. 232–242.
N. Orville Griese: *The "Rhythm" in Marriage and Christian Morality.*
R. de Guchteneere: *Judgment on Birth Control.*
Dietrich von Hildebrand: *In Defence of Purity*, pp. 89–112.
Jacques Leclercq: *Marriage and the Family.*
Charles J. McFadden: *Medical Ethics for Nurses*, chapters iii, iv and v.
Charles C. Miltner: *The Elements of Ethics*, ch. xiv.
Thomas V. Moore: *Principles of Ethics*, chapters xvii, xviii and xix.
Bakewell Morrison: *Marriage.*
Anthony L. Ostheimer: *The Family.*
Pope Pius XI: *Christian Marriage.*

[2] *Principles of Ethics*, p. 212.

Chapter 28

STABILITY OF MARRIAGE

1. INDISSOLUBILITY

Indissolubility a matter of natural law The other attribute of marriage which demands careful attention is its *permanency or indissolubility*. Because the Catholic Church stands alone in opposing civil divorce with the right to remarry, too many think the condemnation merely ecclesiastical and binding only on Catholics. It is true that the Catholic Church condemns these divorces. But divorce is evil not only because the Church condemns it. The Church outlaws it because it is against the natural moral law. Since this law binds all men and women, civil divorce with the right of remarriage is immoral for the non-Catholic as well as for the Catholic.

Two kinds: imperfect and perfect divorce *Divorce* may be of two sorts. It is called *imperfect* when husband and wife separate, but neither has the right to remarry. *Perfect* divorce signifies the dissolving of the marriage bond, during the lifetime of the parties, *with the right of remarrying*. Though unfortunate and regrettable, imperfect divorce, or separation, is allowable for sufficiently grave reasons. Perfect divorce, with the alleged cancellation of the marriage bond and the right to remarry, is not allowable *because of its many conflicts with the natural moral law*.

2. DIVORCE AGAINST WELFARE OF CHILDREN

The good of the offspring In the first place divorce is *opposed to the good of the offspring*. The primary reason for sexual differentiation and the association of men and women in the family relationship is to insure the continuation of the race. Procreation itself needs only a passing union. But considered alone procreation falls immensely short of fulfilling marriage's purpose. This requires that children not only be conceived and born but that they be brought up properly. Many living beings lower than man quickly become independent of their parents—but not children. The human offspring has a richer nature, superior faculties. It needs years for development and it needs both parents.

Education long and arduous   Children are uniquely dependent for the proper development of their mental and moral and physical faculties on the prolonged and diligent care of their parents. The child must be fed, instructed. It must be protected against evil influences. Good habits must be inculcated. Its character must be formed. The child is human and must be so treated.

Procreation not the end   Procreation is *not enough* to satisfy the natural demands for continuing the race. Children must be reared so as to become human beings in the fullest sense. This requires that the parents share actively and personally in the psychological and mental and moral and physical and emotional and spiritual development of their offspring. Careful cultivation is needed by the child, who grows so slowly, whose problems and adjustments are so delicate, whose needs are so great, whose own resources are so scanty, and whose destiny is so sublime.

Both parents needed   Aristotle insisted that children need their parents for the sake of existence, nourishment and discipline. In the early period of child-training the mother bears the heavier share. But later the sterner hand of the father is needed to complement the mother's influence. Just as male and female contribute to the birth of a child, so their cooperation is normally required for its due intellectual, moral and emotional growth and development.

After children From the natural point of view alone, the
are raised rearing of the average family demands the
devoted care and attention of both parents throughout the
greater portion of their married life. Even when this is done,
their continued union is morally necessary to serve as the
living source of the traditions which they have passed to
their children.

Divorce most The selfishness and infidelity of divorced
hurts the parents *wreck their chief ruin upon the child*. For
child while the parents can adjust themselves, the
child cannot. It becomes deprived of its most primordial
right to having a father and a mother. In other contracts
where the interests of a third party are at stake these interests are considered, but divorce proceedings disregard the
essential reason for marriage. Divorce sacrifices the child
and its most fundamental interests to the convenience of
the parents. There may be instances when in concrete
circumstances the child actually loses little in the loss of
its parents' care. But this is abnormal. And laws of moral
human conduct are not based on abnormal and unnatural
behavior and instincts.

Objection An objection may be made to this argument.
It does not seem to apply to couples without
children, either because they never had any or because
their children are fully grown. Either assumption, some
have argued, nullifies the argument for the permanency of
marriage based upon the education due to offspring.

Objection This objection misses the argument's force. By
answered its nature marriage implies children; that is
why it exists. And the argument holds even where there
actually are no children. For the ethical necessity of a
permanent union is *not constituted or created* by the obligation
of rearing children but is *indicated or manifested* by this obligation which is inherent in marriage. Consequently, once
the necessity of properly caring for children is seen to

involve a permanent union of the spouses, it stands established that marriage must be enduring—whether or not there be children actually involved. In other words, the normal necessity involved in marriage of bringing up children gives insight into the nature of the union. Once that knowledge is had, it applies to all marriages—not by reason of the presence of children but by reason of the nature of marriage itself.

3. DIVORCE AGAINST GOOD OF SPOUSES

Human love   Divorce also *conflicts with the love of husband and wife*, which is the essence of marriage. Life in common is filled with like and unlike interests, and unless it is founded in deep affection, the daily routine can be most trying. Of all human friendships, that between husband and wife should be the greatest. For here man and woman are united not merely sensually but by all the implications and involvements of domestic life. Married love should be human, conforming with man's rational nature, a love based on friendship more than on passion, a reciprocal love. The love of passion is selfish, short-lived, lasting as long as the woman stays attractive. The love of friendship is unselfish, enduring, gaining strength by every new expression. The man who clings to his wife while she is young and puts her aside when she loses her charm has never loved her as a human being. True marital love requires that it be unconditional, complete, exclusive and absorbing. Husband and wife share life's failures and successes. Together they grow old and together meet the challenges of the years.

Divorce   But *divorce stands opposed to this deep marital love.*
against love   Even though divorce should never occur, its *possibility* casts an insidious shadow, blighting where it does not actually destroy and putting a premium upon selfishness. Granted divorce as a way out of difficulties, which

inevitably arise, it will become the touchstone for every disagreement. If not referred to explicitly, at least it stands in the background, inviting the destruction of the family, even encouraging the partners to dangerous associations with the promise of a luckier marriage.

Separation　Separation without right of remarriage *makes no such promise*. Equally as divorce it breaks up the home but unlike divorce with the right to remarry it puts *no premium upon separation*. On the contrary separation holds out the prospect of a lonely and often difficult existence.

Divorce un-just disadvan-tage to woman　Woman ordinarily looks to her husband for support, and his duty does not disappear as the years go by. On the contrary it increases as the woman grows older. She has a right to his support and fidelity as long as she lives. For having given herself to him while youth and fertility and beauty remained, she has surrendered her most valuable years, and in return she should get his love and protection for life. By divorce in many instances she loses many, if not all, of these advantages which are hers by right. Compared to the divorced husband, the woman is at a great disadvantage. She is the weaker part and dependent. It is much easier for the husband to enter a second marriage than the divorced woman, especially if she is no longer young. More readily than the woman he can adjust himself and start life anew.

4. DIVORCE AGAINST THE FAMILY AND SOCIETY

Family basic to society　Divorce is opposed to *the good of the family and society at large*. Man's life should be lived in accord with right reason, and since the family is the basic unit of society, its well-being becomes essential to the well-being of the State. What encourages the solidarity of the family will become a direct contribution to the solidarity of the State.

Divorce vs.　　If *perfect divorce* be prohibited, husbands and
indissolubility　wives will try harder to make their marriage
a success, to salvage it when it suffers damage. The domestic
economy will hold a greater interest when they know that
what they amass will be their joint property and be trans-
mitted to their heirs. Misunderstandings and difficulties
will be cleared up more easily and forgotten. Family discord
and quarrels with relatives will be lessened or eliminated
and a healthy spirit of unity will exist among the relatives.
However, if married people face all their problems with
the postulate of easy divorce, there is *far less likelihood* of a
balanced and well-ordered family and consequently of a
balanced and well-ordered State.

Obligations　　Another argument for marriage being perma-
to society　　　nent is *the obligations which men have as members
of society*. The liberty of the individual is not only rightly
but necessarily limited by his organic connection with the
higher social unit of his fellow human beings. The conception of the State as an organism implies its transcendence
in a certain way over all groups and individuals composing
it. By its nature the State is superior to domestic society
and to the individual person. Once the individual person
has become a member of society by birth he is obliged to
make his contribution to the common good. Of all human
actions and institutions, the one which most directly concerns the existence and continuity of society is formal
marriage. It is evident that ephemeral and irregular unions
are not the best way of guaranteeing the welfare of the
State. The more regular and stable the formation of the
family, the more assurance there is of the State's continuance and preservation. Individual members of society, by
reason of their social nature, are bound to contribute to
the well-being, order and continuance of the State. Essential conditions of its existence and proper functioning
demand that the marriage union be permanent.

Ancestry and relationship   Apart from the bilateral relations of the contracting parties in marriage, human beings like to know their ancestry. Such satisfaction in the knowledge of kindred, brotherhood, cousinship and all the others, is impossible without the permanence of marriage. When divorce and remarriage, sometimes followed by several more divorces and marriages occur, the whole picture of relationships is confused.

5. OTHER ARGUMENTS AGAINST DIVORCE

Divorce cannot be regulated   Another argument against divorce is *the practical impossibility of controlling it.* Experience shows that no matter what the grounds, people will seek them out, commit or feign to commit, the legally assigned crimes—provided they can get what they want. The courts themselves shut their eyes to abuses. In the United States divorce has reached alarming proportions. Almost any reason will do, if the right court is selected. Some of the States are rivalling with each other in lowering the restrictions against divorce. Even where the only grounds is adultery, people fulfil the legal requirements to offer it as the grounds for divorce.

Perfect divorce legalized promiscuity   The advocates of legalized divorce are *inconsistent* when they condemn concubinage and sexual promiscuity. Every reason that they allege against these practices proves with equal force against perfect divorce. This is not a new argument against divorce. Aristotle used it against Plato's (427–347 B. C.) plan of having wives and children in common and Aristotle credits the argument to Plato's teacher Socrates (469–399 B. C.).

Divorce no remedy for unsuccessful marriages   Divorce has been argued as a remedy for unsuccessful marriages. Far from *remedying* the evils of such failures, *divorce has contributed more than anything else to the present breakdown of the home*. Divorce as a cure is worse than the disease. "Once divorce has been allowed, there will be no restraint powerful enough to keep it within the bounds marked out or presurmised. Great indeed is the force of example, and even greater still the might of passion. With such incitements it must needs follow that the eagerness for divorce, daily spreading by devious ways, will seize upon the minds of many like a virulent contagious disease, or like a flood of water bursting through every barrier. These are truths that doubtlessly are all clear in themselves; but they will become clearer yet . . . so soon as the road to divorce began to be made smooth by law, at once quarrels, jealousies, and judicial separations largely increased; and such shamelessness of life followed, that men who had been in favor of these divorces repented of what they had done, and feared that if they did not carefully seek a remedy by repealing the law, the State itself might come to ruin."[1]

Permanent union normal The history of the race and the experience of mankind show that the *normal condition* in married life is the permanent union. Though the opposite condition sometimes has existed, it is considered abnormal. Such permanent unions persist in spite of quarrels, unfavorable conditions and even positive distaste of one spouse for the other. All experience supports the truth. The phrase "they are of one flesh" is a concentrated truth of human experience. Permanent marriage is a cultural inheritance and furnishes a strong argument for the stability of marriage. Most normal men and women when they marry think of their union as permanent. And it is normal conduct which is the basis for ethical study.

Right of happiness argument refuted One of the *frequently given arguments* for divorce is the person's right to happiness. It may be conceded with the utmost freedom that persons do have the right to seek happiness. But

[1] Pope Leo XIII. *Arcanum divinae.*

what exactly is happiness? It is not merely personal, sensual satisfaction. Happiness must be sought within the framework of those institutions which are indispensable to the development of the race. The happiness which the individual seeks in marriage must, therefore, be controlled by the essential good of the family and State. It is a tragedy for people to miss the happiness they anticipated in marriage. But their failure does not entitle them to revolt against the fundamental laws of the institution planned by nature for a purpose above man's personal happiness. The ends of marriage can be obtained as they should only by an indissoluble bond, so that no person can claim the right to gratify his own happiness by divorce and for the same reason no human authority can grant it.

See readings following Chapter 27.

Chapter 29

THE USE OF MARRIAGE

1. MARITAL ACT GOOD IN ITSELF

Right use of faculty   Saint Thomas argued that intercourse *exercised properly in marriage is good in itself and needs no justification*—since it is using faculties according to the order established by the Creator. The sex inclination is natural, common to all animals and, being divinely implanted, cannot be evil.

Necessary to a good end   Another argument rests on the principle that anything which is necessary for achieving something good and desirable cannot be evil in itself. The perpetuation of the human race is a desirable good and necessitates sexual intercourse. The act therefore cannot be evil in itself. If sexual intercourse is not evil in itself, it is good. For there are no indifferent concrete individual human actions. Every act has a character which makes it actually good or bad. The marital act then is good in itself, but it must be exercised within the marriage bond and in such a way that its natural end of begetting children is not frustrated.

2. OUTSIDE OF MARRIAGE

Fornication and adultery   Though good in itself sexual intercourse becomes evil *when exercised outside of marriage*. When it occurs between people neither of whom is married it is *fornication*. When one or both of the parties are married it is *adultery*, which, besides violating purity, involves grave injustice. What is said, therefore, to prove fornication evil applies equally to adultery.

Immoral Extra-marital intercourse is *wrong* because it is directly opposed to the welfare of the child which the act naturally tends to produce. Such transitory unions cannot provide for its proper education and up-bringing. Again, every human act which is not in accord with its proper end and purpose is inordinate and evil. Nature has established the function of the genital organs for the production of children, whose welfare is provided for in the family. Any use, therefore, of these faculties except in marriage, which safeguards the education of offspring, is wrong.

Its essential The essence, then, of the sin of extra-marital *immorality* intercourse is that *venereal pleasure is sought contrary to right reason:* it is opposed to the natural purpose of the marital act and to the good of the race. For not only does it fail to provide for the welfare of offspring but directly attacks the love which should bind people together. Extra-marital relations breed selfishness, suspicion, enmities, dissensions, jealousies and hatred. They attack social tranquillity at its very roots. Hence fornication and, *a fortiori*, adultery are evil, considered in themselves, as frustrations of natural functions and also considered in the evils, personal and social, which come from them.

3. BIRTH CONTROL

The principle Within marriage the marital act must be exercised in such a way that *its natural purpose of generating new human beings is not frustrated.* While this principle is clear and simple in most applications, it becomes complex when questions are raised about the extent of the obligation of having children. Must married people have all the children physiologically possible? Or may they exercise some control over births, and if so what sort of control is legitimate?

Marriage naturally considered Marriage as a natural process exists for the procreation and education of children as well as for the good of the spouses and the welfare of society. By its nature marriage keeps the human race in existence as well as other human societies. At the minimum births must equal deaths. But though men inevitably die, they are not so inevitably born—although nature has made ample provision for their multiplication. Human beings are constituted to increase and multiply, and this they will do if nature has its way.

Human generation not excessive But it has been argued that if nature has its way, human beings will over-populate the earth. This is an exaggeration. There is no incontrovertible proof that man's natural rate of multiplication is harmful to the race or too rapid for the world's resources. On the contrary, history shows that mighty nations and luxuriant cultures collapsed when men and women bartered a vigorous and numerous progeny for their own selfish comforts and ambitions.

A misinterpretation The *natural purpose* of marriage is to produce and educate children. Some critics of this view try to make it mean that parents must produce all the children they can, regardless of physical and economic and other conditions and in total disregard of ordinary common sense and prudence. So interpreted, the natural purpose of marriage degenerates into an absurdity.

Trust in God virtuous It may be observed at once that such criticism identifies common sense and prudence with what the *critics* consider sensible and prudent. They forget that some men and women trust little to ordinary common sense and prudence, because they trust absolutely to God's love and providence. These latter take the position that the planner is not man but God, who gives human beings the power of generating new life. So they leave the matter of offspring to God and trust Him to see them through. To consider this imprudent or intemperate indicates crass ignorance both of God and of virtue – of God, because His providence is denied, and of virtue, because sublime trust in God is turned into imprudence and the uninhibited Christian and free use of marriage is scorned as intemperate passion.

No control at all Leaving the number of offspring to God's providence is a *valid answer* to the question about how many children a couple should have. Acknowledging God's design and providence a man and woman may resolve against any interference. On the basis of marriage's purpose, of human physiological equipment, of the needs of the race and the State and of civilization, of the perfection of the spouses, and above all on the basis of God's providential care of the universe in its least detail and the trust man ought to have in God—for these reasons many men and women will hesitate in any way to limit their offspring.

Some control Most people, however, move on a less heroic plane. They have legitimate ambitions coupled with wholesome respect for the responsibilities of parenthood. They may lack heroic virtue, but are none the less eager to avoid evil. Must they let nature take its course or may they exercise some control over the number of their offspring? The question is not of excluding them entirely. This would be against the nature of marriage.

Control not wrong in itself To suppose that any sort of control is wrong is to assume that all control is evil in itself and never allowable. That some control is *not wrong* appears from the fact that celibacy can be laudable and that temperance and prudence are virtues.

Celibacy People who never marry control conception and births effectively. But who will condemn celibacy as immoral in itself? If society is to endure, if the race is to continue and civilization to prosper there must be enough marriages and births to replace losses and give a margin of births over deaths. But the *responsibility for this rests upon society at large, not explicitly upon any one member*. And so under normal conditions people are free to marry or not as they choose. If they stay single, the limitation they in fact put upon new births cannot be reckoned as evil and immoral.

A question When people marry is there to be no temperance and prudence whatsoever in exercising the marital act? The answer must be negative if every interference with conception is evil. For the husband and wife who practice self-control and use intercourse with restraint are limiting conception.

Temperance and prudence virtues To condemn their temperance as vicious is absurd. Christian ethics has never divorced temperance and prudence from virtue. Nor has it ever encouraged their contraries of intemperance in food or drink or sexual indulgence. For married people to use their marital rights in moderation cannot be opposed to virtue. On the contrary, to bring children into the world through unbridled passion, with no regard to prudence, human or divine, and no heed whatsoever to consequences suggests the crude, unthinking, irresponsible and purely physical conduct of brute animals. It cannot be claimed as a characteristic of human marriage.

Legitimate reason required In itself, then, *some control of offspring is not evil*. But this is far from saying that men and women can take the decision of offspring into their own hands lightly or merely to satisfy pride or ambition or the craving for freedom and leisure and other luxuries which a numerous family makes impossible. *For married people to limit conception in any way whatsoever there must be a legitimate reason*.

Some inade- As *invalid* motives for limiting offspring the
quate reasons following may be mentioned—the wife unreasonably fears the ordinary pains and inconveniences of
pregnancy and childbirth. The couple want to enjoy life
while they are young and settle down later to having a
family or they shrink from the sacrifices which having children ordinarily implies. They want to limit their family to
one or two children so as to give them the best in education
or to keep the family fortune together or because it is
stylish to have only a small family or because they simply
do not like children.

Reasons for Among the reasons which make some *perma-*
permanent *nent control of conception legitimate* may be listed
control the following: Conception probably will result
in the mother's death or permanent bad health. She almost
certainly cannot give birth to a living child or with equal
probability pregnancy will end with a miscarriage. Her
children in all likelihood will suffer some serious and incurable hereditary defect, especially some form of insanity.
It may be impossible for the family to support another child
or the mother is physically or morally unable to fulfil her
duties.

Reasons for The following reasons justify some *temporary*
temporary *control* of conception: The mother is ill or
control convalescing. Some extraordinary inconvenience or expense is attached to her having a child. The
mother's exceptional fertility necessitates deferring births.
The family is in bad financial straits or labors under the
difficulty of unemployment or some other misfortune. The
wife is young and physically unfit for the cares of motherhood. War intervenes, with the prospect of the husband's
being drafted. Some temporary nervous condition afflicts
the wife. The birth of another child would make it practically impossible for her to care for the children she has.
The wife must work to support the family.

Doubtfully valid reasons   As motives for limiting offspring the following are *very doubtful*. The wife wants to avoid pregnancy so she can help her husband get out of debt. Or she wants one or two children but no more, so that she can continue working or following her profession. The weakness of these motives is their selfishness. To limit one's family merely for such purposes can hardly be considered moral.

Natural and artificial control of births   Granted that parents have a valid reason for limiting their family, the question arises *how they can do it*. Birth control, or planned parenthood as some call it, can be practiced in two ways. One is the *natural* and moral way of abstaining from sexual intercourse. It includes total abstinence and using the so-called safe period of the rhythm theory. A second and immoral method, called *artificial* or *unnatural*, uses chemicals, sponges, foams, jellies, diaphragms, douches, packings, sheaths and a wide variety of contrivances to frustrate the marital act and avoid pregnancy. Each form of control will be considered in turn.

4. NATURAL BIRTH CONTROL

Total abstinence   An infallible way of preventing conception is *total abstinence* from the marital act. If a *sufficient reason* exists for the parents to avoid having children this is a moral and a sure method. By agreement husband and wife may forego their marital rights. They were given freely; by common consent they may be foregone.

By mutual agreement   But the abstinence must be by *mutual agreement* and not constitute a *grave occasion of incontinence* for either party. For marriage is a contract, whereby the partners exchanged conjugal rights. If either party refuses to grant these rights the contract is violated. Such refusal, however, must be unwarranted, since there are circumstances which justify refusal—for example uncondoned adultery, insanity, drunkenness, grave danger to life, illness, unusual pain or peril in childbirth.

Safe period explained For various and valid reasons *total abstinence* may be impracticable. Then the husband and wife may practice *periodic abstinence* or what is called the safe period. This is based on the view that conception occurs only during a limited time in each menstrual cycle. To know the length of the sterile and fertile periods demands exact knowledge in every instance. But on an average the fertile period supposedly covers about eight days in the middle of the cycle. Outside of this time conception is regarded as improbable.

Origin The theory, though far from new, takes its present scientific standing from the independent work of Japan's Professor Ogino and Austria's Dr. Knaus. It is often called the Ogino-Knaus method of birth control or simply the "safe period," or "rhythm."

Reliability That the method is not absolutely successful is understandable in the light of its physiological basis, the variations in human beings, the care with which it must be used and human carelessness. Yet its fallibility must be weighed against that of other contraceptive appliances, most of which have a 7 to 10 per cent failure.

Use *It can be recommended* for women in good physical and emotional health, whose periods follow a regular pattern and for whom pregnancy, should it occur, would not involve great loss or hardship. But if it be foreseen that pregnancy would gravely endanger a mother's life or involve some other severe physical or economic hardship—in short, if conception must be avoided, then total abstinence should be practiced.

Morality If a *valid reason* exists for controlling offspring, the use of the safe period is a *moral way of exercising such control*. By abstaining from intercourse during the fertile period husbands and wives are not doing any-

thing to frustrate nature. Their action has nothing unnatural about it. It is carried out according to nature. If
conception does not follow it is not because of anything
they do. Nor is the use of the safe period against the marriage contract. For although marriage signifies the inter-
change of rights to intercourse, it does not specify how often
or when these rights should be exercised. Since this is left
vague, men and women legitimately may use their dis-
cretion. Hence, if by common consent they wish to limit
intercourse to those times when conception is less likely,
they may do so—*provided they have a just cause for avoiding
offspring.*

*Just reason
necessary*   Even if recourse to the sterile period is moral
in itself, *a just reason is required.* Married people
cannot say that as they were free to marry, so now they are
free to abstain, if they want, from marital relations and
thus limit their family. They were indeed free to marry.
But when they married they contracted new responsibilities
and *stand pledged* to fulfil them as far as they physically and
morally can.

*Responsibili-
ties of mar-
riage*   Marriage imposes grave burdens, which the
persons did not have before, of raising a family. That is marriage's natural purpose and
cannot lightly be turned aside. *Their vocation now calls for
children.* The good of the family, the welfare of the State
and the Church require children. The good of the spouses
themselves demands them. Offspring are now their clear
duty, which can be avoided only for serious reasons.

*Natural con-
trol can be
immoral*   It takes more than mere whim or selfishness or
unreasonable ambition or unjustified fear to
warrant family limitation. Abstaining from
intercourse is not evil in itself. But *when it is done without
justification it becomes wrong,* not only because of the selfishness which prompts it but also because of the harm which
it does the natural order and the commonweal.

5. ARTIFICIAL BIRTH CONTROL

Definition   Birth control can mean a moral and legitimate limitation of offspring. *Currently it is practically synonymous with direct, artificial and immoral methods of preventing conception.* Though differing widely, the various forms of contraception can be classified under onanism, drugs and chemicals and mechanical devices. Unlike total or periodic abstinence artificial birth control positively obstructs nature. Contraception seeks to insure the enjoyment of sexual pleasure without its normal consequences. Whereas the use of the safe period conforms to nature, artificial control nullifies the natural process.

Immoral frustration   The *immorality of artificial birth control* is clear. Basic to ethics is the principle that violations of right human nature in its essential aspects are intrinsically evil (p. 78). Directly and on purpose artificial birth control violates an essential aspect of human nature. No matter how accomplished, artificial birth control deliberately obstructs the due effect of intercourse, which is the procreation of children. There are other purposes and other results but they are secondary. Artificial birth control reverses this order. It seeks to divorce sexual satisfaction from its primary objective of procreation, to allow indulgence and frustrate natural consequences, to isolate pleasure from responsibility.

Essential of the natural law   The frustration caused by artificial birth control bears upon *an essential aspect of the natural law.* For the act of procreation springs from the very constitution of human beings. It is intended to serve not only personal biological and psychological needs but also and primarily the essential needs of society. Nothing is more essential to society than that it endure. But it cannot endure without new births. Procreation is fundamentally social not personal—although this truth is in the way of being lost. Intercourse exists to maintain the human race.

Hence when the act is frustrated by positive interference, its essential purpose is obstructed and defeated.

Fundamental evil   This is the fundamental argument against artificial birth control, that it is *a positive and deliberate effort to frustrate a natural and essential function.* Even though no physical or psychological evils followed, artificial control would be wrong, because its immorality is not a consequence of its evil effects but follows of its own inherent evil character.

Other arguments   Yet as a matter of fact contraception has proved *gravely injurious*, especially to women. The use of drugs and appliances can inflict serious damage upon delicate tissues. Sterility can result. A sense of guilt, marital discord, social unrest, divorce are reckoned among the evils of contraception. Over 70 per cent of divorces in the United States are among childless couples. Psychologically, frustration causes numerous personal and social ills. Another evil of artificial control, as opposed to the natural mode of limitation, is that it easily becomes widespread, fosters selfishness, results in a dangerously low birth rate and threatens the security of the State.

Artificial control universally evil   The multiplication of birth control clinics plus the diffusion of birth control knowledge and appliances on the one hand and on the other the solitary opposition of the Catholic Church have brought about the idea that such control is wrong only for Catholics. It most certainly is true that the Catholic Church condemns contraception. But it is wrong not because She condemns it. She condemns it because it is wrong, wrong on the basis of the natural as well as the divine law. It is not a matter of religious affiliation. It is a matter of being human and falling under the natural moral law. This is what makes artificial birth control wrong for everybody, Catholic and non-Catholic alike.

Reply to argu-   That there are valid reasons for limiting births
ments for   has been admitted. Poverty, illness and many
birth control   other causes may make it prudent if not man-
datory. But to paint up these evils in all their tragic reality
and then submit that the *only solution* is artificial birth control amounts in some instances to charlatanism. If poverty
is the obstacle to a normal family, then financial aid ought
to be given. If medical care is inadequate, it should be
made adequate. If housing is so cramped that a normal
family is impossible, then remedy the housing situation.
However, if the obstacles to having a family simply cannot
be removed, then the only solution is limiting offspring.
But this does not mean that the control must be artificial
and immoral. There remains the moral method of total
abstinence. No way is more certain. Or finally recourse
may be had to the safe period, which has solid scientific
authority for its effectiveness under normal conditions.[1]

[1] Here may be cited Pius XI's condemnation of onanism, or
artificial birth control, in his letter *On Christian Marriage:* "As St.
Augustine notes, 'Intercourse even with one's legitimate wife is
unlawful and wicked where the conception of the offspring is
prevented. Onan, the son of Judah, did this and the Lord killed
him for it.'

"Since, therefore, openly departing from the uninterrupted
Christian tradition some recently have judged it possible solemnly
to declare another doctrine regarding this question, the Catholic
Church, to whom God has entrusted the defence of the integrity
and purity of morals, standing erect in the midst of the moral
ruin which surrounds her, in order that she may preserve the
chastity of the nuptial union from being defiled by this foul stain,
raises her voice in token of her divine ambassadorship and
through Our mouth proclaims anew: any use whatsoever of
matrimony exercised in such a way that the act is deliberately
frustrated in its natural power to generate life is an offence against
the law of God and of nature, and those who indulge in such are
branded with the guilt of a grave sin."

6. UNJUSTIFIED BIRTH CONTROL OF ANY SORT EVIL

Not needed to make every child wanted Some arguments against artificial birth control prove equally against natural control when practiced without adequate reasons. Thus it is argued that controlled births insure every child being a "wanted child." Its prospects will be brighter and it will contribute more to the happiness of its parents. This argument limps in the light of many examples of children who may not have been wanted especially and yet who grew up to be useful members of society. Benjamin Franklin was the fifteenth of seventeen children; Rembrandt was the youngest of nine; Leo Tolstoi was a fifth child, Samuel Coleridge was the tenth, and St. Catherine of Siena was the last of a family of twenty. As for children being wanted or unwanted, for the most part they are wanted by their parents once they are born. There is little evidence to prove the wisdom or worth of the small limited family either for the parents or for the children.

Birth control against good of society As Winston Churchill said, if birth control controls, a lowered birth rate is bound to result, and a lowered birth rate is a threat to the nation's well being. Franklin D. Roosevelt went further in saying that the severest of all condemnations should be visited upon wilful sterility. The first essential in any civilization is that the man and woman should be the father and mother of healthy children so that the race will increase and not decrease. Contrast this statement with the fact that some 42 per cent of married women in the United States have no children or only one child and that only approximately one third of married women have children enough to keep the population at a stationary level. The situation in the United States is tragically clear.

Two-year interval not necessary It has been argued that babies ought to be born at two-year intervals. The planned parenthood people think it best for the babies and for their mothers. But this cherished tenet received *a crushing blow* from Dr. Nicholson Joseph Eastman, of The Johns Hopkins University. Dr. Eastman[2] asserted that the two-year interval was deduced from obsolete statistics. After going through some 35,188 obstetrical cases, he concluded that babies born twelve months after a previous birth have just as good a chance to be healthy as those born later, and that the longer the interval between births, the more likelihood of a mother's suffering from a type of pregnancy toxemia associated with high blood pressure. Yet in the face of such testimony birth controllers still propagandize the two-year interval.

Childbearing normally not harmful It is asserted that women are worn out by frequent childbearing. As a matter of fact they are if they are not nourished and cared for. That is the answer to this difficulty and not the dangerous expediency of controlling births. Childbearing does not seem to have sapped the energy of such well-known mothers as Mrs. Franklin Roosevelt or Mrs. Dionne. Mothers of large families compare most favorably in mental and physical health with childless or one-child mothers. Neurotic preoccupation with their own health is one disease which the mothers of large families escape.

7. ARTIFICIAL INSEMINATION

Description *Artificial insemination* in the strict sense is a process whereby the semen of a man who is *not* the woman's husband is introduced into the cervical canal. In this way, as has been proved, pregnancy can be brought about. There are some difficulties but most of them involve the factor of ovulation rather than any obstacle in the operation itself. This is simply a matter of injecting a few drops of semen into the lower part of the uterus. The percentage of success by unofficial reports varies widely—

[2] *Time*, May 22, 1944, p. 46.

from about 15 per cent up to 80 per cent with 60 per cent looked upon as being the average which reasonably can be expected.

Reasons for   Artificial insemination has been recommended
artificial   as an appropriate way of helping couples have
insemination   children when the wife is physically and men-
tally capable but the husband is sterile. It is supposed to have the advantage over adoption of providing a child whose background will be known and who will be the wife's own offspring. Artificial insemination is also recommended when the woman's husband, even though he is not sterile, is unfit to be a father, because of some hereditary disease or weakness, or to prevent erythroblastosis due to maternal immunization to the Rh factor.

Morality   Whatever may be said in favor of *artificial in-*
              semination and of the care with which the male
donor is kept anonymous and of the success with which legal dangers are forestalled, *it remains immoral*. Its evil character is not due chiefly to its involving masturbation on the part of the male donor—although this is the immoral way in which the semen is ordinarily obtained. Even if the semen be had in some ethical manner the process of arti-ficial insemination is still immoral.

Essentially   *It is essentially adultery*, contrary to the funda-
adultery   mental concept of marriage, that only a
woman's husband has the right to father her children. This right cannot be waived any more for artificial insemination than it can for adultery in the usual way. The husband's consent for his wife to have intercourse with another man does not make it right. Neither can his consent to artificial insemination rectify the inherent impurity and injustice of the act.

See readings following Chapter 27.

Chapter 30

THE CHILD

1. INTRODUCTION

Keep child in view   Polygamy and promiscuity, divorce and birth control, with their obnoxious variants, are rejected chiefly because of their opposition to the primary objective of marriage, which is the procreation and education of the child. Yet in the earnest and detailed process of trying to preserve this primary objective and safeguard the interests of the child, the child itself as a human being *can be lost sight of.*

Child not a means to end   It must be remembered that marriage exists *for the child* and that children make the family. It is proper to dwell upon the vital contribution children make to the State and to the perfection of the parents. Yet in all of this the child must not be reduced to an instrumentality of human or political perfection.

A person   The child once he comes to exist, exists as a person. Henceforth, in a true sense, the State exists to protect his rights just as the family exists to make its contribution to his perfection. *The child is a person*, a new being upon the earth, helpless to satisfy his most primitive needs yet full of exquisite promise.

Primary objective needs analysis   His parents have given him existence, but the kind of person he will become lies in the process of growing up. The primary objective of marriage is quickly expressed: the procreation and education of offspring. But its *realization along all human lines* needs analysis in some detail if it is to receive the emphasis it deserves.

Parents'   With the coming of a child the married couple
obligation   becomes a *family*. From now on they have the
responsibility of giving their child all they physically and
morally can to insure its proper development. Their obligation rests upon their relationship to their offspring. He
is theirs. *Because they gave him life they are bound to try to provide
all that is comprised in the vast word "education."* This means in
general that negatively parents must not injure the child
either by what they do or neglect to do and positively they
must provide for its welfare.

Cannot be   Parents' responsibility for the education of
shifted   their children cannot be shifted. As Father
Lord writes, "No parent can hide behind the teacher, the
school, the priest, the parish, the club and say, 'I asked
them to handle my child for me.' Parents' duties toward
their children cannot be tossed into the lap of anyone else."[1]

Child's right   A child has no right to come into existence.
             But once in existence he has the right to have
all that is *necessary or helpful* for his development along all
human lines. He has the right to be born into a political
society which will be a fit place for him to live. He has the
right to a home which will surround him with the love and
intelligence and care and everything else that he needs to
grow into the full development of maturity.

Child and   By reason of her intimate association with
the nurse   parents and with children, the nurse needs a
clear notion of the relation of the child to his parents and to
society and above all of the importance of the child *considered in himself*. Especially upon the nurse working in
pediatrics falls the obligation of being familiar with the
rights of children and the duties of parents as well as the
necessity of having a good foundation in Christian psychology. She should be aware of the need of study and

[1] Lord, D. A.: *Some Notes for the Guidance of Parents* (St. Louis,
The Queen's Work, 1944), p. 30.

instruction and experience in order to understand the child. That the nurse must seek the welfare of the entire person and not treat the patient merely as a sick animal is a truth that finds special application in her association with children. To give them good nursing care and to be helpful to their parents, the nurse ought to have an understanding of the child and his development and a just estimation of his worth.

2. BEFORE BIRTH

In general   Before conception the child did not exist and had no rights. But with conception, his rights as a person begin. This imposes the obligation of doing nothing directly to terminate the pregnancy (p. 254). But the obligation involves more than a prohibition to murder. It means that the child will have *two competent parents in love and in law*.

Two parents   The child of illegitimate parents is *handicapped* *in love and in* as well as the orphan and the half-orphan. *law*   Experience shows that even if the mother is capable and faithful, the fatherless child suffers. The child of separated or divorced parents is also handicapped as is the child born to parents who have ceased to love each other or are hostile to his birth. To give the child a right start two parents are needed in love and in law—two parents who want the child and are prepared to give him what they can, two parents to live until he has reached independence, two parents united in the bonds of the family for the child's welfare as well as for their own happiness and perfection.

Parents a   "The history of the family proves," writes A. *step to suc-*   G. Spencer,[2] "that to actively engage two *cessful life*   adults in the business of rearing children is an immense asset to those children. The two parents insisted

[2] Spencer, A. G.: *The Family and Its Members* (Philadelphia, J. B. Lippincott Co., 1923), p. 167.

upon as foremost necessity for child care may, however, be of a poor sort, perhaps only furnished with good-will toward their task. Even so, whatever the lacks may be, however small the capacity, feeble the will and poor the purse, however society-at-large has to make up for deficiencies in the parents, it is at least one step toward a successful life to have two recognized parents who mean to do the right thing by their offspring and never fail in love toward each other and toward the family whom they call their own."

Competent   The mother should try to be as *healthy* as she
mother   can. Food, rest, medical care, exercise and a tranquil environment are some items which she will consider and cultivate for the sake of her unborn child. Likewise she will avoid not only what will certainly injure her child but even such things as *may interfere* with his health, such as the use of tobacco and alcohol. To give up some pleasures for a time may mean sacrifice. Still it does not seem too much to ask of the mother who wants to give her child the best.

Knowledge   *Knowledge* is an obligation of motherhood. As
               with knowledge generally, knowledge about being a good mother and housewife must be acquired. The contrary view was picturesquely rebutted by Heywood Broun[3] when he wrote that "it is pretty generally held that all a woman needs to do to know all about children is to have some. This wisdom is attributed to instinct. Again and again we have been told by rapturous grandmothers that: 'It isn't something which can be read in a book or taught in a school. Nature is the great teacher.' This simply isn't true. There are many mothers who have learned far more from the manuals of Dr. Holt than from instinct. . . . I have seen mothers give beer and spaghetti and Neapolitan ice cream to children in arms, and if they got that from

[3] *The Reader's Digest*, July 1941, p. 57.

instinct the only conclusion possible is that instinct is not what it used to be."

Competent father   Before the baby comes, the father too has his duties to fulfil. It is his *obligation* to provide financially for the home, for his wife and for his family. He should make arrangements with the hospital or clinic as well as plan to care for the home and children during the mother's absence. One of her greatest anxieties when she is in the hospital concerns her home and family. A thoughtful husband will do all he can to remove this anxiety—just as he will be solicitous in other ways to help his wife during pregnancy and when she returns with the new baby.

Wages   The right of the child to a competent father raises the problem of wages and economic conditions. The father should be able to earn enough to provide for himself and for his family. Otherwise the child is not likely to have competent parents. No wife should have to carry the double burden of motherhood and wage-earner. In the home where the father cannot provide adequately for minimal needs the family is likely to be undernourished, sickness to flourish and the children to grow up physically handicapped. Moreover, where a family lives under the continual threat of unemployment and eviction there is not likely to be the background children need for growth and emotional stability. Everyone recognizes that in many instances the father cannot be blamed for economic deficiencies. The State shares this responsibility with him. Yet he should do what he can to provide. Both parents have the strictest moral obligation to know what is for their children's welfare and to put this knowledge into action.

3. THE BABY

Home environment   With so much insistence on the *importance of environment*, it is amazing how often parents minimize its influence upon the new baby. He is much more alive to his new surroundings than some parents think. Tones of voice, the way parents treat each other, regularity in the household and intelligent but firm discipline all make their impression upon the youngest child. From the very beginning, environment begins to work on and to mold the child, to make its slow but inevitable contribution to the child's formation or deformation.

Mutual love of parents   Another vital factor in the baby's early life is the *mutual love of the parents*. "The child," Leclercq writes, " . . . is closely bound up with conjugal love. He is the fruit of love, and its most potent stimulant. He needs it for himself. Not only has the child a right to his parents' love, conceived as the love of each of his parents for him; but he has also a right to the mutual love of his parents. He is entitled to have parents who so love each other as to make of this love the foundation of the common life in the home."[4]

Jealous parents   "How terrible when the child actually divides the parents! when the father in the hearing of the child—even though the child be an infant—taunts his wife with her neglecting him for the sake of the baby and loving the baby more than she loves him! or the mother early develops a jealousy of the father's devotion to the child and lets that jealousy radiate above the child's awakening perceptions."[5] That parents should be so jealous of their child would be unbelievable were there not more than enough evidence to prove it happens.

Affection   A child can get along without many things and yet not suffer grave damage if he is surrounded with *the right sort of love*. Children need to be loved, to be taken up and treated with affection. It is not enough that a father provide shelter and food and clothing and

[4] Leclercq, J.: *Marriage and the Family* (New York, Frederick Pustet Co., 1941), p. 11.
[5] Lord, D.: *The Guidance of Parents*, p. 63.

education for his children. Neither is it enough that a mother slave and sacrifice for her family. Both parents must give their offspring love and show it in wholesome marks of affection.

Nursing her There is one evidence of love which some
child mothers refuse to give their children. Though mother's milk normally increases the chances of a child's being healthy, many mothers do not breast feed their children. For some of them it is physically impossible. But they are only a minority of the total number who do not nurse their babies. No doubt these latter mothers have been influenced by the indifference of many physicians. Hospitals themselves have somewhat discouraged mothers from breast feeding their children: it means more work for the staff. But probably most dissuading of all are the notions that breast feeding is not only a dreadful nuisance but is somehow a little vulgar.[6] The mother who takes her responsibilities seriously will rebel against these lamentable fashions and accept the burden as well as the satisfaction of nursing her own baby.

4. INTELLECTUAL EDUCATION OF THE CHILD

Pre-school A child's intellectual awakening does not wait until his first day in school or kindergarten. It begins with the development of his mind, with his curiosity about the world in which he finds himself. This is why it is important that parents give careful consideration to the *child's questions*. It is unnecessary to insist they should be answered truthfully. Lying to children is as evil as lying to grown-ups, and may have even worse effects. In these early days of childhood is being laid the basis of intellectual companionship between parents and child. Unfortunately too many parents do not understand what is happening or they just leave things to take their natural course.

[6] *Time*, June 24, 1946.

Reading,
music, pic-
tures
Long before children can read, they delight in being read to; long before they can study music, they can enjoy it; and long before they can discuss pictures they can look at them. But what readings will they listen to and what pictures will they see and what music will they hear? Parents who have the welfare of their children at heart and who take their duties seriously will understand that *books and pictures and music are important items*—not luxuries. They will make sure that their children are initiated at an early age to such music and reading and pictures as will furnish a wholesome foundation for their development.

Radio
It is no condemnation of the radio to say that young children should not be *exposed indiscriminately to what a twist of the dial or the push of a button may bring*. Programs are not created for pre-school children. While the child should be put in the way of getting the right things, it is just as important that he be protected from the wrong things.

Movies
This applies especially to the movies. It is indefensible for parents to take young children to the theatre. If parents live up to their obligations, they may not be able to see as many pictures as they would like. They have the alternative of seeking their own pleasure at the expense of the child or of sacrificing their pleasure for the sake of their child.

Wholesome
outlets
It is not enough to say what should not be done any more than it is enough to keep telling children not to do this and not to do that. Children are alive with energy and on fire with curiosity. Wise and good parents will not try to smother their children's vitality; *they will provide wholesome outlets for it*. Every game and every toy is an educational instrument for the child. Every walk, every trip to the store, every automobile ride, even simply watching father hang a screen door or mother make a

cake, every item in the child's day is a fascinating adventure. At least it will be if the child gets his parents' cooperation. The choice is theirs: whether they will share themselves with their child and give him of their best, or, having given him life, will be content in keeping him well-fed, well-clothed and well-housed.

Home and school   Many parents anticipate with relief their children going to school. Apparently they expect to shift the entire burden to professionals. This is a sad and, at times, irremediable mistake. Schools at best are unnatural. The home with parents, brothers and sisters is the natural milieu for the child's education.

Choosing a school   When the time comes for selecting a school, parents ought to give it their most intelligent consideration. In many instances the choice will have been determined by their choice of residence. This is why the question of where a family will live often means where the children will go to school. In so far as they can, parents ought to select their homes with the future schooling of their children in mind.

A good school   In choosing a school parents should have a clear notion of what a school ought to be. It is not an elegant information booth. School is an extension of the home, where the child's education is continued. This embraces all lines of development: intellectual, physical, religious and moral. To the extent that a school falls short in any of these fields it fails in its purpose.

Not by name alone   Because a school has a big name, big enrollment, big gymnasium and sports program, because its charges are high or low, does not prove (or disprove) that it is a good school. Probably the best criterion is the student body. A school should be judged by what actually goes on in the classroom and on the playground. There the child is being molded, not merely by teachers but also, and perhaps even more so, by his associates.

Parents' co-   *Parents cannot shed the natural obligation of edu-*
operation   *cating their offspring.* At best the school can
continue the process which the parents have begun or
perhaps to some extent make up for their deficiencies. But
the parents and the home must bear their part even after
the child enters the classroom. Parents should encourage
their children by showing interest in their work. They
ought to provide time and suitable environment for study.
They should check on the daily assignment. An occasional
visit to the school and a chat with the teacher will be evidence that they form a team. A poor report will not touch
off an explosion but will raise the question of why the
report is poor and suggest a better plan of study. A good
report will not be taken casually but will receive the approval it deserves. From first to last parents must take an
active part in their children's education. In no other way
can they *fulfil the duty laid upon them by the primary purpose of
marriage.*

Youth   Young men and young women should not be
                   treated as children. Yet perhaps more than
ever they need their parents, when they no longer are
facing the challenges of the elementary classroom and playground but the more earnest problems of life. Youth needs
the good example and guidance of parents in intellectual
pursuits. What leadership and example will the parents
give? Will they evidence their own conviction that truth
exists and that the pursuit is long and laborious and obligatory? Or will they be cynical and show themselves little
in harmony with their children's spirit of inquiry?

Obligation of   All too seldom do parents think of their obli-
parents   gation to look after their growing children's
intellectual interests. They feed and clothe and house them
and directly or indirectly pay their school bills—but leave
education itself to professionals. In principle this is a mistake. For they are trying to do the impossible; they cannot

divorce themselves from their children's intellectual growth. More important still, such parents are failing in their personal obligation. They are the child's natural educators. High school teachers and college professors can cooperate but they cannot shoulder the entire burden and responsibility. That remains with the parents.

5. SEX INSTRUCTION

New problems　　As the child grows his problems multiply. He leaves the early years of grammar school to enter a sterner world. There will be new adjustments with parents and brothers and sisters and school associates. Deep psychological changes will appear. New interests, new likes and dislikes will battle in the child.

Parents needed　　*It is a difficult time*—not to be set aside with a benevolent smile. The measure in which parents can help will have been determined largely by what their relations have been with their children. If the years have seen understanding, if parents and children have been intimate, free and easy in each other's company and used to talking things over, they will see this trying time through together and successfully. If close bonds have not been established, it is unlikely that they will appear suddenly and function.

Sex　　This is especially true of difficulties with the awakening sexual appetites. Sex instruction for small children is, or ought to be, simple. When they ask questions they should be given answers which are honest and satisfying to the child's curiosity but with no needless amplification.

Real difficulties in adolescence　　The real difficulties come with adolescence. Functions and organs associated with generation develop. Annoying curiosities startle the child. From being happy with friends of their own sex,

girls manifest interest in boys and boys begin to like the
girls. Temptations and new desires and imaginings afflict
the child—the boy more violently than the girl. Frequently
the boy becomes sullen, morose, abstracted, rude and
solitary. The girl looks anxious and afraid. Reluctantly the
parents admit that their children are growing up and perhaps become regretful and anxious.

No substitute At this time children need *accurate knowledge*
for the parents and parents should see that they have it. But
it is a mistake for parents to look to the school or to the
clergy to do what they should have done and were best
situated to do. No one can substitute for the quiet truthful
explanation which the father and mother can give to their
children about the processes of life's beginning.

The alterna- The alternative is that their children may not
tive get the information they need and suffer
through ignorance. Or they may get it indeed; but in such
a way that what by nature is good and pure and sacred
becomes coarse and obscene and the theme of lewd in-
nuendoes and jokes.

Begin early Father Lord insists that the first warning to
parents must be this: "Sex instruction and
training rightly begin with infancy. It continues during the
days of the child's development. It should be fairly well
established by the time of the child's adolescence. . . . I
doubt," he goes on to say, "if once adolescence is reached
a father or a mother can start the sex instruction of a child.
. . . The minute the subject is approached, the adolescent
child, now aware of at least the preliminaries of sex, grows
acutely self-conscious. If he has had any experiences, even
guiltless ones, he suspects that his parents know about them
and are talking because they suspect him. He wants to run
away. In fact he may dodge with an effectiveness that
leaves the parent completely thwarted."[7]

[7] *The Guidance of Parents*, pp. 121–122.

6. MORAL FORMATION

Both parents needed Nowhere does the child need *both* parents more than in the field of *his moral formation*. Parents have the obligation of teaching their children the meaning of right and wrong. But their guidance will be futile unless they illustrate it in their own lives. The interest and watchfulness of both parents are required. Needed too is their agreement on principles and on enforcing them. Punishment, when it is necessary, should be inflicted calmly and judiciously and find the parents in agreement. Once the child can turn from one for sympathy to the other, the parents are in the way of losing a hold on their child and the child is in the way of suffering from his parents' disunion.

Companions Parents may do their best to have a home in which the standards are of the highest. But much of this will be wasted unless they guard their children against evil companions. It is not snobbish to insist that the children's associates do not endanger their morals.

Hobbies Many a boy and girl has found hours of happiness and a safety he little suspected in wholesome hobbies. It may get on parental nerves to have the boy hammering in the basement or scraping his bank to buy a miniature motor or monopolizing the conversation with talk about his latest hobby. But wise parents will endure all of this because they know it is playing an important rôle in their child's development. And the same must be said for girls. Their hobbies will be different from the boys' but just as important.

Movies Moving pictures have a tremendous influence upon the moral ideals of children. To admit that some children suffer from their attendance at the movies is a sad reflection upon the parents. Many parents who are otherwise careful about their children let them go to the movies without in the least knowing what they will see. They underrate the impact of the dramatic and spoken word, the sensuous and emotional appeal of the images in shadow and color upon the young person. Moving pictures can be sources of instruction and pleasure; they can be poison. To let such a crucial issue rest in the children's hands is to do them a grave injustice.

The opposite sex   There comes a time in the normal boy's and girl's life when from being disdainful of the opposite sex they discover it attractive. The boy's respect for the girl and her regard of boys are going to be conditioned by home training. If this has been of the right sort and there is a friendly relation between parents and children, there is usually nothing for the father and mother to worry about. If the child's interest is morbid or exaggerated, they may then take steps to control it. But understanding and insight ought to govern their approach. To joke about juvenile love affairs is an excellent way of losing the confidence of the children. On the other hand it would be a mistake seriously to consider them as inevitably leading to the altar. In most instances the bright flame burns out quickly. The main thing is that *when young people come to face these experiences, they have sympathetic and companionable parents to fall back on.*

Parties   Children are destined to take their place in society, and so must learn *to associate with each other pleasantly.* For this reason parents ought to give occasional parties in their home. A collateral effect will be bringing the children's friends together under the eyes of the parents. Moreover, if children find their home enjoyable, they are not likely to look upon it as a place to avoid when they plan a good time. Parties mean trouble and some expense, but wise and responsible parents will not regret them.

Work   It is as much an error to treat children as slaves as it is to treat them as little gods. They are neither. They are human beings, more or less painfully climbing life's ladder. At an early age they should realize that they *must contribute their share to the household.* Their tasks may be slight, but parents ought to see that they are fulfilled punctually. Spending money can be alloted on the basis of the child's fidelity to his duties. In this way he can look upon the money as a salary and not as a gift, and both he and the money take on added significance.

Money   Within the home parents have the right and the duty of controlling expenditures. But they should try to teach their children *the value of money and how to use it wisely.* As in so many other ways, here too the parents' example is the deciding factor. If they use money wisely and generously, the children are likely to follow their example. If they have been miserly or wasteful, so too are the children likely to be.

Parental jurisdiction As long as children are under the parental roof, *they ought to submit to their parents.* Reasonable rules about coming in at night and jurisdiction over the companionship of their children fall well within parents' rights. In some homes a painful cause of friction is the family car. Since the car belongs to the parents, the responsibility of its use rests on them. When they let the children have it, parents can insist upon the party consisting of four and can check the speedometer. Either too little or too much mileage can be dangerous.

7. PHYSICAL EDUCATION

The complete child The child must be thought of *in his entirety:* as living, sentient, rational and social. His education must include all aspects of his nature, under penalty of producing a warped human being. While the intellectual and moral and religious formation should receive due attention, so too must his physical training.

Body worship rejected This is far from approving the current addiction to physical fitness which amounts almost to body worship. Health and a beautiful body are valuable auxiliaries to successful living and a person is obliged to give them reasonable care (p. 206). But they are not absolutes. *The body exists for the soul to be its instrument.* A sickly or crippled body can handicap a person. Yet there are too many instances to the contrary to allow anyone to say that physical fitness is absolutely required for a happy and useful life.

Parents' responsibility Because of the close association between the soul and the body and the fact that the soul functions in many and important ways through the body, and also out of respect for the body as God's creation, the body must receive due respect. Since the child is the parents' responsibility, so is it their obligation *to look after his health.* They should provide periodical physical examinations to detect any physical defects, for some children should not play certain games or take part in certain sports. But granted that the children are without serious physical defects, parents should plan and encourage wholesome athletic activities.

Games Games are not ends in themselves but *means to helping the child to the exercise he needs.* He plays to win and he plays hard. But parents should guide their children to balance the instinct for winning with other motives. Games are for fun and companionship, for the development, as Father Lord writes,[8] "of bodily muscles and skill and the display of camaraderie, charity, good sportsmanship. The matter of winning is entirely of secondary importance." The famous victory will be forgotten quickly. But years later the man "will realize that in the heat of the game he was free from the heat of young passion and that, having worked off his excessive animal energies

[8] *Guidance for Parents,* p. 98.

as he circled the base for the . . . winning run, he returned home too tired to be troubled by temptation. There on the vacant lot he was learning much about cooperation and sportsmanship that was to help him to be a better democrat."[9]

Danger   Attached to swimming and football and baseball and boating and boxing and tennis and badminton and riding and to all sports *there is some danger*. But the same can be said for life from birth to death. The normal human being must face these dangers if he is to face life. They must be recognized and reckoned with; safety precautions should be taken and children taught to obey them.

Active partic- Even today when more and more people
ipation enjoy various forms of exercise, too many still are spectators. It is much better for their physical development that boys and girls *take part* in games, swim and skate and ride and golf and play softball and tennis—even though they play most awkwardly—than that they sit on the sidelines. Here as usual the example of the parents generally will prevail. If they play with their children, it is true that one day the boy is going to beat his dad's golf score and the daughter outswim her mother. But what evil consequence is likely to follow from this? It should not mean that dad can no longer golf with his sons or mother swim with her daughters or all the family swim or golf together. And meanwhile parents will have been drawn close to their children through their shared interest in sports and all the family will be physically better off.

8. RELIGIOUS EDUCATION

Parents' re- "Long before the priest, the religious teacher,
sponsibility or the catechist enters the life of the child,"

[9] *Guidance for Parents*, p. 44.

writes Father Lord,[10] "the parents have been turning him toward God or away from God. They have been making religion attractive, unimportant, or positively distasteful to him." It has been pointed out (p. 344) that religion is an obligation. Since children are under the jurisdiction of their parents, parents have the *responsibility of guiding their children's religious formation.*

An error   Some parents today pride themselves so much on their "broadmindedness" and love of liberty that they insist on permitting their children to go without any religious education and guidance: "They must be free to make up their own minds when they are old enough." Such an argument is as sensible as saying that they will let the children's physical development wait until they can make up their own minds about it.

Parents' ex-   Parents must teach their children *by word and*
ample   *example* about God and their duties to Him. "We have all come to feel," writes Father Lord, "a sentimental love for the picture of the young mother sitting in a chair while her little child kneels at her knee. The mother's-knee theme is however more sentimental and pretty than actually effective. If the parents wish to leave in the child's mind an example the child will never forget, let them kneel along with the child. Then they are not teachers instructing a child in the course of conduct they recommend; they are companions doing the thing which the child loves to do right along with them."[11]

Instruction   Yet *formal instruction* has an important place in the child's religious development. At an early age the child should be told about God's existence and revelations to man, how God is his destiny and that he has an immortal soul, which will survive his death. His daily

[10] *Guidance for Parents*, p. 81.

[11] *Ibid.*, p. 81.

life should be tied in with his religion by explaining how conduct is a means of attaining his goal.

Prayer   In all too many instances family prayer has disappeared. But, as it was shown (p. 344) how man is obliged to worship God, it follows that parents must help their children carry out this obligation. With good will and planning, family prayers, even though it be only grace at meals, can find a natural and satisfactory place in family life.

Church   *Church going* is also part of man's duty to God (p. 347). This follows from his human nature and the debt man owes to God as a member of society. As in every phase of the child's life the example of his parents is the strongest motive, so also in the matter of going to church. If the parents themselves are faithful, the children are likely to follow their example. But it is not encouraging to children to be sent to church while one or both parents stay home. With great probability such children will stop going as soon as the parental compulsion, without good example, is withdrawn.

READINGS

Ray E. Baber: *Marriage and the Family.*
F. J. Kieffer: *The Child and You.*
Jacques Leclercq: *Marriage and the Family*, ch. vii.
Daniel A. Lord: *Some Notes for the Guidance of Parents.*
Anthony L. Ostheimer: *The Family*, pp. 75-96.
Anna G. Spencer: *The Family and its Members.*

Chapter 31

THE STATE

1. DEFINITION

A perfect society   The most elementary natural society is the *family*. It suffices to bring children into the world and to provide the necessities of life. But the family cannot supply *all* that human beings need for the full realization of their powers. This is why the family is called an imperfect society in contrast with the *State*. Of all social institutions in the natural order the most complete is the State. It has everything required for human development and is subject to no other natural society. For these reasons the State is called *perfect* and is defined as a natural association of families, united under a definite authority, in order to secure the common temporal good.

State and government different   The State means the political organization of society. As such it should be kept *distinct* from any special form of government. Government may be a monarchy, a democracy, an oligarchy, an aristocracy or any form which suffices to establish and to maintain the authority required for the State to function. The concern here is not with any one of the forms in particular, but with the State considered apart from the actual government it may have. Whereas the State is necessary, the form of government it may have is not. It is the result of the people's choice or agreement.

Governments unequally good   If it be asked whether all forms of government are equally good, the reply is *negative*. From the point of view of man's rational nature and personal dignity, the most appropriate form of government would seem to be democracy. But it is a mistake to claim absolutely that for all men everywhere democracy is best. Democracy is the best form of government only where universal suffrage is tempered with due regard for the social condition of the citizens. In principle it is much safer to say that for a certain people at a certain time that form of government is most suitable which best promotes the general welfare.

2. COMPOSITION

State made up of families
The units which coalesce to form the State are not individual persons, but *families*. Only remotely may the State be said to be made up of human beings. The family is the link between the most social of man's institutions and man's individual self.

State a moral union of wills
The State's unity is not produced by the sacrifice of man's individuality. *The State is a moral unity, generated by the pursuit of a common goal*. At the same time the State is both one and many. It is many in so far as it consists ultimately of individual members. It is one inasmuch as it is an organization. The unity of the State, then, is not the oneness of being, but the oneness of activity, achieved amid diverse functions and arising from the union of wills focused upon the common purpose of seeking the good of all. The State represents a relation of parts to the whole, of individual persons to a multitude of persons. As a unity of order among persons the State is a real relation. For the terms of the relationship are real. But the State, real as it is, cannot be divorced from the individuals which constitute it. Without them it is nothing.

3. AUTHORITY IN THE STATE

Authority defined
The definition of the State includes the need of authority. *Authority* means the right and power which the State, or the persons deputized to represent it, have to use suitable means to insure order and peace and the general welfare of the community. The State exists

on the basis of the subordination of the plurality of citizens to the unity of administration. This unity can be brought about only by some one having authority, who rules and directs the civil organization to its ultimate goal. Notice carefully that the State's authority falls far short of being absolute. It is limited to its own field, which is securing the temporal welfare of the citizens.

Its necessity   But before the limitations are examined, it may be well to stress the natural *need of authority* in the State. Not only is the State a society; it is a perfect society. But for all that it needs direction just as any other human society. The State is made up of multitudes of men; it has its proper goal. If left to themselves, the citizens even with the best intentions might choose different means for attaining that end. If their activity is to be concentrated, as it must be, some person or group of persons will be needed to settle upon a plan and see that it is put into operation. The need for authority likewise appears from the fact that men, if left to themselves, will seek their own individual good. Unless there is a principle of authority to unite them, the State will be simply a mob and no State at all. Then, again, men manifest marked individual differences, have varied ideas and temperaments. They are bewilderingly diverse, and some are perverse, if not indolent and weak. To amalgamate all these elements there is required some guiding power which will unite men in a plan of action and, if necessary, force their cooperation. The only alternative to a State with authority is anarchy, which means the absence of law and order and the State's contradiction and annihilation.

4. PURPOSE OF THE STATE

Purpose differentiates societies   Societies are unions of human beings for the purpose of achieving a common goal. Thus the familial society exists to provide for the procreation and rearing of children. This separates it from the State, which exists for the sake of securing the common good of the entire community.

Common good   The State, as distinct from government, is the social organization of families for the purpose of securing the common good (p. 61). *This is the good of all the members of the State taken in its entirety.* The common good is not something existing in itself or some vague abstraction which must be apotheosized and slavishly served. It exists for the good of the citizens and cannot be separated from them. Nor must it be conceived as the sum-total of individual goods. For the common good is not identical with the good simply of the person. Everyone seeks his own good, but all must unite in seeking the common good. In this sense the common good is the objective of each member of the community. It is the social ideal for which all must strive as intelligent beings.

Citizen's sac-rifice to com-mon good   This may involve some sacrifice of a person's individual good, as when he pays taxes or does military service. But the sacrifice of the citizen's private good is only apparent. For in contributing to the common good a man in effect *furthers his own good*, since the individual good cannot be achieved completely without the common good. Every man's welfare is a factor of the general welfare. He is part and parcel of the State. Its preservation and well-being cannot be weakened without injury to the individual. Consequently, in renouncing his private good for the general good a man is fulfilling his highest social duty and his loss becomes a real gain in virtue.

Priority of common good   On more than one occasion Thomas Aquinas declares that the common good is more imperative than the individual's good, that the common good transcends the private good and that the good of the many must be preferred to a man's own good. Such statements easily can be turned to suggest that the individual exists solely for the common good and is completely subordinated to the State.

Correct inter-   *Nothing could be more foreign to Aquinas' thought*
pretation   *than to dissolve human beings in Totalitarianism or State Absolutism.* His insistence upon the priority of the common good bears on the situation where the goods are on the same level. When the temporal good of a citizen conflicts with the temporal good of the community, the good of the community must prevail. For example, money is a legitimate good. Individuals need it and so does the State. Yet a man's right to his money does not prevent the State from taking what it needs by the way of taxation. The good involved is of the same order. But when the private good is of a higher order than the common good, the private good takes precedence. In other words, the common good is superior to the good of the individual *as a member of society, but not absolutely.* For man has goods which are superior to the State and to the common good, such as his spiritual perfection. And when these conflict the good of the State does not take precedence.

Citizen's   Private citizens have the obligation to con-
share in the   tribute to the common good; *they likewise have*
common good   *the right to share in it.* Since the common good concerns both the good of the State and the good of the citizens, each member of the organization has a right to enjoy the benefits of temporal happiness and well-being. The equality of the sharing, however, is not absolute but relative. It depends upon the dignity of the person, his position and worth to the State, the contribution he has made to the common welfare, in short it is measured by his social worth. In this, as in so many other ways, human beings are not equal. Justice demands that these inequalities be evaluated when it is a question of what the State owes a citizen. Every man should contribute according to his

ability and receive in turn what he needs for his proper development.

Human in-equality   To assert that men are not equal stirs the wrath of those who insist that the State should be without classes and the citizens absolutely equal. It is true that men are born equal in the sense that they are all human beings with absolutely equal rights to be treated as human beings. But beyond this fundamental and essential equality, there is little equality among men. They differ from one another from the first moment of their existence, in ancestry and parentage, in talents and abilities, in intelligence and physical characteristics and preferences and temperament, in industry and generosity.

And the State   These are facts which cannot be minimized in connection with the State. For the State is nothing apart from its citizens. If inequalities exist in the basic material of society, they must be reckoned with when the State is thought of in its perfection. The State must recognize and utilize them. There is work for every citizen to do, a contribution for every one to make according to his ability. The tasks are multiple and dissimilar and unequal and yet all of them, from the highest to the most humble, contribute to the well-being of the State. Far from being opposed to the common good, the natural differences of men can be said to be necessary to the well-ordered State. An unstratified society is one of the most pernicious illusions of the day. Nothing is gained by denying the obvious, and everything can be lost by pursuing the Utopian dream of a classless society.

Primary objectives of common good in general   The State does *not exist for itself*, as certain Hegelian and totalitarian thinkers would insist. Its primary objective is *to supply what neither the individual nor the family can furnish*. The State exists for a common purpose, for the good of the people, for the attainment of what men must have not only

to live but to live *well*. The State is constituted of men by
men for men. Consequently, in addition to furthering man's
economic and social and physical and intellectual interests
the State must provide adequately for his moral and religious development, since the good human life must evidence growth along all lines of human perfection. The
State must aim at the natural welfare of the community
and of its individual members. It must safeguard peace and
justice. It must provide such of this world's good as is
necessary for physical existence and comfort along with
those moral conditions which are required for private well-
being and public prosperity.

Primary ob- More particularly, the State must protect the
jectives in community by setting up national defenses.[1]
particular   It must enact laws, found courts and protect
all rights. It must safeguard the citizen's life, liberty, property, livelihood, good name, his spiritual and moral security. Laws must be made and enforced against all forms
of physical assault and arbitrary restraint, against theft,
robbery and every kind of fraud and extortion, against all
apparently free contracts which actually make a reasonable
living impossible, against calumny and detraction, against
the spiritual and moral scandal produced by false and immoral preaching, teaching and publication. The State
should protect all these rights as exercised by the private
citizen and by lawful associations. The family, the Church
and all legitimate societies justly can claim the protection
of the State in defense of their rights. For men have the
right to seek their perfection not only by individual effort,
but also through mutual association.

[1] On the ethics of war consult: Aquinas, Thomas, *Summa
Theologica*, ii–ii, q. 123, a. 5; ii–ii, q. 40, a. 1. Moore, Thomas V.:
Principles of Ethics, ch. xxxi. Ryan, J. K.: *Modern War and Basic
Ethics* (Washington, D. C., Catholic University of America
Press, 1933).

Secondary objectives of the common good

The *secondary objectives* of the common good are those which cannot be exercised properly by the effort of the individual citizen or by the joint activity of a group of citizens.

Public works

The first of these objectives is the organization, ownership and management of *large public works,* such as coinage and postal service, flood and fire control, the aids to safe travel on land and sea and in the air, the utilization and conservation of natural resources. Such enterprises as telegraphs and telephones, radio, railways, water supply, light and power are optional. For the general welfare does not always demand that the State own and operate them. In practice the principle is that when public operation is clearly superior to private operation, all things considered, the State fails in its duty if it neglects to take over these utilities.

Public education

Although the child's education belongs primarily to the parents, the State has the right and duty to insist upon *the education of its citizens.* It should cultivate such a love of learning that without constraint parents will look after their children's education. But if they neglect it, the State has the right to establish schools and to take every other legitimate means to safeguard itself against the dangers of ignorance. In particular the State has the right and the duty to exclude the teaching of doctrines which aim to subvert law and order and therefore undermine the State itself. All this is within the State's right because it is vitally connected with the general welfare.

Public charity

The principle that the State exists to undertake such burdens as individual citizens cannot carry has special significance in the realm of *charity.* As much as possible the relief of distress should be private. Actually, however, the demands upon charity go way beyond the scope of individual citizens. It falls, then, upon the State first, by way of prevention, to do all it can to make relief unnecessary. It should make such industrial, educational, sanitary, moral and social provisions that people are assured of reasonably good living conditions. Secondly, and according to need, the State must maintain hospitals, asylums, almshouses and corrective institutions. It must grant subsidies to private institutions and agencies engaged in these works, and, if necessary, provide for the needs of persons outside of institutions. In a given instance, whether or not the State should undertake any of this work is determined by questioning whether the State can do it, all things considered, better than private agencies.

Public health, safety, morals, religion In the light of the State's primary duty to promote the over-all welfare of the citizens it is clear that the State should *fight against disease*. It should initiate and enforce enlightened sanitary regulations, such as quarantine, inoculation, medical inspection of school children. It should supervise the disposal of garbage and protect the people from impure drugs and adulterated and dangerous food. It should formulate traffic laws and lay down minimum standards of safety for public carriers and buildings. The State should seek to provide a healthy moral environment through the regulation of the liquor and narcotic traffic, the suppression of divorce, prostitution, public gambling and indecent papers, books, moving pictures and theatrical productions. Finally, the State should strive to protect and to promote religion in every lawful way.

Public regulation of business Modern industry and business are complex and dominant as never before. In a matter so vital to the public welfare no one can deny that the State has the right and the duty of protecting the weak and helpless. The State has the obligation *to exercise needed control* over banks and banking and other financial institutions. It must interest itself in commerce, in utilities serving the public, in manufacturing of all sorts, so that the commonweal may not suffer. The State can justly break up monopolies and take necessary precautions to prevent exorbitant and selfishly pegged prices and to insure a just distribution of essential commodities.

The State and labor   Then there is the thorny field of the State's relations with *labor and the organizers of industry*. It is not merely the good of the workers or the good of the owners which is involved; but, as is too often completely overlooked, the good of the State and nation itself. For this reason the State has the right and duty in behalf of the common good to take an active part in labor disputes. It may legislate for labor contracts and labor conditions. It may enforce appropriate laws about wages and hours, child and woman labor, safety, sanitation and compensation, sickness, old age and unemployment. Here again is to be applied the principle that whenever the general interest or any particular class suffers or is threatened with injury which can in no other way be met, it is the duty of the State to intervene.

False theories of State's purpose   This view of the State's objectives contrasts with that of such writers as Hobbes (1588– 1679), Locke (1632–1704) and Kant (1724– 1804). Their notion, called *limitative* or *minimizing*, regarded the State as having a single function, *merely to keep people from hurting one another*. The State existed simply as a policeman to guard the peace against foes from within and from without. This was also practically the opinion of Herbert Spencer (1820–1903). He thought the State's sole business was to define the limits of human activity, so that men would not interfere with one another. These views fall far short of Aristotle's conception. He would have the State touch upon every aspect of life as man should live it and *in a way that the family or the individual person could not themselves provide.*

5. ORIGIN OF THE STATE

Family in-   An earlier section of this book was devoted to
adequate   showing the social nature of man (p. 33).
Physically, intellectually, morally, religiously and emotionally man needs human companionship for his proper
development. This association is found basically in the
family. But it cannot give men all they need if they are to
achieve the fullness of their powers.

The village-   But as a family grows and families multiply
community   more and more they can satisfy these social
needs. There can be wider divisions of labor, greater ex-
change of services, more adequate provision for internal
peace and welfare and for defense against enemies from
without. To this inter-related association of families Aristotle
gave the name village-community. It represents an advance
over the single family and is a step towards the evolution
of the State.

Village-   Yet the village-community fails to furnish all
community   that organized society needs. It falls short of
incomplete   adequate military defenses. Its government is
primitive, its laws and juridical procedures elementary.
Police protection may be absent entirely as well as formal
machinery for supporting public institutions. Its economic
organization also leaves much to be desired, both as regards
trade and providing against poor or lost harvests. Above
all, it lacks the unifying principle of a recognized authority,
which is so necessary to the welfare and advancement of
society.

The State   Gradually with the growth of the village-
emerges   community these deficiencies disappear. Authority comes into being. Tribunals of justice appear and
law and order reign. Public institutions are created and
supported by taxation. In short, the community reaches a
stage where it can look after its own needs. The families
remain but a larger unity welds them together. That unity

is the State which now functions as a single unit, independent and sufficient unto itself.

Self-suffi-　　Self-sufficiency does not mean the *absence of*
ciency ex-　　*needs.* It means that the State has the organiza-
plained　　　tion to provide the means for supplying its
wants either of itself or through others. Famine or financial panic can afflict even the most advanced community, but if it has the necessary resources to meet the evils it proves its right to be considered a State. Neither does self-sufficiency imply that the State can provide for all its needs out of its own territory. But it does mean that the State can import what it cannot itself furnish.

Other ex-　　Other explanations of the origin of the State
planations　　are not impossible. Theoretically it may have
improbable　　originated by the union of people unrelated by
blood. Drawn together by geographical or physical advantages, they could elect a ruler, establish a government, make laws, set up courts, organize police and military forces, in brief constitute themselves a State and claim recognition. as such. But that this actually occurred is improbable or at best was by way of exception. For in prehistoric times blood was the fundamental principle of unity and the normal generation of the State would be, as Aristotle thought, through the growth of the family.

The State　　*The State is evidently a natural institution, the*
a natural　　*culmination of the divine plan for man's perfection.*
institution　　It is not the result of chance or some artificial
agreement or contract. It is natural because it is founded upon the family, which is the natural unit of social institutions. It is natural, above all, because it corresponds to natural needs in man. If man was to achieve his perfection the State had to appear. It is his natural environment. It makes the fullness of his natural life possible. "All that has been attained," writes Cronin,[1] "in the way of knowledge

[1] Cronin, M.: *The Science of Ethics* (Dublin, M. H. Gill and Son, 2nd. ed. 1920) ii, 471–472.

and all that has been accomplished by human energy in the way of art, science, commerce, all, in fact, that goes to make up our natural civilization, with the exception of the merest rudimentary beginnings, all or nearly all of this has been attained through the instrumentality of the State."

6. RELATION OF THE CITIZEN TO THE STATE

Thomas Aquinas' view

Thomas Aquinas viewed the citizen not as a means to the State's perfection but as a part of the whole. Just as the parts of the body are necessary to the entire body and exist for its good, so men in civil society exist for the common good. As the parts of the body cannot exist without the body, so man is insufficient for himself. In this way, Aquinas emphasized man's subordination, and conditioned his perfection upon the perfection of the State.

Man transcends the State

Yet man is *not merely a part* of the larger complexity of the State. He is a being in his own right. As a part he is subject to the State; but *as a rational autonomous entity, he has a goal and perfection of his own.* As a social being he is constrained to serve the common good, but as a self-determining being he tends to his own individual and proper good. Thus man bears a twofold relation to the State. *He is both part of it and transcendent to it.* As a social being and as a natural part he is immanent in the State. But in other respects he is above the State. Man is not destined to the body politic in all that he is and has.

The State a relative end

The end of the State is only a relative end, not the final end and destiny of man. Through the means of society man is helped to his ultimate perfection, which is strictly personal and superior to the State. Hence in this respect man transcends the State.

State's supremacy limited

However, the State is supreme in *everything which bears upon the common good.* In this field and according to need the State can control man's activity. But what pertains to his final destiny, to his eternal welfare, this is outside the State's jurisdiction.

Suspension of rights   Because of this part-whole relationship of the citizen to the State, it may happen at times that *necessity* demands the suspension of individual rights. Thus the State in order to protect itself against attack may induct a citizen into military service. It can expose his life to danger, and can take the life of a criminal in order to preserve internal law and order (p. 286).

General principle   The general principle can be laid down *that the State's interference with the individual should be limited as much as possible*. The individual good is the individual's concern only. Yet the State legitimately can concern itself with the individual good when something is strictly needed and the individual cannot supply it himself. The State has no obligation, therefore, to help any private citizen amass a fortune or escape bankruptcy. Yet it does have a clear duty, for example, to care for the poor and the weak-minded. In the instance of a failing industry the State can bolster it up if the industry is necessary to the common good and critically needs help. Under no circumstances is the State justified in using State funds for the benefit of private citizens only.

To control selfish interests   When men are left to themselves they are likely to neglect the wider needs of the common good. In such instances the State may be obliged to interfere, as it does, for example, in making laws for the conservation of timber, the preservation of wild life, to control the rate of opening oil wells, the use of natural resources in general. Likewise, and without questioning the right of labor to strike, the State has the obligation to arbitrate or force arbitration when labor disputes disrupt the peace and threaten the prosperity and welfare of the nation. Labor should never be allowed to strangle the nation's economic life.

For individ-
ual's good   There are instances when the State, without playing nursery maid, must safeguard the citizens. For instance, individual men and women might be left to themselves to avoid false weights and measures, fraudulent business deals, to safeguard themselves from the unprincipled physician or unqualified pharmacist, and to protect themselves against poisonous foods, patent medicines, unsanitary meats, injurious narcotics and intoxicants. Practically, however, the citizen cannot protect himself against all these dangers adequately. And when the number of citizens is considered it is obvious that the State is justified in exercising its authority.

State must
respect essen-
tial rights   *Yet on no account has the State the right to assume jurisdiction over man's essential rights,* which are basic in human nature, which antecede the State and are its foundation. Among such rights are the right to life and liberty, the right to marry and have a family, the right to food and the necessities of life. Most of these rights are generally conceded. But today there is a dangerous tendency to grant the State certain rights over marriage which it does not have. The State has no right to limit the number of marriages or, in the cause of eugenics, to say who should and should not marry. Likewise the State, while it has certain rights in the education of citizens, must respect the prior rights of the parents.

Need of
vigilance   The limitation of State authority is *a delicate but crucial question, fraught with danger and difficulties.* But for this very reason citizens should be vigilant, quick to follow the drift of legislation and courageous in combating any usurpation of power by the State or unjust denial of it by the individual. *Apathy towards the problem most certainly will result, as history proves, in the loss of freedom, in the disappearance of personal rights, in the rise of a monstrous and counterfeit State which will absorb the citizen and make itself his beginning, his end and his all.*

7. DUTIES OF CITIZENS

In general   While the State has duties to the citizens, they also have duties to the State. These obligations are not just gentle persuasions or merely optional at one's pleasure or obligatory only under the duress of law and force. As men are bound to give each other their due, as children are bound by piety to love and respect and support and obey their parents, *so are citizens bound to obey and respect and be loyal and serve the State.* In addition to commutative justice there is legal justice, which is the virtue which obliges citizens to give to the community what is required for the common good (p. 61). The duties of legal justice are covered by the word patriotism.

Patriotism defined   *Patriotism signifies love of one's country.* More explicitly it means obedience to law, respect for public authority and loyalty. It is not partial and narrow and exclusive, in the sense that love of one's country begets hatred or contempt for other peoples. It is not national jealousy, boasting, imperialism, aggression, and provincialism. Patriotism is a virtue bearing as much, or even more, upon the State's internal affairs as upon its relations with other nations. The truest patriot, let it be noted, is a good man—a man true to himself and true to all his relations with his fellow men, whether or not they are of his own race or color or nation or religion. Patriotism means loyalty to knowledge and to truth, to justice and to humanity. It implies a generous measure of good will and unselfishness. Yet men love the State not as an end in itself, but as a means to an end, as an instrumentality whereby they may become nobler, wiser, stronger, happier and more beneficent human beings.

Paying taxes   More specifically and under any lawful government citizens have the obligation of taxes and military service. The State needs money to support itself and public institutions. It gets the revenue by taxation. As citizens are bound to contribute to the common good, so are they bound to pay their share to support it. Their obligation is real and binds in justice. This is the general principle; its application is admittedly complex.

Application   But in the light of the principle citizens clearly are bound to give the State *financial support*. To say that all tax laws are penal, obliging the citizen to pay only if his evasion is detected, is not universally true. Generally citizens are bound to pay taxes only when the amount has been specified by the authorities. When the law directs them to make a statement of their property, they are bound to do so. But this raises the question whether they must volunteer such information. For example, is a person morally obliged to state that his income is large enough to be taxable? Such a statement is demanded by the law. It seems clear, therefore, that citizens are bound to make a statement of their taxable income not only when it is officially required but sometimes in the absence of such official demands.

Military service   One of the essential functions of the State is national defense. This includes more than building up powerful fighting units. It means the mobilization of the entire population to provide such services and material as successful prosecution of war demands (p. 412).

Draft laws   *Voluntary service* for national defense most accords with human dignity, but is not likely to meet the emergency. The State, therefore, can pass draft laws, inducting citizens not only into combat service but also into all the activities which war implies. It may draft physicians and nurses and other professional men and women. It may allocate workers to factories and shipyards. In brief, the State can do all that is necessary or expedient to preserve itself.

Patriotism in a democracy   Taxes and military service apply under all forms of government. When citizens live in a democracy, they have *the added obligations of performing their electoral functions.* These, it must be remembered, bear directly upon the common good and express concretely the citizen's participation in government. Consequently, he is morally bound to exercise his voting franchise. *The ballot box is the sanctuary of good citizenship and, it may be added, of good government.* The sole aim of the voter must be the welfare of the State. Failure to use the right of suffrage wisely spells the doom of the democratic way of life. Yet voting means more than casting a ballot. It means casting it honestly and intelligently. This supposes an understanding of the citizen's power and responsibility, of the political institutions, of the candidates and policies and issues involved. It means also that citizens with the necessary qualifications be willing to be candidates for office.

The good citizen　Sometimes it is said that the good man in other aspects of life is automatically the best citizen. This is only partly true. *The good man is the good citizen if he is aware of the duties of good citizenship and exercises them.* The worthy citizen knows his obligations and reasonably and continuously tries to live up to them. He is aware not only of his domestic and social duties but also of what he owes to the commonwealth. It is only the man and woman who embrace their duties to their families and neighbors, to the Supreme Being and to the State who deserve to be called good citizens.

8. THE FAMILY OF NATIONS

Efforts to organize　Of late years there has been a growing tendency to unite the nations of the world into a family. After World War I the League of Nations came into being, full of promise but ineffectual in the event to save the world from another tragic war. Following World War II, the nations again gathered to unite in a workable organization.

No alterna-   It should not have required the atomic bomb
tive   to awaken men to the *absolute necessity* of
forming a world organization of nations, pledged to outlaw
war and to preserve peace. But now that the threat of
atomic demolition hangs over civilization, men have no
alternative. Either they set up the machinery to knit the
nations of the world together and prevent the monstrous
catastrophe of war or they will perish.

Means   To achieve the goal of a world family of
                  nations men must take the means. They have
to agree on fundamentals. Yet the refusal of some civilized
nations to accept even the existence of a Supreme Being
reveals the sad state of affairs. With no agreement on such
a basic truth, how can an organization arise dedicated to
preserve the world from man's own barbaric violence!

God's place   As personal ethics presupposes a Supreme
                  Being, so must ethics as applied to nations
begin and end with the acknowledgment of His existence.
In Him the natural moral law finds its adequate foundation, and from it springs the virtues of justice and love,
which must bind men together and safeguard their rights.
For men to think of a world organization without God
may not prove them insincere; but it does doom their
efforts to failure.

> Unless the Lord build the house, they
> labor in vain that build it. (Ps. 126)

READINGS

Michael Cronin: *The Science of Ethics*, ii, chapters xv–xviii, and
  pp. 663–680.
Durant Drake: *Problems of Conduct*, ch. xxix.
Edward F. Garesché: *Ethics and the Art of Conduct for Nurses*, ch.
  xxiv, Part I.

Paul J. Glenn: *Ethics*, pp. 255–295.
J. F. Leibell: *Readings in Ethics*. pp. 860–1090.
Charles C. Miltner: *The Elements of Ethics*, ch. xvii.
Thomas V. Moore: *Principles of Ethics*, chapters xx and xxi, xxxi.
John A. Ryan and M. F. X. Millar: *The State and the Church*.
John K. Ryan: *Modern War and Basic Ethics*.

BIBLIOGRAPHY

Aikens, C. A.: *Studies in Ethics for Nurses*, 5th ed. (Philadelphia, W. B. Saunders Co., 1943).

Aquinas, St. T.: *Summa Theologica*, English Dominican trans. (London, Burns, Oates and Washbourne, 1912-1925).

Aristotle: *Nicomachean Ethics*, tr. by W. D. Ross (Oxford, Clarendon Press, 1925).

Attwater, D. (translator): *Body and Spirit* (New York, Longmans, Green & Co., 1939).

Baber, R. E.: *Marriage and the Family* (New York, McGraw-Hill Book Co., 1939).

Barker, E.: *The Values of Life* (London, Blackie and Son, 1939).

Barrett, C. L.: *Ethics* (New York, Harper & Bros., 1933).

Boethius: *The Consolation of Philosophy*, tr. by H. E. Stewart, and E. K. Rand (Cambridge, Mass., Harvard University Press, 1936).

Bradley, F. H.: *Ethical Studies*, 2d ed. (Oxford, Clarendon Press, 1927).

Brogan, J. M.: *Ethical Principles for the Character of the Nurse* (Milwaukee, Bruce Publishing Co., 1924).

Bruehl, C. P.: *This Way Happiness* (Milwaukee, Bruce Publishing Co., 1941).

Cabot, R. C.: *The Meaning of Right and Wrong*, revised ed. (New York, The Macmillan Co., 1936).

Cabot, R. C.: *What Men Live By* (Boston, Houghton Mifflin Co., 1929).

Carrel, A.: *Man the Unknown* (New York, Harper & Bros., 1935).

Carritt, E. F.: *The Theory of Morals* (London, University of London Press, 1928).

Carroll, R. S.: *What Price Alcohol?* (New York, The Macmillan Co., 1942).

Cox, I. W.: *Liberty, Its Use and Abuse*, 2d ed. (New York, Fordham University Press, 1939).

Cox, J. F.: *A Thomistic Analysis of the Social Order* (Washington, D. C., Catholic University Press, 1943).

Cronin, M.: *The Science of Ethics* (Dublin, M. H. Gill and Son, 1930).

Cunningham, B.: *The Morality of Organic Transplantation* (Washington, D. C., Catholic University Press, 1944).

Densford, K. J. and Everett, M. S.: *Ethics for Modern Nurses* (Philadelphia, W. B. Saunders Co., 1946).

Dewey, J. and Tufts, J.: *Ethics*, revised ed. (New York, Henry Holt & Co., 1932).

Dicks, R. J.: *Who Is My Patient?* (New York, The Macmillan Co., 1941).

Dimnet, E.: *The Art of Thinking* (New York, Simon & Schuster, 1938).

Drake, D.: *Problems of Conduct*, 2d ed. (Boston, Houghton Mifflin Co., 1935).

Drake, D.: *The New Morality* (New York, The Macmillan Co., 1928).

Duzy, E. S.: *Philosophy of Social Change* (Washington, D. C., Catholic University Press, 1944).

Eby, L. S.: *The Quest for Moral Law* (New York, Columbia University Press, 1944).

Edgell, B.: *Ethical Problems* (London, Methuen & Co., 1929).

Everett, W. G.: *Moral Values* (New York, Henry Holt & Co., 1918).

Farrell, W.: *A Companion to the Summa*, 4 vols. (New York, Sheed & Ward, vol. i, 1941; vol. ii, 1939; vol. iii, 1940; vol. iv, 1942).

Ferree, W.: *The Act of Social Justice* (Washington, D. C., Catholic University Press, 1942).

Finney, P. A.: *Moral Problems in Hospital Practice* (St. Louis, B. Herder Book Co., 1938).

Foerster, F. W.: *Marriage and the Sex-Problem*, tr. by M. Booth (New York, Frederick A. Stokes Co., 1936).

Fullerton, G. S.: *A Handbook of Ethical Theory* (New York, Henry Holt & Co., 1922).

Gabriel, Sr. J.: *Professional Problems*, 2d ed. (Philadelphia, W. B. Saunders Co., 1939).

Garesché, E. F.: *Ethics and the Art of Conduct for Nurses*, 2d ed. (Philadelphia, W. B. Saunders Co., 1944).

Gilson, E. H.: *Moral Values and the Moral Life*, tr. by L. R. Ward (St. Louis, B. Herder Book Co., 1931).

Gladwin, M. E.: *Ethics: A Textbook for Nurses*, 2d ed. (Philadelphia, W. B. Saunders Co., 1937).

Glenn, P. J.: *Ethics* (St. Louis, B. Herder Book Co., 1938).

Goodall, P. A.: *Ethics* (Philadelphia, F. A. Davis Co., 1942).

Goodrich, A. W.: *The Social and Ethical Significance of Nursing* (New York, The Macmillan Co., 1932).

Griese, N. O.: *The "Rhythm" in Marriage and Christian Morality* (Westminster, Md., Newman Book Shop, 1944).

Guchteneere, R. de: *Judgment on Birth Control* (New York, The Macmillan Co., 1931).

Gurian, W.: "The Philosophy of the Totalitarian State" in *The Proceedings of the American Catholic Philosophical Association*, vol. xv, 1939.

Harding, G.: *The Higher Aspect of Nursing* (Philadelphia, W. B. Saunders Co., 1919).

Harrison, G.: *Ethics in Nursing* (St. Louis, C. V. Mosby Co., 1932).

Healy, E. F.: *Moral Guidance* (Chicago, Loyola University Press, 1943).

Heidgerken, Loretta A.: *Teaching in Schools of Nursing* (Philadelphia, J. B. Lippincott Co., 1946).

Hildebrand, D. von: *In Defence of Purity* (New York, Longmans, Green & Co., 1931).

Kane, R.: *Worth* (New York, Longmans, Green & Co., 1920).

Kant, I.: *Fundamental Principles of the Metaphysics of Morals*, tr. by T. K. Abbott, 6th ed. (New York, Longmans, Green & Co., 1927).

Kerins, J. F.: *The Social Role of Self-Control* (Washington, D. C., Catholic University Press, 1943).

Kieffer, F. J.: *The Child and You* (Milwaukee, Bruce Publishing Co., 1941).

Kirsch, F. M.: *Sex Education and Training in Chastity* (St. Louis, Benziger Brothers, 1930).

Kreilkamp, K.: *The Metaphysical Foundations of Thomistic Jurisprudence* (Washington, D. C., Catholic University Press, 1939).

LaRochelle, S. A. and Fink, C. T.: *Handbook of Medical Ethics*, 9th ed. (Westminster, Md,. Newman Book Shop, 1946).

Leclercq, J.: *Marriage and the Family*, tr. by T. R. Hanley (New York, F. Pustet Co., 1941).

Leibell, J. F., (Editor): *Readings in Ethics* (Chicago, Loyola University Press, 1926).

Lennon, Sr. Mary Isidore: *Professional Adjustments* (St. Louis, C. V. Mosby Co., 1946).

Lewis, C. S.: *The Screwtape Letters* (New York, The Macmillan Co., 1943).

Lindworsky, J.: *The Training of the Will*, tr. by A. Steiner and E. A. Fitzpatrick (Milwaukee, Bruce Publishing Co., 1929).

Lord, D. A.: *Some Notes for the Guidance of Parents* (St. Louis, The Queen's Work, 1944).

McAllister, J. B.: *Emergency Baptism* (Milwaukee, Bruce Publishing Co., 1944).

McDonald, W. J.: *The Social Value of Property According to St. Thomas Aquinas* (Washington, D. C., Catholic University Press, 1939).

McFadden, C. J.: *Medical Ethics for Nurses* (Philadelphia, F. A. Davis Co., 1946).

Martindale, C. C.: *The Difficult Commandment* (New York, P. J. Kennedy and Sons, 1932).

Martindale, C. C. (introduction): *Into Their Company* (New York, P. J. Kennedy and Sons, 1932).

Mill, J. S.: *Autobiography*, 4th ed. (London, Longmans, Green, Reader, and Dyer, 1874).

Mill, J. S.: *Utilitarianism* (New York, Belford, Clarke, 1888).

Miltner, C. C.: *The Elements of Ethics*, revised ed. (New York, The Macmillan Co., 1931).

Moore, T. V.: *Dynamic Psychology* (Philadelphia, J. B. Lippincott Co., 1926).

Moore, T. V.: *Principles of Ethics*, 4th ed. (Philadelphia, J. B. Lippincott Co., 1943).

Morrison, B.: *Marriage* (Milwaukee, Bruce Publishing Co., 1934).

Murphy, R. J.: *The Catholic Nurse, Her Spirit and Her Duties* (Milwaukee, Bruce Publishing Co., 1923).

Nightingale, F.: *Notes on Nursing* (New York, D. Appleton, 1860).

Nightingale, F.: *Florence Nightingale to her Nurses: A Selection from Miss Nightingale's Addresses* (London and New York, The Macmillan Co., 1914).

Ostheimer, A. L.: *The Family* (Washington, D. C., Catholic University Press, 1939).

Parsons, S. E.: *Nursing Problems and Obligations*, 3d ed. (Boston, Whitcomb and Barrows, 1919).

Phillips, R. P.: *Modern Thomistic Philosophy* (London, Burns, Oates and Washbourne, 1934).

Pope Pius XI, *Christian Marriage* (Washington, D. C., National Catholic Welfare Conference, 1931).

Rand, B., (Editor): *The Classical Moralists* (Boston, Houghton Mifflin Co., 1909).

Rauth, J. E. and Sheehy, Sr. M. M.: *Principles of Psychology for the Basic Course in Nursing* (Milwaukee, Bruce Publishing Co., 1945).

Reardon, J. J.: *Selfishness and the Social Order* (Washington, D. C., Catholic University Press, 1943).

Robb, I. H.: *Nursing Ethics for Hospital and Private Use* (Cleveland, J. B. Savage, 1903).

Rooney, M. T., *Lawlessness, Law, and Sanction* (Washington, D. C., Catholic University Press, 1937).

Ross, J. E.: *Christian Ethics* (New York, Devin-Adair Co., 1924).

Ross, W. D.: *Foundations of Ethics* (London, Oxford University Press, 1939).

Ryan, J. A. and Millar, M. F. X.: *The State and the Church* (New York, The Macmillan Co., 1930).

Ryan, J. K.: *Modern War and Basic Ethics* (Washington, D. C., Catholic University Press, 1933).

Scheffel, C.: *Jurisprudence for Nurses* (New York, Lakeside Publishing Co., 1931).

Snell, Sr. R.: *The Nature of Man in St. Thomas Aquinas Compared with the Nature of Man in American Sociology* (Washington, D. C., Catholic University Press, 1942).

Spalding, E. K.: *Professional Adjustments in Nursing*, 3d ed. (Philadelphia, J. B. Lippincott Co., 1946).

Spalding, H. S.: *Talks to Nurses* (New York, Benziger Bros., 1920).

Spencer, A. G.: *The Family and its Members* (Philadelphia, J. B. Lippincott Co., 1923).

Strecker, E. A. and Chambers, T.: *Alcohol One Man's Meat* (New York, The Macmillan Co., 1928).

Sutherland, H.: *Laws of Life* (New York, Sheed & Ward, 1936).

Talley, C.: *Ethics, A Textbook for Nurses* (New York, G. P. Putnam's Sons, 1925).

Thouless, R. H.: *How to Think Straight* (New York, Simon & Schuster, 1939).

Titus, H. H.: *Ethics for Today* (New York, American Book Co., 1936).

Wolfe, Sr. M. J. of A.: *The Problem of Solidarism in St. Thomas* (Washington, D. C., Catholic University Press, 1938).

Wright, W. K.: *General Introduction to Ethics* (New York, The Macmillan Co., 1929).

INDEX